THE ANTHROPOSOPHICAL
APPROACH TO MEDICINE

An Outline of a Spiritual
Scientifically Oriented Medicine

Volume I

Established by

FRIEDRICH HUSEMANN

Newly edited and revised by

OTTO WOLFF

With contributions by Walter Holtzapfel, Werner Kaelin,
Hellmut Klimm, Hans Krüger, Hanno Matthiolius,
Wilhelm Pelikan, Alla Selawry, Wilhelm Spiess, and Otto Wolff

Translated by Peter Luborsky
Translation Edited by Lisa Davisson

THE ANTHROPOSOPHIC PRESS
Spring Valley, New York

This volume is a translation of *Das Bild des Menschen als Grundlage der Heilkunst Band II, Halbband 1* published by Verlag Freies Geistes-leben, Stuttgart. It is published with the kind permission of the German publisher.

Cover Designed by Peter Stebbing

ISBN   0-88010-031-1
Series ISBN 0-88010-032-X (4 volume set)

Printed in the United States of America

Table of Contents

Foreword to the
Second German Edition

Since the publication of the first German edition of this volume (1956), ten of its sixteen authors have died (F. Husemann, W. Kaelin, A. Leroi, W. zur Linden, K. Magerstädt, W. Pache, H. Reuter, A. Rust, W. Spiess, and G. Suchantke). Because the situation in medicine has since changed considerably, a fundamental revision of the contributions to that edition was necessary. Fortunately, there were several new colleagues ready to take up the work of making new contributions or of revising the earlier work.

It is the desire of the editor to continue Friedrich Husemann's work, which he designated as "a literature bridging the gap between spiritual science and the sciences of the senses," thereby following the intention of Rudolf Steiner. This endeavor represents an effort not to oppose the current orthodox medicine but to widen the increasingly narrow, "accepted" scientific bases of medicine. The conceptions founded on spiritual scientific paths repeatedly find corroboration in experimentally discovered facts. Between these conceptions and discoveries there are no contradictions; the interpretations of facts, however, diverge ever more widely. This divergence is a problem of epistemology.

Today's medicine is strongly influenced by natural science and now puts into practice what decades ago was only conceptualized: "Medicine will be a natural science or it will not exist" (Bernhard Naunyn, 1839–1925). To this statement, which has until now been a guideline for medical research, A. Goerres answered, "Medicine will be more than a natural science or it will be a half-science." This assertion is quite remote from the predominating role of natural science within medicine, but it appears increasingly to be the case today that doctors are ready to question or deny their own practical bedside experience if a physician who is oriented to the natural scientific approach "proves" something different with his method. As an example, one could mention the debate between orthodox (allopathic) medicine and homeopathy, which cannot be understood by contemporary natural science and whose justification is being questioned in spite of clinical experience. The problem of the foundations of medicine is becoming more acute and the postulate, "Molecular biology is the foundation of modern medicine" (Butenandt) signifies an even further narrowing within natural science itself.

Consequently, today's medicine chases after technology, the most rapidly progressing sector of natural science, and in this way loses or denies its own essence as it moves increasingly into fields that do not deal with the human element and takes these as its standard. Thus, medicine with a natural scientific bent can claim to be objective, unprejudiced, and uninfluenced by any world view. Nonetheless, the confinement to natural science, the exclusion of specifically clinical faculties (a clinical eye, therapeutic intuition, empathy, contact, etc.) and the denial of the individuality of the patient (his destiny, constitution, etc.), for example, in the evaluation of remedies, signify an arbitrary restriction to a narrow sector of medicine. The intentional, conscious omission, even negation, of realities creates half-truths, of which the conclusions can no longer be in any way objective but rather are stamped with the prejudices of their own world view: that the natural scientific approach to medicine is the only valid one, the only one to be explored and to be trusted. Present-day medicine is thus based on a restricted world view that cannot do justice to the whole reality of the human being.

With the one-sided over-valuing of physical and material processes, there is a neglect of spiritual knowledge; even the possibility of its development is questioned. From this attitude comes an uncertainty in the sphere of knowledge, an agnosticism. In its modern form, this uncertainty in thinking can be seen in the alleged impossibility of grasping real connections without experiment and in the opinion that only what can be statistically ascertained can be considered proven.

The crisis of medicine, which is publicly acknowledged in spite of therapeutic successes, can only be overcome by supple-

menting the characterized one-sidedness. Here it is not a matter of discovering new facts but rather of understanding them
from a spiritual point of view. The methodical path toward
this lies in an enlivening of thought without renouncing the ex-
actness gained by natural scientific training. To achieve this
one must develop an artistic sensitivity as a faculty; the way is
described in detail in the work of Rudolf Steiner. Through the
commingling of science and art—without depriving them of
their essences—the methodological foundation is created for a
knowledge and practice that will do justice to the essence of
man. To develop the above statement further in terms for the
future: Medicine will be broadened by a spiritual conception
of man to an *art of healing,* or else it will remain a soulless
technology that removes only symptoms. Through the concrete
inclusion of the spirit and soul of man, a *humanization of
medicine,* as it was inaugurated by Rudolf Steiner, is possible.

—Otto Wolff, M.D.

October, 1973

Publisher's Note

This work is a translation of the first half of the *second* volume of *Das Bild der Menschen als Grundlage der Heilkunst*. For lack of time, the first volume, the second edition of which appeared in 1951, could not be revised. Because the first volume is being considered for revision, it will appear later in the English series. When complete, the English edition will consist of four volumes. The correspondence between the planned English edition and the German original is as follows:

The Anthroposophical Approach to Medicine	*Das Bild der Menschen als Grundlage der Heilkunst*
Vol. 1	— Band 2, Halbband 1
Vol. 2	— Band 2, Halbband 2, first half
Vol. 3	— Band 2, Halbband 2, second half
Vol. 4	— Band 1

The first volume of the German edition (Band 1) contains a spiritual scientific study of nature and the human being, together with a presentation of the human being's relationship to the four elements of earth, water, air, and warmth, which form the basis of the supersensible members of the human constitution. Since this material is not available in English at this time, this first English volume begins with an introduction summarizing the fundamental concepts of spiritual science (or anthroposophy), in order that what follows can be better understood.

Chapter I
Introduction

Life

The origin of life is not sufficiently explained when it is described merely as the result of the aggregation of physical constituents. An essential factor must be added to carbon dioxide and water, for example, in order to form living substances (carbohydrates) from these dead materials; this essential factor is light. The process of photosynthesis as such has, of course, been investigated in detail. Light, however, is more than an electromagnetic wave phenomenon. Besides its visible aspect, light has an essentially supersensible quality as well. The visible spectrum is only a part of what is necessary for the development of plants. Besides sunlight, many other, quite different, cosmic forces, especially planetary forces, are active in this process. These forces are not bound to the physically detectable rays of the light. Although the basic outline of this idea can be clearly grasped, and although it has already been partially investigated experimentally, it is, in fact, a new field for research. In the future, such research will make possible the understanding of the different actions of these forces, just as physical substances can be analyzed today.

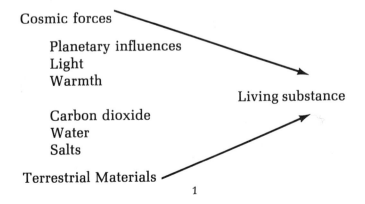

Cosmic forces

Planetary influences
Light
Warmth

Living substance

Carbon dioxide
Water
Salts

Terrestrial Materials

Thus to form living substance, two elements must work together: terrestrial materials and cosmic forces. The formation
and development of living substance—starch, for example—are
both functions of, and expressions of the specific nature of the
particular living organism. The imprint of a plant's essence
(*Wesen*) can be traced all the way into its inner structure.

The organizational principle underlying life is called the
etheric body (life body, body of formative forces) in the spiritual
science of Rudolf Steiner. The etheric body is of a supersensible
nature and can be perceived only with supersensible organs
developed for such perception. Thus the etheric body is not a
hypothetical force or something the existence of which has
been logically deduced, but a reality that is nonetheless no
more directly perceptible to the sense organs than are magnet-
ism and electricity. In earlier times, men generally were still
able to perceive the etheric body. In ancient Egypt, they spoke
of the *Ka*; the Greeks spoke of the *Threptikon*; Paracelsus used
the term *Archaeus*, which approximately corresponds to the
etheric body.

Every living being has its own etheric body, which has an
organizing activity and contains the structural plan of that being. Hence, the materials of metabolism are used in a way that
expresses the essence of the particular organism, not the
nature of the materials themselves. In the example above, plant
starch, being a carbohydrate, always has the same composition:
carbon, hydrogen, and oxygen. The way these materials combine to form a starch, however, is not determined by the basic
materials themselves, but by the etheric body of the plant that
regulates growth and form. The etheric body makes use of the
materials with all their properties, but not arbitrarily or according to the nature of the material alone, as occurs in the inorganic realm. Instead, the etheric body uses those materials
in a way that corresponds to a "structural plan." The purest
and most "undisturbed" manifestation of life as such is the
plant world.

The Animal Kingdom

From the developmental level of the plant, it is an entirely
new step up to the level of the animal. An animal cannot be

understood as a more highly developed plant. On the contrary, in the typically animal metabolism, the pattern of metabolism found in the plant is reversed and is based on oxidation rather than reduction. The plant inhales carbon dioxide and exhales oxygen; new substance is built upon the carbon framework by means of light. In animals and man, the opposite takes place. The living substance of the body is continually burned up, that is, decomposed, and exhaled as carbon dioxide. Thus, two opposite processes are present in the animal organism: anabolism, the formation of living substance, and catabolism, the breakdown of living substance. An animal is not only living, like a plant, but is also capable of drawing an aware soul into its body. The awake, conscious state typical of higher animals is connected with the catabolic type of metabolism. That the soul is active through the senses is characteristic of this state. In contrast, plants can be described as sleeping. It is extremely important to recognize the fact that the wakeful state necessarily accompanies catabolic processes in the realm of life and that consciousness is not based upon anabolic life processes. This fact has far-reaching implications for medicine and pedagogy, which will be shown in detail later.

In the plant it is practically the surface alone that serves as a functional vital organ. In the animal, there is typically the formation of internal cavities—lungs, intestines and body cavities, frontal and maxillary sinuses, gall bladder, urinary bladder, etc. This formation of internal cavities as a typically animal trait is related to the catabolic side of metabolism and thus to the ability to sense.

Through these formative impulses and the catabolism that is their expression, what is essentially living is constantly overcome, reversed or limited. The animal principle that comes into a living organism as an active psychic force is called, in the spiritual science of Rudolf Steiner, the soul body or astral body, because of its connections with certain regions of the stellar world. These connections were once generally appreciated but have since mostly been forgotten. Only the word "zodiac" (Greek *zodiakos kyklos*: "animal circle") attests to this ancient knowledge that is no longer understood today. Paracelsus still employed the concept of the astral body (star body).

The Human Being

On yet a higher plane, an equivalent difference exists between man and animal as between animal and plant. The human being is not a more complicated and specialized animal. All the evidence of human and animal morphology points unmistakably to the fact that man is *not* physically more specialized than the animal except in the brain. While it is true that man owes the working of his intelligence to it, the brain does not constitute what is uniquely human and forms only the physical basis for a part of his spiritual faculty of thought. Animals also accomplish tasks that demonstrate intelligence but not the essence (*Wesen*) of thinking. When the human being calls upon the full range of his cognitive capacities, he can attain wisdom, which is only possible through the intense activity of the spirit, the "I" of man. Certainly there are expressions of great wisdom in the animal kingdom, such the construction of honeycombs, the building of nests, the flight of migratory birds, etc., which are often attributed to instinct. These extraordinary, wisdom-filled actions of the animals, however, are completely unconscious. Despite this obvious wisdom, animals can demonstrate only minimal intellectual functioning. Only in man can wisdom become conscious. It is also an essential characteristic of man that he can draw out the wisdom inherent in his body—more precisely, in his etheric body—and can bring it into consciousness.

Man actually does with the animal principle (the astral body) in his organism what the animal does with the plant principle (the etheric body); he "pushes it back" so that something else can unfold. Man does not have stronger drives than the animal. He is not a more highly developed animal; rather, he acts on the basis of totally different motives. These do not originate wholly from sentient reactivity but can, depending on the individual, also originate in the spirit. Of course, the drives and all that is "animal" (Latin: *anima* = soul) do play a role in man—he could not live without them—but they do not define what is specifically human. This lies on another plane, that of the spirit. The part of the spirit that man calls his own he designates as "I."

A real understanding of these connections is hindered when

the distinction between soul and spirit is not understood; the two are completely different from, even partially opposed to, one another. The spirit is set above the soul and rules it, just as the animal element rules and suppresses the plant principle. The expression of animal drives can be ruled by the spirit only in man. In ancient times, this relationship between soul and spirit was represented by the image of a rider on a horse. The spirit is a superordinate principle, which man senses as the "I" in himself. With this "I" are connected the typically human traits, standing upright, speaking, and thinking, which allow the human spirit to express itself. In Goethe's words, "Let man be noble, helpful, and good! This alone distinguishes him from all beings we know." Here, a moral quality is invoked that is an expression of the uniquely human spirit.

Man	I (Ego)	Spirit
Animal	Astral body	Soul
Plant	Etheric body	Life
Mineral	Physical body	Death

   Knowledge of the four kingdoms of nature listed above is extremely ancient. With the one-sided orientation of modern research in the natural sciences toward the physico-chemical, merely the physical nature of man is investigated, and insight into the interweaving of body, soul, and spirit has largely been lost.

   Man is, nevertheless, first and foremost a spiritual being, an "I" that receives from the divine world of creation a body that corresponds to the spirit and that, in the course of the incarnation process—that is, in the embryonic period and childhood—he increasingly makes his instrument. Man is not the product of heredity and environment. Rather, he uses heredity and environment purely as raw material for transforming and molding his individuality into an expression of his "I." Without an understanding of the four members of man and his supersensible parts, one cannot fully comprehend or appreciate bodily processes.

It is also possible to study the interrelationships of forces active in the human organism. These are likewise a reality, but the approach to them is different. Such a study, though, is necessary for understanding the multiformity of the human organism. Many pathological manifestations become comprehensible and are recognized as significant only through an approach based on a study of the force structures operating in man.

The Threefold Human Being

The investigation of individual organs provides important information about their function. To discover the organs' significance for the whole human being, however, one must investigate what is "expressed" in the organs' respective functions; that is, one must proceed from an observation of the organ to an observation of the dynamic acting in it. In this way, one can come to see how different organs together make up a functional unit. Looking at the sense organs, for example, it is easy to see what they share. They give the human soul information from the outside environment (for example, the eye and ear), or from inside the body itself (for example, balance, warmth, and touch). All sense organs have a clear connection to the nerves, and thereby to the brain. It is in fact no accident that the most important sense organs are concentrated in the head (eye, ear, nose, tongue, semicircular canals in the ear, etc.). Also in the head is the greatest mass of nerves, the brain. These two groups of organs can be viewed together as a functional unit, the nerve-sense system. If one follows the dynamics, the gestures, and the force relations observable in the nerve-sense system, one must admit that it cannot be an accident that there are in the head organs of perception whose direction of action is from outside to inside. Light, sound, and nourishment flow through these organs to the inside of the organism. Indeed, the sense organs act as gates. They are meant to let something pass through as unchanged as possible: through the eye, light; through the ear, sound; etc. The less the sense-organs change these, the better they fulfill their function. For such sensory activity, rest is an essential state. Therefore, the head is the part of the body that moves the least during motion. Since no organ is as sensitive to shocks as the brain, it has many devices to neutralize the shocks of movement, such as the elasticity of the spinal column and of cartilage, the cushion of the cerebro-spinal fluid, etc.

Of all the characteristic relations of the nerve-sense system to various qualities, those to warmth and cold are of the most interest. Anyone can recognize how the distribution of warmth in the human body is of the greatest importance for its activity. Many observations indicate that the head/nerve system cannot exceed a certain level of warmth and still function healthily. It is said, for example, that to think clearly, one must keep a "cool head." In contrast, too much blood flow, as occurs in fever, clearly impairs the functioning of the sense organs. For undisturbed functioning, the nerve-sense system needs not only rest, but also moderated warmth, a certain "coldness."

When one considers that "rest" and "cold" prevail in the nerve-sense system and that for this reason "nothing happens" there —there is scarcely any metabolic activity compared to the liver, for instance—then one can understand why the nerve and sensory cells show the least life. A nerve cell loses the capacity to divide almost immediately after birth. There is hardly any real growth, as a manifestation of life, in this region. The greater part of the eye manifests practically no "life" in this sense. If one pursues this line of thought, which can be mentioned only briefly here, one must conclude that in the nerve-sense system the opposite of life, namely, death, is active. Portions of these organs are already almost dead during life and are able to fulfill their function just because of this. Thus, in the lens of the eye, one finds no blood and a minimal metabolism. The same is true of the white matter of the brain. It is obvious that man cannot live only from organs so constituted, that life itself must be connected more with other organs. The dynamics described, with the tendency toward rest, cold, and death, are so clearly one-sided and concentrated in one region, that the opposite must be present and active elsewhere in the organism.

In fact, there are organs in which the opposite tendency is

dominant. For example, there is hardly an organ for which movement is so characteristic as for muscle. It is generally known, especially by athletes, that warmth is vital to undisturbed functioning of muscles. With warmth, metabolism is accelerated; activity is increased. Movement and warmth belong together, as do stillness or rest, and cold.

The word "movement," however, should be taken to mean not only externally perceptible change of position, but also transformation of substances in metabolism. Thus, warmth arises through combustion, oxidation, a most intensive transformation of matter.

There are organs whose main function is this conversion and transformation of substances. The most important organ of metabolism is the liver, in which transformation of all kinds of substance takes place continuously.

Such transformations—intense metabolic processes—are not present only in the muscles and liver, but also in the intestines, kidneys, and blood. These organs can be seen as the foci of metabolic transformation. Together with the processes they manifest, they can be called the metabolic-limb system.

In fact, these organs show a clear relationship to life; the words "life" and "liver" are etymologically related in many languages. If one follows the functioning of the liver in all its manifestations, one can see that it is really a principal organ of life. Life manifests and expresses itself in the transformation of substances.

Looking at the nerve-sense system and the metabolic system as polar opposites, one discovers not only that their chief organs are spatially separated, but also that their described tendencies and attendant phenomena always oppose one another.

While we have seen that the tendency in the nerve-sense system is to let the outer world penetrate into the organism, the tendency of the metabolic system is to "eliminate." Instead of "taking in" and passivity, we find here "giving out" and activity, as well as influence on the external environment.

If merely these two opposing systems were present, they would be engaged in a ceaseless battle that would negate both their functions, just as cold and heat combine to form a lukewarm mixture, or positive and negative electricity destroy one another in a short circuit. This danger is removed by the formation of a third system, which functions as a mediator between the other two. It is this mediation that guides the tension between the opposites to further development. This phenomenon is aptly described by Goethe's concept of "enhancement of polarity." Pursuing the above train of thought, we shall have to seek this system spatially in the middle region of the body.

The interplay between the two systems exists not only between above and below, but also between activity and rest, in a temporal alternation. The latter produces a rhythm. All rhythmic processes in the organism demonstrate this temporal alternation and can be grouped together as the *rhythmic system*. In reality, the two opposing systems described are not active simultaneously, but alternate constantly and rhythmically. During the day, man is awake and "lives" from the forces of the nerve-sense system. At night, during sleep, the actual life processes unfold; a general warming, enlivening, and stimulation of metabolic processes occurs. At this time there is a "switching off" of nerve-sense activity; the human being sleeps. We see that the rhythmic system acts over time. Investigating further, we see that the rhythm of waking and sleeping expresses the alternation of dominance by one or the other polar system, by nerve-sense activity or metabolic activity.

This alternation or rhythm is found again in virtually archetypal manifestation in the heart and lungs. Their rhythmic activity is so obvious that these two organs can be viewed as representatives of the rhythmic system. The heart alternates uninterruptedly between contraction and expansion, and one can see in contracting and tensing the opposite of expanding and relaxing. The dynamics described are directly apparent here. The same is true of the lungs with their continual alternation between inhalation and exhalation. We are not concerned here so much with what is generally viewed as the main activity of these two organs, the movement of blood and air. Obviously, these are of the greatest importance, but in considering the nature of the rhythmic system, we are concerned here primarily with the pure activity of the organs, with their dynamic, that they are placed between two poles and mediate between them. In contraction lives the dynamic of the nerve system; in expansion, the dynamic of the metabolic system.

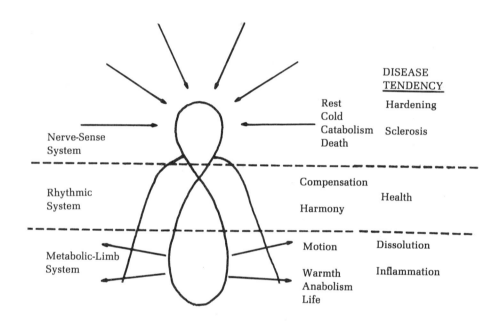

The Threefold Human Being

This conception of the human organism as consisting of three members provides a key to understanding health and sickness that will prove fruitful for pathology and therapy as discussed in the following chapters.

It is necessary for the doctor not only to discover which tendency is predominant in an organism, but also how this tendency is related to the person's age, that is, to time. Man has not only a spatial form (*Raumgestalt*), but also a temporal form (*Zeitgestalt*). The action of the forces in the threefold man, as described above, as well as that of the supersensible members of man's being, changes in the course of man's development.

Specific tendencies and characteristics are observable in seven-year periods. A description of these characteristics will be found in the following chapters.

Chapter II
The First Epoch of Life:
From Birth to the Change of Teeth

The Development of the Child

The Newborn Child and His Field of Forces

When we look with an unprejudiced eye at the growth of a child, we can observe in this growth the interplay of two groups of forces. The product of one group is the bodily "substantiality" of the newborn child, his physical forces and general health. These we regard as the products of heredity, of forces present in the bodily nature of the child's ancestors. We can see in them the action of the past reaching into the present.

The second group of forces reveals itself in the changes that a child undergoes over time; that is, in the differences we can observe when comparing the child at age one, two, three, etc. Then we see what tremendous changes have occurred in him. In the course of one to two years, the unformed infant, lying helpless on its back and aimlessly flailing its limbs, becomes a more strongly formed entity, walking upright, actively observing and participating in the surrounding world. Some time later, he is able to speak and reveal himself as a thinking, feeling, and willing being, one who can even sum up the whole of his physical and soul-spiritual existence by calling himself "I"—an act of unbelievably high philosophical abstraction and of concrete spiritual-physical experience as well! At this age, however, the child does not yet have any insight into the nature of his "I."

The impartial observer will recognize this transformation as the result of the forces of the soul and spirit coming into play over a period of time, and finally revealing themselves as "I." These forces stand opposed to those inherited from the parents; their dynamic is different in that they tend, gradually, to mold the physical body, which was initially built and governed by inherited substances and forces, into an instrument and expression of the "I," the individuality. Many years—the whole life, in fact—are needed to attain this goal, years that must include not only the unconscious, playful efforts of childhood but also conscious exertion and many illnesses.

If one does not choose to see mostly pure chance in the illnesses that affect man (in the final analysis, will is included in this view), one comes to recognize them more as processes by which the individuality gradually withdraws itself from the working of the forces of heredity.

This view is what is new in a medicine oriented toward spiritual science, a medicine that recognizes not only that the individuality is a reality of soul and spirit but also that *diseases occur in meaningful connection with the processes of individualization.* This is particularly true of childhood diseases, as we shall later see.

For the newborn, however, all this lies in the future and will manifest itself physically only in the course of time. Thus one can say that in the newborn not only the past but also the future is at work and, indeed, this future is not merely the future in general, but the totally individual future that every human being carries with him in his supersensible being. That the future is itself dependent on the person's *own* past (that is, earlier incarnations) we will mention only in passing. A detailed presentation of these connections is not possible here and is hardly necessary for a doctor's needs. To be sure, for the anthroposophically oriented doctor it will become a goal to recognize the individual bodily nature, with its disposition to disease, as the result of a past life, as Rudolf Steiner illustrated in numerous typical and individual examples.[1] The path of recognition, however, can proceed only from observation of the physical body and strive to reach its connection with the soul and spiritual nature. Medical study can and must be confined to concrete, observable connections at first. Still, even now, an impartial contemplation of relationships revealed by science could lead the physician to conclude that the human body cannot be understood on a physical basis alone, but that the physical is the expression of a supersensible system of forces.

The Development of the Child[2]

In the presentation of the water, air, and warmth organism, we have seen what a number of regulatory mechanisms is necessary to maintain the equilibrium of these systems in what we call health. The problem becomes more complex, however, when these mechanisms operate not in a mature organism, which is already in a certain state of balance, but in a growing organism. Each day puts new demands on the regulatory mechanisms, since the relationship between the individual organ systems changes continually.

Growth is not merely an increase in size; it is also a slow process of mineralization and formation. This process does not affect all organs to the same degree; certain organs are at times more affected, others less. Even contemplation of the outer forms can tell us what is essential concerning the development of form. The shaping of the outer form (*Gestalt*) is also a manifestation of the "time-form" (*Zeitgestalt*) (L.R. Grote), which is a membering of the flow of life in time and which occurs rhythmically, that is in life-epochs.

The *embryonic organism* originates from a sphere (the ovum), and one can say that the consequences of the spherical form are apparent up to the time of the change of teeth, though decreasingly so with the passage of time. The second characteristic of the embryonic form is the disproportionate size of the head. In the second month of gestation, the head still accounts for half of the body, while the limbs appear as secondary appendages of the trunk. Naturally, the change in proportions is most dramatic during the embryonic stage. The head of the newborn still makes up a fourth of the length of the body and has not yet evolved far from the spherical form, while that of an adult represents only one eighth of his height, having changed greatly from the spherical form with the growth of the facial bones. At the very beginning of life, the head is relatively large and weighty. It is distinguished not only by its size but also by its proportions, which characteristically differ from those of an adult's head. The cerebral portion of the head is predominant, with the strongly defined occiput, and in the face, the region of the eyes is pronounced. The forehead is high and large, usually curved slightly forward (a Madonna forehead). In comparison, the middle and lower parts of the face appear less formed; this area is small, soft, and as yet little delineated. The nose is merely indicated, and the slight jaws, especially the lower jaw, are set back. It is the rhythmic sucking on the mother's breast that initially brings the lower jaw further and further forward and allows new formative forces to flow into the whole skull region. The center of gravity of the child's head lies further back than the adult's, so that the head falls backward, not forward like the adult's, when the child is tired.

The trunk is also rounded, cylindrical, and the same tendency can be seen in the limbs. The whole form of the small child appears spherical, closed into itself, complete. The extremities still contribute to this total impression of roundness. Thus, the posture of the embryo is not dependent solely on the spatial conditions in the uterus; the extremities are held in an angular position, which is also retained for many months after birth. It is of particular note that the trunk does not yet appear segmented into chest and abdomen. Unity, the closed shape, is the dominant theme in the figure of the small child; all that is segmented, divided, or separate recedes in favor of the whole.

The mode of *movement* of the young child is also directed from the head. The movements occur as if the child were held from above, comparable to the movements of a marionette. They proceed in spirals, circles, and curves; a certain swaying back and forth can arise from the great weight of the head. The small child is still a "circler," the circle appearing as in the path of motion in countless children's games. The small child is also a tiptoer; he touches the ground only with his toes in the first attempts at walking; this is a careful, tentative touching of the earth. Not only walking and running are directed from the head; all the impulses for movement that can be observed in the infant proceed in a cephalo-caudal direction. The behavior

and movements first noticed developmentally are head and eye
movements; then comes fixation of the gaze. At a later stage,
coordination of eye and hand occurs. Finally, the legs become
strong enough to permit walking and standing freely upright.
Thus, the organism of movement is incarnated step by step
from head to foot. The extent to which the young child approaches everything from the head or from the center of the
organism is shown by the proximo-distal course of movement
in a limb; in the attempt to reach an object, first the shoulders
and elbows are moved and only then the wrists and fingers.

Connected with the predominance of the head pole is the ex-
panded importance of the sense organs. Just as the child's eye
first takes in everything indiscriminately, trusting that the
world is good, so his whole organism is actually like a sense
organ. The small child perceives and experiences his environment as an extension of his own body. If the surroundings are
sound and beautiful and if true thoughts are thought in them,
then health-giving forces flow through the child; he thrives and
attains his proper state of development. If his environment is
permeated by malignant influences, by hatefulness and false
thoughts, then the child's further development is seriously
hampered or altogether blocked in important ways, as in many
institutionalized children.

It is of fundamental importance for parents and educators to
have an immediate sense and certain knowledge of how every
impression from the outside penetrates as far as the body of
the child, having a beneficial or injurious, a wholesome or a
sickening influence.

This wholeness of form, harmonious in itself, is maintained
until the time of the change of teeth. Around the first half of
the sixth year, a gradual metamorphosis sets in, in which the
"small, pre-school child form" becomes the "school child form."
This signifies a "change in a sense relating to the whole psycho-
physical person."[3] Detailed description of this will be given in
the chapter on the school physician.

For a complete understanding of these processes, however,
we must consider what occurs in the supersensible members
of man. During growth, important changes take place in the

etheric body of the child. From birth on, he has remained in close connection with the surrounding etheric world; now he gradually loosens himself from it and becomes independent. This loosening proceeds in stages, occurring first in the head. Beginning with birth, the etheric forces organize the brain, which before then is a product of the forces of heredity, in such a way that it can become a suitable instrument for the incarnating individuality. This molding activity ends around the middle of the third year of life. That is the time when the etheric body of the head begins to become free. The complete release of the etheric forces from the region of the head does not take place until later (see the section on the change of teeth). From this point on, the etheric formative forces are partially lifted into the region of the soul and become available to serve as forces of memory and intelligence. Naturally, before this time the child already demonstrates the capacity to hold impressions in his mind and to gather experiences. But up to this point this occurs in such a way that all experiences immediately become formative forces; the experiences imprint themselves on the organism, molding it. In this way, however, they are almost totally forgotten. It is not until the middle of the third year of life (with individual differences) that experiences are increasingly preserved from being forgotten, and some stand out that remain permanently in the memory. This brings the first possibility of a conscious experience of the individual self; only when the child has inner experiences that he recognizes as his own, though they are in the past, can he experience himself as a being that transcends time.

Pedagogic Aspects

It is important for the child that those around him be fully aware of the special connection of the child's etheric body with the etheric environment. At this time, the child has a strong instinctive sense for the quality of the soul activity in his environment. He unconsciously participates in the soul processes of the environment and imitates them. This makes it possible for him to learn to speak and inwardly to grasp the meaning of what is spoken. Rudolf Steiner distinguished these functions as the "sense of the sounds of speech" (sense of language), and the "sense of thought." They are inconceivable without the foundation of an intimate capacity for imitation, which is made possible by means of the "etheric contact" with the environment. The "sense of 'I' or ego" is also very alive in the child, though it is unconscious and instinctive.

Owing to this "etheric contact," the child assimilates from the environment not only positive properties, but unfortunately also negative ones: discontent, discord, psychic turmoil, even disease syndromes. Often a child with "nervous symptoms," for example, stomach disturbances or insomnia, is in reality only reflecting what is occurring in the mother's soul or organism, and often undesirable behavior must be blamed not on the child, but on the mother or father. As a neutral observer, one is often astonished at the naïveté with which parents overlook these obvious connections. Much of what is ascribed to "heredity" is in reality only "induced."

The present-day tendency is still to view too great a part of the soul qualities as inherited. The mistaken interpretation of these connections has the most undesirable consequences in pedagogical terms for parents, for teachers, and especially for children. This concept of heredity has a blinding and crippling effect on the soul life of those involved, since it destroys, or at least minimizes, consciousness of freedom and responsibility.

One can see even today that children often hold their parents responsible for characteristics supposedly "inherited" from them. To be sure, the thinking is clearly unscientific, since parents cannot, after all, influence the natural course of heredity with their consciousness. Still, in some cases it would be quite justifiable for children to blame their parents for certain things—for example, that they may have quarrelled excessively in their presence or taken out their bad moods on them—in a word, that they did not educate themselves and thus transmitted their social immaturity to their children.

Concerning the basic importance of the education of the child up to the time of the change of teeth, Rudolf Steiner gave the following indications:[4]

In the whole of the rest of life, one cannot make good again what one neglected as an educator in the period up to the seventh year. As nature provides the right environment for the physical body before birth, so must the educator see to the right physical environment after birth. Only this right physical environment will affect the child in such a way that his physical organs will be molded into the right forms.

There are two magic words that indicate how a child enters into a relationship with his environment—*imitation* and *model.* The Greek philosopher Aristotle called man the most imitative of the animals, and this statement describes no period of life so much as the period of childhood before the change of teeth. Whatever goes on in his physical environment the child imitates, and through this imitation his physical organs are molded into the forms that they will retain. We must take this physical environment in the widest conceivable sense. It includes not only what occurs around the child, but also whatever occurs in his environment that can be perceived by him and that can act from physical space on his spiritual forces. This also includes all moral or immoral, all intelligent or foolish actions that he can sense or experience sympathetically.

Moral teachings and reasoned explanations do not have the desired effect on the child; rather, what adults do visibly before his eyes affects his behavior, and this affects the etheric body.

> Whatever . . . is to develop by way of concepts, habits, memory, etc., must develop "of itself" like the eyes and ears, which develop in the mother's womb without the influence of the outer light . . . What Jean Paul says in his excellent pedagogical book, *Levana oder Erziehlehre,* that a world traveller learns more from his nanny in his first years of life than on all his travels together, is undoubtedly correct. But the child simply does not learn by instruction; he learns by imitation. His physical organs develop their forms through the influence of the physical environment. Good sight will develop when the right relations of color and light are brought into the child's surroundings, and the physical foundation for a healthy moral sense will develop in the brain and circulation of the blood

when the child sees what is moral in his surroundings. If up to his seventh year, the child has seen only foolish actions in his environment, then the brain will take on such forms as will make it suited only for foolishness and silliness in later life.[4]

In other words, the education of the child up to the second dentition is based on the self-education of the parents.

Impressive examples of the child's extraordinary imitative capacity, involving the whole organism, are given by Alfred Nitschke, a Tübingen pediatrician. A girl almost three years old suffered from a severe functional disorder, which seemed to be located in the hip. She was unable to walk fast, to run, or to jump. Meticulous clinical examination showed no pathological findings.

> At first, we did not know what to think of this serious disability. The nature of this disturbance, which had been present since she began learning to walk, had a peculiar and initially surprising explanation. The father of the child was an author and scholar; he worked only at home and spent a great deal of time with the children. He was admired and honored by the family. The young daughter was especially attached to him. He had been badly injured in war, wore a partial prosthesis on the left side, and had stiffening of the hip joint. In conversation about this, it became clear to us, and then also to the mother when it was pointed out to her, that the gait of this physically healthy child was the same as that of her handicapped father. This is why she limped with a stiff hip and had never been able to jump; this is the reason for her peculiar way of going down stairs. The healthy child had taken on the gait of her injured father. How is that possible? Did she want to feign a disease, an ailment that was not there at all? It is certain that such wishes were not present in this child, not even hidden. Despite this disturbance of her gait, she seemed neither abnormal nor sick.
>
> But why did she walk like her father? What might cause the child to do this? You have often seen how children play the role of adults, as merchants, teachers, or sometimes father, and they can often take on the posture, gestures, manner of speech, and gait of their teacher, for example, surprisingly well. But this is just play, an assumed role that is dropped at the right time. This young patient was certainly not playing "father" in her strange

condition; she was not playing a role at all. This form of walking, which to our eyes was pathological, was the only way she had ever walked.

There are surely thousands of cases where, with a given external situation, this sort of imitation takes place in a way that is not so evident. The key to this imitative behavior toward the father lies in the phrase, "The young daughter was especially attached to him." This strong psychic bond led practically to identification, and in so intense a form as is possible only at that age.[5]

In a second example, Nitschke reports on a ten-month-old girl who began to vomit quite soon after birth, and had had problems with nourishment afterward. For this reason, the over-anxious mother had kept the child still and almost without stimulation.

> The child had no pathological physical symptoms but was wretched and thin, the musculature weak and slack. She could eat nothing, and had the habit of assuming a strange posture in which her body rested like a collapsed pocketknife between her thin, extended legs, while her arms often lay stretched out limply in front of her on the carpet. Her slightly raised face had a cross and apathetic expression. What struck one was her large, calm eyes and especially her expressive mouth with which she often played with her fingers. During the next three months in the clinic everything remained unchanged despite intensive efforts. In consultation with the parents, we attempted to discover some further cause, which we suspected but could not find.
>
> On the day when the child was to be shown in the lecture hall as someone whose condition we had not succeeded in explaining and overcoming, but whose impairment probably stemmed from the life situation, this girl was allowed to bring something she was fond of so that she would not be miserable. She brought from home a large stuffed rabbit, her favorite playmate, which she always kept in bed with her. At the sight of this animal, I was suddenly struck with the insight that this was the culprit! Now we remembered how, when the child was first admitted, we had jokingly commented, "That child looks like a rabbit." It was a large animal, one of the grotesque forms that children are

given to play with nowadays. It had long, thin, limply hanging arms and legs, a head with great big eyes, a pronounced mouth, and lips that the child was constantly touching with her fingers. The child had often laid this limp, sadly cross-looking rabbit opposite her on the coverlet, putting it in her own posture—the trunk between the limp hind legs, the front legs stretched out, the face, with its odd expression of eye and mouth, toward her. At home it had been almost the only partner of this otherwise isolated child. This was the model of posture, movement, and mood that had kept the child company and on which she had formed herself.

I would not be so bold as to give this decisive interpretation if its implications had not proved so effective in treatment. We replaced the rabbit with an almost equally large, upright, and well-delineated, friendly little lamb. The child grew fond of the new animal in a short time. Though we changed nothing else in the treatment, she began to eat with pleasure after just a few days; she soon grew childlike and happy, held herself erect, and forgot her old posture without our help. The transformation reached into the depths of the little person. It was beautiful and stirring for us after the long and futile effort, and for the mother, it was incomprehensible. This happy development remained uninterrupted at home. Given such a strong effect, one must assume that the child felt a lack of interest on the part of the mother or of any other person, and because of this attached herself strongly to the stuffed animal.[5]

Examples of the intimate connection of the child with the psychic organization of the mother are reported by the zoologist and parapsychologist, Karl Gruber, under the heading, "Telepathy Between Mother and Child." The mother of two boys, aged seven and nine, reported that she was reading a story one evening while the children were already asleep in the same room. The story, "The Princess of Babylon" by S. Lagerlöf, tells of a father who explains to his little daughter the origin of the confusion of languages in Babylon.

The next morning, when, as often happened, they told their dreams, Klaus had the following dream to report. "There was a great big tree up by our little house, and many men were there. I think they were Englishmen, they were dressed so strangely.

They wanted to get up the tree, up to the top, and they were helping each other; they had ropes and ladders. Then, the one who was the highest called to another to give him a rope but that one thought he meant he should fetch an axe, and now nobody understood anyone anymore, there was such a noise, and one of them thought he was supposed to set fire to the tree. So they all had to come down fast, and the tree burned down."

Assessment: Unquestionably, this is a case of telepathic transference from the mother, sunk deep in her reading, to the sleeping child. It is remarkable how the mother's mental image, produced by the poetical presentation, was symbolically transformed by the child's subconscious; that is, the stone tower becomes a tree.

Here is another case reported by Gruber of a Mrs. M. T.:

In the beginning of February, 1925, I was reading *The White Gods* by Eduard Stucken one evening. At one point it is related that when the Spanish army landed, a gallows had to be erected immediately in order to execute a man but that he was saved at the last minute. I was preoccupied with the thought that this unbridled army was greatly longed for by the Mexicans, who regarded them as "the white gods."

Suddenly Wuddi cried out with fear in his sleep. I went to his bed at once and tried to wake him, which is never easy with him. Half asleep, he said, "It's so horrible—a big empty square and there is a gallows on it where they are going to hang someone, and many others are standing far away!" I could not remember ever having heard the word "gallows" spoken by Wuddi, but after this dream, he was trying to build a gallows for days.

Assessment: In this case it is noteworthy that the telepathic transference evoked a strong affective impression, although the child was not awakened from his deep sleep by this psychic stimulus. In this way, the experience was able to act even more deeply, bodily, on the child.

An unbiased judge will agree with Gruber that the essential correspondence of the dreams and the readings of the mothers cannot be attributed to chance; rather, they must be seen as evidence of a "telepathy" existing between mother and child. One cannot but agree with Gruber when he draws the conclusion:

> This fact, however, makes us think further! Is it likely that only such impressions and images from books are transmitted? Or must we not rather assume that all contents whatsoever of the mother's subconscious can be received telepathically by the child? Are we not suddenly made aware by this of the enormous significance of the mother's physical behavior and psychic state for the child? What if all thoughts and sensations of the mother, good as well as bad, love and hate, grief and joy, hope and fear, can in principle be assimilated by the child's subconscious? What if these impressions take hold and become an inalienable part of the child's psyche? Not all of the mother's thoughts need be transmitted, as is probably the case, but it is quite enough that such a transmission to the child's subconscious from the mother is possible. After all, we know today from findings of psychoanalysis how great a role subconscious complexes developed in childhood play in man's life.

Gruber even considers the possibility that the embryo can be influenced telepathically by the mother, thus giving the appearance of the inheritance of psychic qualities.

It was necessary to insert this excursus into the field of pedagogy because no period of life is so important in giving rise to health or disease as this one. Further important details are to be found in the pedagogical works of Rudolf Steiner and his students.

The Awakening of Ego Consciousness

About the middle of the third year of life—today often considerably earlier—the child begins to speak in the first person. Before this, he calls himself what he has been called by those around him. I have even been told of a child who at first spoke of himself as "you," while the mother called him "I," until one day the names were switched. The child appropriates the "I" form in his speech without any external instigation; indeed, it goes against the names given him by the world around him. With this act, he initiates his spiritual existence in this world, which he asserts for the rest of his life.

If we have the opportunity to observe this process or hear adults describe it from memory, we often find that the first awakening of consciousness of self, or ego consciousness, was induced by some change in the external situation such as a little trip, moving into a new house, or, often, an experience of anxiety or fright. In the last case, the shock is generally also the earliest memory.

> At first, Christhilde called herself "you," pointing at her mouth with her index finger. Later, she spoke only of "we." Then, she spoke of herself as "Christhilde." After that, she dropped all names and said only, "Want that," etc. She said, "I" for the first time on the occasion of a minor car accident. At first, she was a little frightened and said, "Christhilde won't fall; *I* won't fall!" Her expression showed that she now felt quite sure of herself.

> Franz was left alone downstairs while his mother was upstairs. He was not allowed to climb the stairs and up to then he had not been able to do so. But now he felt lonely. Laboriously, he clambered up, step by step, and finally stood beaming in front of his mother. "Here I am; I am here!" For the first time, he experienced himself as "I." The sense of movement, the sense of balance, and the joyful consciousness of having overcome a difficulty together formed the basis for this experience.[6]

The Development of the Organs and the Constitution

Each organ must be formed before it can perform its function; that is, by means of the etheric body an instrument is created through which spiritual impulses—the higher parts of man's being, primarily the astral body or the ego—can influence the body in a specific way. One can recognize the connections of the individual organs to the higher members of man's being, as well as their relation to one another, by the structure and function of the organs.

An organ whose relation to the etheric body is readily apparent is the *thymus*. Its great importance to the immune system of the organism has been recognized only in the last decade. The following considerations will enable us to understand the functioning of this gland.

The fact that the thymus is the most active lymphocyte-producing tissue (especially in the cortex) speaks of a relation to the etheric body because lymphocytes are typical of the child's organism of anabolism and growth. The finding that the thymus is by far the biggest lymphatic organ in the newborn child and that it is necessary for the development of the lymphatic system suggests the same thing. Even before birth, however, the relative weight of the thymus begins a continuous regression. The thymus reaches its highest absolute weight (30-40 g) at puberty, after which a gradual atrophy sets in.

In experimental investigations, a decrease of the lymphocytes in the blood was found in conjunction with involution of the thymus and a diminished number of lymphocytes in this gland. In addition, it is found that the thymus often decreases rapidly in weight during consumptive and infectious diseases, as well as after shock and stress, that is to say, when catabolic processes predominate.

The reaction to ionizing rays is especially instructive. Of all the cells in the body, the lymphocyte is the most sensitive to radiation. Similarly, the thymus is the most radiation-sensitive organ, the small lymphocytes of the cortex being more so than those of the medulla. Ionizing rays have the most radically destructive effect on the inner structure of the etheric body.

The role of the thymus in the immune system is also informative. A thymectomy performed on a young animal leads to a lasting cessation of normal immunologic reactivity. Transplants of skin are no longer sensed as foreign and therefore not rejected. Thymectomy alone has no effect on a mature animal, but a combination of thymectomy and x-ray treatment leads to a permanent breakdown of immune reactions.

The so-called T-lymphocytes originating in the thymus mediate cellular immune reactions—the destruction of transplants, for example. They are immunologically competent cells, mediating a specific immune reaction in response to an antibody stimulus. These cells make up a large part of the circulating small lymphocytes; they play a large role as the so-called killer cells in the body's defense against tumors.

This phenomenon is also of great significance for the disease of cancer, since the body's defense against tumors is based above all on cell-mediated immune reactions. In this connection, it is worth noting that stimulation of the thymus and of lymphocytic reactions can be accomplished with mistletoe extracts.

Thus, the thymus is indispensable for the development of cellular immunity and in the formation of humoral antibodies against many antigens.

Definite connections also exist between the thymus and myasthenia gravis, a disease often associated with benign and malignant thymal tumors. Myasthenic patients also show lymphocytic infiltration of the muscles. Thus, an "infantile tendency" is predominant here, which prevents the impulse to motion (originating in the ego and astral body) from taking effect in an organism too involved in anabolic processes.

All these processes are the expression of the activity of the etheric body. It is the etheric body that builds not only species-specific, but also organ-specific proteins, and "takes note of" a sensitizing agent. Later, it "remembers" what the basis for the immune response was (see section on protein metabolism). The functioning over time is a typical expression of the activity of the etheric body. This constitutional tendency of the organism is particularly disturbed in malignant tumors because formative forces are no longer held by the totality of the etheric body, but grow independently, and thus proliferate. The thymus is the "executive" organ of the etheric body; by its functioning, it enables it to give form to growth.

As mentioned above, atrophy of the thymus begins around puberty. The interaction of the etheric and astral bodies can be studied with clarity at this point; the extent of thymus and adrenal cortical activity are in direct proportion to one another. Administration of corticoids (cortisone, cortisol, corticosterone, but not DOCA) leads within hours to involution of the thymus with destruction of or inhibition of the dividing of the lymphocytes; androgens and estrogens also lead to atrophy of the thymus. In contrast, thymal hypertrophy is found in Addison's disease; this can be understood from the material found in the section on steroid metabolism, on p. 260 ff.

These circumstances suggest that the astral body, which

becomes free around puberty (see chapter on the third epoch of life), supports itself henceforth in the "finished" organs. The incorporation of the etheric body and the formation of organs must be completed by this time; now the ego and astral body make use of them.

The thymus can thus be seen as a hormonal gland whose function is accented by a time factor. It has the task of serving the incorporation of the etheric body; this accounts for its relative largeness even before birth. Everything that injures the etheric body (ionizing rays, stress, catabolism), or transforms it (astral forces) has a destructive effect on this gland. The thymus can even be seen as the protective wall of the etheric body, preserving the forces of childhood, which must remain as a reservoir for a later time. We can also describe its "protective function" thus: before puberty, the etheric forces flowing in from the periphery are directed, through the thymus, in such a way that they serve, in the main, the building up and maturing of the organism. Only with the conclusion of the second seven-year period, when the astral body is partially freed (see below), is the thymus then subject to regression through the catabolic influence of the astral forces.

The organism of the newborn generally still has a rather high water content. This is especially true of the head; we speak of hydrocephalus when the water content of the head becomes abnormally great. It must be noted, however, as Rudolf Steiner pointed out, that a certain degree of "hydrocephaly" is a prerequisite for the normal development of the brain and nervous system.

> They must, so to speak, be drawn out of the fluid element existing in man. Thus in childhood we can observe a battle between hydrocephaly and what enters the human organism to combat hydrocephaly. One should really not speak of hydrocephaly alone, but also of the opposite, of an excessive loss of water in the brain. This is a disease that is perhaps not sufficiently noted; it is really nothing but the opposite pole from hydrocephaly and as such demands notice. As children, we are actually always swinging back and forth between these two extremes, hydrocephaly and later its opposite.[7]

This swinging of the organism between "excessive water content" and "desiccation," that is, between hydrocephaly and its opposite, which is not yet recognized as a clearly defined disease syndrome, can be confirmed by the observation of a physician. If the tendency to shrinkage, which corresponds to a normal physiological aging process, is too weak, then the organism tends to retain water in the tissues. Formerly, this condition was called "hydropic constitutional anomaly." Afflicted children often look fat but are only bloated. Many show great variations in body weight, which reflect accumulation or sudden elimination of water. Therefore, the term "constitutional hydrolability" was used, since this tendency to variation in water content can be observed even in newborns. Water loss (dystrophy) poses a special danger to tiny infants, since this element must still predominate in them. Such hydrolability frequently exists up to the end of the second year of life, often connected with a tendency to rickets, eczema, spasmophilia, etc. With the designation "poikilosmosis," these variations in water content were set alongside those of temperature found in cold-blooded (poikilothermic) animals.

When improper nourishment is added to this constitutional tendency, as was the case in the past with the frequent occurrence of illness resulting from an almost exclusively carbohydrate diet, then this condition can be easily produced by limitation of the (water-forming) carbohydrates. A temporary diet of milk alone, for example, usually results in an immediate drop in weight as an expression of water loss.

Thus, the hydropic constitutional anomaly stems from too weak an activity of elimination and formation, which is effected by the astral body. It is natural that under such circumstances the opposite pole, the metabolic process, must take the upper hand. When the metabolic process is not properly directed by the formation process, however, there will be a disorderly and excessive activity of the metabolic process, which expresses itself in infants and small children primarily as a tendency to sores and to weeping and crusting skin lesions (scab, milk crust); here we have the picture of an exudative lymphatic diathesis. It is interesting that in the first years of

life, the organism reacts with the whole skin to abnormal metabolic functioning. The organism at this age is still much more a
whole than later, and the individual organs do not yet stand
out much from each other. This is generally the case with all
illnesses of this age group. Behind the condition of remaining
too "watery," we can recognize a retarding element, because
the high water content is characteristic especially of the period
of early childhood.

Later in life, exudative lymphatic diathesis will become
manifest more in catarrhal inflammations and swelling of the
mucous membranes of the eyelids, nose, throat, bronchi, and
intestines. At the same time, or later, the glands in general,
especially the faucial and pharyngeal tonsils, can be enlarged.
Thus, the pathological symptoms move even more toward the
center of the organism. We can see here, as well, that the formative process begins at the periphery and gradually proceeds
toward the inside of the organism. The greater or lesser emphasis on the development of individual organs by man's
supersensible members lays the foundation for characteristic
constitutions.

These relationships need more detailed description. Even
after birth, the child's etheric forces remain completely incorporated into the surrounding etheric world, bound to it. From
this, the penetrating effect of the environment results, even into
the physical body of the infant, as described above. Gradually,
the etheric forces separate from the environment and consolidate. They remain closely connected with the whole physical body, continuing to build it and give it form. Were this to
remain so, then, although man would have an individually
formed etheric body, he would be able to use it only for growth
and the formation of organs, not for processes of consciousness. This is, in fact, the case in infancy and early childhood.

It has already been mentioned (p. 17) that approximately in
the second or third year of life, the forces of memory develop;
this stems from the freeing of the etheric body in the head
region, that is, its release from its organic connection. Consciousness can exist only on the basis of catabolic, life-trans-
forming processes. Without this death process, there could be

no real spiritual life—life manifesting in a new form. Rudolf Steiner pointed to this fact in a most emphatic way:

> The spirit unfolds within the human being *not* on the basis of *anabolic* activity, but on that of *catabolic* activity. Where spirit is to act in man, matter must hold back from its activity. The arising of thought within the etheric body is not based on a continuation of etheric existence, but on a disintegration of it. *Conscious* thought occurs *not* in processes of forming and growth, but in those of completion of formation and withering, of dying—processes that are continuously incorporated in etheric activity.[8]

This etheric decomposition, this atrophy, is prefigured physiologically in the nervous system, in which, after birth, there is practically no cell division, which is an expression of developing life. It is only in the region of the head that the etheric body is first gradually released; this brings about the basis for thinking and activity of memory. This process is completed around the time of the change of teeth. Only then is the child ready, from an organic standpoint, to learn. The implications of this will be discussed further later (see chapter on the second epoch of life).

It should be mentioned, however, that time has an essential role in this process. Thus, the brain is "ready" at a relatively early time, without yet exercising its function. Only when the development of the rest of the organism has been completed at its proper time can the supersensible members, now free, make use of the organs already formed. This occurs in definite rhythms, particularly the seven-year rhythm. The end of the first seven years is signaled by the change of teeth; that of the second, by puberty. What was said above of the etheric body and its release at the change of teeth is the case for the astral body at puberty. Naturally, the genital organs are "there" before birth. Maturity, however, does not come until puberty, the time when the astral body withdraws from the inner formation, becomes free and can begin to make use of the organs (see chapter on the third epoch of life).

We would like to mention here another indication given by Rudolf Steiner concerning the metamorphosis of the occurrence of disease. We have seen that the water organism is still predominant in infants and that control must be gained of it in the course of the first developmental period. This occurs in the head region through the interaction of the forces of hydrocephaly and its opposite, a certain drying out. Here, the time factor plays an essential role. If the tendency to a certain hydrocephaly—a weakness in dealing with the water organism —remains too long, then this disturbance moves further down into the organism. The underlying cause is an insufficiently defined part of the etheric body, which manifests itself as wateriness. This "etheric remnant," which could not be properly incorporated into the organism, now moves toward the chest. "It is simply hydrocephaly pushed one step lower in the human organization, where it forms the disposition for pneumonia or pleuritic symptoms, as well as for what is connected with these symptoms in childhood."[9]

Here we have basically the same situation as in hydrocephaly. It is a case of insufficiently organized water, especially recognizable in exudative pleurisy. In pneumonia the initial watery phase is also clearly recognizable in the "hepatization" of the lung. This explains why lobar pneumonia practically never occurs in early infancy. Bronchial and interstitial pneumonia, typical for children, have other bases (see chapter on the lung in Vol. III).

Rudolf Steiner warned against incompletely curing or suppressing pneumonia and pleurisy in children; he saw in such suppression the danger that the "hydropic constitution" would be displaced one step further inside the organism, appearing as a disposition to heart disease and polyarthritis. Rather, the doctor's task must be, if possible, to treat pneumonia and pleurisy with physical dietetic measures, especially in childhood, and thus not disturb the normal course of these illnesses. This will permit the disease process to complete itself in this form and to avoid the further metamorphoses mentioned above. Besides this, pneumonia can be a "recovery disease" at this age (see chapter on infectious disease in Vol. III).

A pair of forces to which Rudolf Steiner repeatedly and emphatically referred is important for the formation of the constitution, especially in the first seven-year period. These are represented by the substances magnesium and fluorine. Before the end of the first period of life—the change of teeth—the balance must be correctly set in the actions of these two substances.

In the first seven years of life, the principle consolidation of the organism, the incorporation of solid substance in bone formation, takes place and ultimately leads to the pushing out of the second teeth. The change of teeth is by no means a purely physiological event, merely providing man with better chewing instruments; above all, it has a spiritual meaning. Therefore, it is a sign of a significant step in development.

Teeth consist mainly of calcium, of course, but this substance is not formed according to its own, innate forces. As one can see from any snail, mussel, or foraminifer—the typical calcareous animals—the characteristic rounded, closed form predominates in them. This is not, however, what is found in the tooth. Every section of a tooth shows that the inner dentine is built up in a raying-out pattern, whereas on the outside, there is a well-defined boundary formed by the enamel. These two opposing tendencies in tooth formation, namely, the radiating formation from the inside and the defining, hard boundary on the outside, represent the two forces of magnesium and fluorine, which are found even materially in the respective parts, dentine and enamel. Thus, we can see the interaction of these two processes in tooth formation. An understanding of these two processes in childhood and a corresponding conceptual use of them are significant to the constitution during the whole life. The significance and practical use of magnesium and fluorine are described in detail in the chapter on mineral remedies (see Vol. II).

With the change of teeth, the first epoch of life is concluded. The etheric body has been freed, and a new configuration of the four bodies of man has come about. Before we direct our attention to this different period of life, however, we must discuss the disease of rickets as well as the group of typical febrile childhood diseases, as these not only occur mainly in the first epoch of life, but often also contribute decisively to the formation of the constitution for the whole life.

Rickets

We will discuss this disease in detail, since it reveals certain fundamental concepts.

Today rickets occurs most frequently in the first year of life. A lassitude finally increasing to the point of obvious muscular weakness is often the first thing the mother notices. Then comes increasing insomnia, which is clearly connected with increased sensitivity. This can be so strong that the child is startled when someone merely comes near him, and twitching of the face and arm muscles can arise (spasmophilia). In the face of this excitability of the nerve-sense system, the immobility of the rest of the body is striking; the legs, trunk, and sometimes the arms lie limp and flaccid. Only the head is thrown about restlessly in many cases, as if the increased movement might help an inner discomfort. Often connected with this is abnormal sweating of the head, which, together with the head movement, can cause partial baldness of the back of the head. The bone is so thin that in some places it can even be pressed in like parchment. Craniotabes, however, is not only a symptom of rickets; as is known, it can also occur alone.

A glance at the rest of the organism will show us immediately that the disease is not confined to the head. The abdomen protrudes quite far, though it does not appear to be painful. The musculature is poorly developed, and in severe cases it is in a sort of constant tension. It is the flexors that are characteristically most affected. When the tensed muscles are touched, the children react with vigorous expressions of pain.

Examination of the chest shows that the ribs, at the points where they become cartilaginous, are thickened and painful ("rachitic rosary").

Thus, we find disturbances of the bone system alongside those in the nerve-sense system. These disturbances include

not only the described thickening, but also an abnormal softness of the bones, which, when the disease lasts long enough,
can lead to thickening and distortion of the extremities and
vertebral column. In reference to craniotabes, it should be
mentioned in passing that the significance of a disease symptom differs when it appears in the head or in the lower part of
the body, because the dynamic is a different one in these
different places.[10] The consequences of this extend to the
therapy; while the general disorder of rickets can be treated
with phosphorus, craniotabes requires a mineral salt-like substance such as calcium carbonate.

With metabolic research and the clarification of the significance of vitamin D for rickets, certain extremely instructive
patho-anatomical data have quite wrongly receded into the
background. We will look at them first simply as phenomena.

The disturbance present in rickets is characterized by a *deficient tendency to calcification.* Cartilaginous cell columns,
separated by the matrix, are formed as in normal growth, but
the matrix does not calcify, at least, not sufficiently. Similarly,
the final bone tissue does not calcify at all or altogether insufficiently, so that it retains an abnormal flexibility. This defective
mineralization process is one thing to be noted in rickets; we
must also direct our attention to another.

In normal bone formation, the branches of blood vessels
pushing out from the medullary space advance in a regular
way, parallel to one another. In rickets, this occurs in an irregular way: the blood vessel branches form in all directions.
The cartilaginous columns show *no ordered direction of
growth,* and tissue is formed in which the cellular and matricu-
lar elements are mixed together irregularly, finding their way
by themselves without developing after the common plan that
is so beautifully manifested in normal bone, with its "direc-
tional phenomenon." Naturally, this makes it impossible for
the outer part of the bone to form properly. The newly formed
tissue does not sufficiently show the tendency to grow longitudinally; it swells out on the sides in a broad layer, giving the
joints a plump appearance. Longitudinal growth lags behind.

The *absence of plan* in the formation process is also visible in other *proliferative symptoms.* One site of their occurrence is the periosteum, which covers the bone on the outside and provides elements for the formation of marrow and bone. The periosteum begins to proliferate and produces a flat tissue without calcium, with the result that the bones that are covered with it—for example, the skull—take on a misshapen appearance. In addition, the endosteum, a delicate membrane lining the medullary space inside the bone, also proliferates. It produces a fibrinous connective tissue that gradually penetrates into the medullary cavities and displaces the marrow. In this connective tissue, bone trabeculae form without calcium, and these also show the peculiarity of being placed without order or plan. We need only think of the great extent to which normal bone is permeated with an architectonic principle.

Thus, there are two primary features to be noted in rickets: a *metabolic disturbance,* the deficient incorporation of calcium, and a *structural disturbance,* manifesting itself in the chaotic growth of the cartilage cells and the irregular architecture of the bone trabeculae.

In the recent decades since the discovery of the role of vitamin D, research into the pathogenesis of rickets has served to shift attention away from pathological anatomy toward physiological chemistry. As is well-known, vitamin D_3 is absolutely necessary for the deposition of calcium in bone. Still, it would be erroneous to draw the conclusion from this fact alone that administration of vitamin D_3 is necessary. The fact that vitamin D occurs so rarely in nature is really a clear hint from nature. After all, the organism itself possesses the capacity to produce the provitamin, and this is then changed into the active vitamin through the influence of light. Thus, vitamin D is not a real vitamin, by definition, since it does not need to be supplied from the outside; this indicates that rickets is not a pure a-vitaminosis, but rather a disturbance in which much more is implicated than a dietary vitamin D deficiency.

What must absolutely be taken in from the outside is light, rather than the vitamin, which is the result of the interaction of light and the provitamin that is produced in the organism. Therefore, it is no truly therapeutic measure to relieve the organism of its task of forming the provitamin by supplying the finished product. A true therapy must rather aim at promoting provitamin production in the organism. How this can be achieved will be shown later, but it will be clear from what has been presented that therapy will not be based on the substance that is lacking or its "building blocks." Rather, it will take into account the processes that first give rise to the substance and that are able to work through it. It should go without saying that we must provide for sufficient sunlight. In this connection, there are different and contradictory practices today. There is the fashion of exposing infants to full sunlight, and it is also thought that with the administration of vitamin D, light from outside is unnecessary. The latter practice poses a danger in that frequent over-feeding and excessive protein intake impede the utilization of light.

It must be emphasized once more that the rickets problem cannot be solved with vitamin D alone. This is shown simply by the fact that not every case of rickets can be successfully treated with vitamin D and that bottle-fed children are more inclined to rickets than those who are breast-fed, although cow's milk contains more vitamin D than human milk. This is also indicated by the discovery that citric acid is prophylactically effective against rickets, even though citric acid is chemically unrelated to vitamin D. What the two do have in common is that they are two carriers of the same process. Both have assimilated light into their substance and are therefore in a position to let the light become active in a certain chemical activity. This shows clearly that chemical considerations alone, which do not rise from the substance to the process, cannot do justice to the reality of a living organism.

Rickets is a disturbance of the light metabolism (see the section on light metabolism) stemming either from lack of light (exogenous rickets), or insufficient capacity to absorb light, which is connected with insufficient capacity to form the provitamin (endogenous rickets). The result is that the (astral) nerve-sense process does not penetrate the entire organism but is dammed up in the head. The complete vitamin, having absorbed light, is its latent carrier ("light mineral") and is therefore able to be chemically effective. In cases of deficiency, the metabolism is no longer properly penetrated by light and by the nerve process; as a result, the organism lacks precisely those formative forces necessary for bone growth. The architectural disturbance of the bones described is the consequence of this.

It is the entire metabolism, however, that suffers from rickets. From another point of view one could say that the solid and fluid organisms are not sufficiently organized by the light forces, by the air and warmth organism. This becomes evident in the characteristic metabolic disturbance. The organism succumbs to gravity. Food reaches the fluid organism, but this is not sufficiently "aired through"; oxidation breaks down and intestinal activity is sluggish ("vagal atony"). The organism accumulates more and more water, and precipitation of solid calcium salts comes to a halt, since the ego organization, lacking light with which to affect, through vitamin D, the chemistry of the organism, does not reach the bone system. In this way, separation of mineral calcium from the living tissue ceases. This very transference from the living to the dead state is a function of the ego organization. It alone can accomplish the last step of devitalization in both food (see section on nutrition, p. 211) and the organism, where something solid, dead, is separated from the realm of what is living. The ego organization brings this about through the lead process, which is in its essence a death process. The meaning of this process for man is presented in detail in the chapter on the metals (Vol. II).

Thus, rickets is a disease or weakness of the ego organization. Since this organization is specific to man, when it is disturbed, deviations of the human form occur, which the genius of language connects with animal forms—for example (in the German language), frog-belly, dachshund legs, pigeon breast, etc.

In rickets, the "organizer" of the bone system, namely, the ego organization, is lacking, and this becomes apparent in the patho-anatomical findings in the absence of structure in bone formation. Furthermore, the bone cannot be permeated with solid substance; it remains too living and plastic. The accumulation of water in the organism extends to the brain, which often may be greatly distended from enlargement of the ventricles (hydrocephaly). Postmortem, the brain is often found to be quite firm, presumably as a result of a secondary hardening of the connective tissue.

The psychic symptoms to be observed with rickets are only an expression of the processes observed. The damming up of the nerve-sense process in the area of the head leads to insufficient movement of the arms and especially of the legs; in compensation, there is abnormal restlessness of the head and a tendency to sleeplessness (clinging of the astral body to the nerve-sense system). If the lack of calcium in the brain reaches a certain point, then this process is intensified, showing a tendency to cramps (spasmophilia).

Whenever there is a "hindrance" in the metabolism, the astral body tries to compensate with increased activity in the muscles, resulting in cramps.[11]

The secondary alteration of the brain, then, has further psychic consequences because the higher members of man's being cannot act properly in it. Such children learn to speak late, are often spiritually sluggish, and develop slowly. In extreme cases they remain retarded for the rest of their lives.

The prevention of rickets is one of the most important tasks in the care of infants. It is important to recognize the mineralization process, disturbed in rickets, as the time-dependent process of incarnation. Today, we have the technical ability not only to stimulate the physiological processes by means of synthetic vitamin D, but also to accelerate them excessively. In this stimulation there is the danger of eliminating one disorder only to create another that is not seen or recognized as such. This problem is discussed at various points (see p. 257 f. and the chapter on pediatrics in Vol. III). It follows from the approach described here that for a child to grow and thrive, a basic prerequisite is loving care, permeated by a knowledge of the child's spiritual essence. From this, such behavior will naturally develop as will make possible for the child's soul a gradually stronger connection with the physical body. Such an inner attitude will cause the simplest actions to express what is right.

The medicinal prophylaxis and therapy of rickets is described in the chapter on pediatrics (Vol. III).

Childhood Diseases

As was explained in the preceding sections, the human organism is at all levels an expression of the individual ego. This penetration of the organism by the forces of the ego is not given, however, but is the result of development, during which the ego must prevail in confrontations with obstacles. The childhood diseases, especially measles, German measles, and scarlet fever, are an expression of this necessary struggle.

The term "childhood diseases," which corresponds to the immediate observations, has become unpopular today. These diseases are no longer connected with the essential being of the child; rather, the fact that mostly children are affected is thought to be purely accidental and is given the explanation that the infectious agents are ubiquitous, so that every person is exposed as a child. Therefore, one speaks of "cyclic infectious diseases" (Höring), of "acute exanthemas," or of "acute contagions of civilization" (de Rudder). These designations are quite correct descriptions but are not suited to grasp the essence of the phenomena.

Not every illness that occurs during childhood is a childhood disease in the sense we give this expression. Thus, rickets and "infantile" paralysis do not qualify for this term.

The most characteristic feature of the typical childhood diseases is fever. Impartial observation reveals repeatedly that children easily and quickly get high fevers and also can overcome them alone, usually without treatment. This ability to produce and control fever easily is typical of the child's organism, and it clearly diminishes in the course of life. In adults, highly febrile illnesses are much rarer and have a different significance for their organisms. While in an adult a fever appears as a symptom of a serious illness and represents a great strain on the organism, in the child high fever is managed much more easily. Dangers for the circulation, heart, and other organs are not at all so great as for the adult. The fact of the relative harmlessness of high fever for the child is often overlooked in this age of therapeutic optimism in regard to infectious diseases.

This "canny" management of warmth is so characteristic for the child that one may have the impression that he is using the illness or the viruses to produce fever. In such a case, they would be the means to an end. In favor of this is the occurrence, by no means rare, found almost alone in children, of "psychogenic" fever without external cause; that is, without agent, in a situation of psychic crisis.

Precisely such an observation suggests that we investigate the meaning of the febrile reaction. Undoubtedly, there is a somatic meaning in the sense of an influence on the defense system (see chapter on inflammation and chapter in Vol. III on infectious diseases); this is certainly only part of the phenomenon, however, as the above example shows.

In spiritual science we speak of a warmth organism, which as such not only permeates everything solid, but also controls the water and air organisms. As the water organism is the expression of the etheric body and the air organism is a manifestation of the astral body, so the ego lives in the warmth organism. Thus, the warmth relations are a concrete index of the extent to which the ego is involved in the organism. With heightened warmth activity in a fever, there is intensified involvement of the ego in the organism. Since the connection of the ego with the body is only complete in the course of time, it will be seen why the child has the "need" of fever more often; that is, the ego makes stronger contact with the body for a time. In other words, the ego enters into the metabolism to a greater extent, which can be seen in the enormously heightened turnover of substances. The increased warmth is, after all, produced by increased combustion of body substance. More specifically, it is body protein that is broken down and excreted in greater amounts. The dark urine typical of fever indicates this intensified elimination of end products of protein metabolism (not only urochrome).

Protein is the body substance that is most "individually" constructed; only because of this is it able to be the carrier of the individual ego (see section on protein metabolism). Since the ego develops continuously in the course of life, however, the physical vehicle, as its specific vessel, must continuously adapt itself to the changing content. These developmental steps, however differently they are accomplished, are greatest in childhood. The organism of the newborn child is really still the substance of the mother, into which the individuality is drawn with the first breath, incarnating itself and literally being bound to the flesh. It is only in the course of the first years of childhood that the "received" protein is transformed to correspond to the individuality. In general, this happens as a gradual part of development, but it can also proceed dramatically in a short time; in this case, it manifests as fever or childhood disease in which the fever is the instrument of the ego in dissolving the "old" corporeality, the protein that is no longer adequate. For this reason, each fever is both a kind of rejuvenation and a new connection of ego and body.

This explains why the child, though his weight may have decreased from loss of protein substance, is usually altered positively in soul and spirit after recovering from a childhood disease. To be sure, doctor and parent seldom pay attention to such phenomena. Before the disease breaks out, children are often whiny and utterly disagreeable. They give the impression of being uncomfortable "in their own skin." This expression, relating the bodily sensation to the skin, comes from a correct intuition. It can hardly be an accident that the typical childhood diseases of measles, German measles, and scarlet fever, are manifested in the skin ("breaking out") and, in part, even lead to a change of skin substance, that is, of a specific protein, through desquamation.

Ever more voices are making themselves heard who see a deeper meaning in the child's mode of reaction and think it by no means desirable always to protect children from these diseases. H. Müller-Eckhard devoted a monograph to the problem of "the illness of not being allowed to be ill." He writes:

> We now have come to the heretical formula that a child has childhood diseases in order to become healthier because it is evident

that without them the child cannot accomplish the adaptation required in the adult order so well or so quickly. He must continually change; he must learn and practice without pause.

Summarizing in conclusion, he says:

Every childhood disease has a meaning and an immanent function that can become active in many directions. Quite often a childhood disease is an irreplaceable help in life, which the child cannot do without in many situations on the difficult journey out of his magic and mystical state of consciousness into the world of the crass reality of the adult order. In all the well-meant protective immunization against childhood diseases, especially against those involving desquamation, one thing seems to have been forgotten: with the childhood diseases that are "eliminated," and whose appearance and arising is made impossible, the active and wholesome functions of these diseases are also taken from the child.

Every febrile illness brings about a radical change in the constitution of the organism. The fundamental polarity of inflammation (fever) and sclerosis (diseases of abnormal deposits such as atherosclerosis, diabetes, or carcinoma), which is treated in the chapter on inflammation, is influenced by every process in the warmth organism. This means that any suppression of a fever or inflammation pushes the balance in favor of a disease lying on the sclerotic side. It has been found, for example, that people who have not gone through any childhood diseases have a greater inclination to cancer. These connections are presented in detail with references in the chapter on inflammation and sclerosis. Here, as well, one can see an indication of the positive significance of the childhood diseases for the course of man's life.

In every measure taken, the physician should keep in view the entire course of the patient's life, above all, the later part; this is of particular importance in pediatrics. Self-deception with short-term "successes" and "recoveries" can have negative effects later. It is in this connection with the whole life that we must view therapeutic measures. Of course, by now no one sees fever as a completely meaningless reaction. Still, as we have seen, a fever is not only a somatic occurrence; it is a developmental step that the child accomplishes with the help of specific processes, namely, the childhood diseases. The common practice of mechanically ordering fever tablets for every ordinary disease manifestation is based on a way of thinking that sees every disease as an irksome breakdown of operations that should be eliminated quickly without inquiring into its significance. The meaning and consequences of such measures for the entire life can only be judged when medical practice is founded on an approach capable of seeing a manifestation of man's soul-spiritual being and development in every physical occurrence.

Naturally, every disease is a crisis and, like every real challenge, it entails dangers, but it is just this that makes development possible. Of course, the fever can climb too high or last too long, thus endangering the entire organism with toxic products or excessive tissue destruction. The heart and circulation are especially threatened with overtaxing. These dangers are not so great in the child, however, because of the character of his organism.

An essential and meaningful defense against increased toxic catabolic products is found in the febrile patient's lack of appetite. The organism is so occupied with its own body-specific protein that it cannot manage digestive activity in the gastrointestinal region. Therefore, during fever, the intake of food, but not of fluid, should be limited as much as possible; in particular, the diet should be poor in, or free of, protein. The excessive catabolic activity can be checked with Argentum D30 daily or twice daily as an injection, possibly with Echinacea. This measure will hardly be needed in childhood diseases. For these, physical therapeutic measures—cold packs on the calves or body—will suffice to dampen the excessive reaction without suppressing the fever. The use of antipyretics is neither appropriate nor necessary. The medicinal therapy is described in the chapter on pediatrics (Vol. III).

Until the middle of the eighteenth century, measles, scarlet fever, and German measles were considered to be one disease. What they have in common is given in the designation "acute exanthema," mentioned above. But how different these diseases are in their physiognomy!

Measles

Measles is a "normal" disease, so to speak; almost every person used to have it.

After an incubation period of ten to eleven days, the catarrhal initial or prodromal stage begins. The temperature rises to 38.5 –39.5°. The mucous membranes of the eyes, nose, pharynx, larynx, and trachea become inflamed and begin to secrete. Lacrimation, photophobia, sneezing, coughing, and hoarseness appear. Thus, the processes of the *water organism* are already coming to the fore. These indicate the predominance of the (inherited) body of formative forces, which makes use of the watery element. In fever we observe the increased involvement of the ego.

On the second or third day, the temperature falls almost to normal and rises again on the third or fourth day to 39–40°, accompanied by the breaking out of a skin rash. This appears regularly fourteen days after exposure to the infection. With the exanthem, the ego carries its counterthrust by way of the blood to the skin. The rash starts on the head (behind the ears) and face, spreading over the neck, trunk, and extremities in the form of large, irregular spots that are often confluent. Thus, the ego begins to operate on the organism from the head, corresponding to the natural tendency in development, since the forming of the child's organism also proceeds from the head.

> In addition to the heavy rash, the face is further disfigured by conjunctivitis and rhinitis, which increase. Redness and secretion of the conjunctiva, blepharitis, often with crust formation and adhesion of the lids, swelling of the nose with reddening of the nostrils, defects of the mucous membranes, and dried secretions, along with the exanthem and a diffuse puffiness, combine to produce a characteristic appearance that often permits diagnosis at first glance. (Staehlin)

This description also reveals the pronounced "watery" character of the disease.

The disappearance of the rash in three to four days, is accompanied by a quickly falling temperature; simultaneously a bran-like desquamation begins. In its alterations, the blood picture mirrors this confrontation of the ego with the etheric-astral forces: the neutrophilic leukocytosis and eosinophilia existing during incubation reflect the predominance of etheric-astral forces in the blood system. In the initial stage the number of white blood cells decreases quickly and, during the exanthem, there is pronounced leukopenia. Thus, the ego has driven the etheric and astral elements from the blood, expelling them through the skin. As the disease wanes, the "lymphocytic-eosinophilic healing phase" begins, an expression of the regenerated higher members of the sick child's being; then the pendulum comes to rest again.

After this regular course of measles, the child proves changed for the better in spirit and character, as parents and educators repeatedly notice. Through the disease, the ego has overcome old, inherited counterforces that hindered his development. Related to this is the fact that with the measles, weeping (water organism!) eczemas often dry up, chronic festering wounds close, and nephrosis can be healed.

The ego's strongest thrust is expressed in the breaking out of the exanthem; it is like a spraying of the blood into the skin. This can lead to hemorrhagic symptoms. If the exanthem develops weakly or recedes quickly, then the fever usually climbs again. The ego must then make up through increased temperature and inner catabolic processes for what it could not attain by the normal elimination process through the skin.

This can be the basis for complications, which in general are not common with measles. It is popularly called, "The striking back of the measles," rather than its "coming out" in an undisturbed course. This represents an immediate and correct grasp of the relationship between skin symptoms and internal damage. Contemporary medicine also registers the connection but only in the sense of a temporal sequence. For a deeper understanding of the dynamic manifested here, the concept of meta-morphosis is needed.

Eczemas that "take the place" of liver diseases, for example, are well-known. Too little attention, however, is given to the skin as an organ of a specific kind of elimination. From what has been presented above, we may assume that a pathological protein[12] is excreted through the skin, leading to exanthema there. The latter is the expression of the struggle that ends in the breakdown of the protein or its elimination through desquamation. If the ego does not have sufficient force to accomplish the centrifugal blood-skin process, which relieves the organism of this protein, then the pathological protein remains in the organism and damages the internal organs. Here, a clear transformation of the disease can also be observed. Formerly, pneumonia was the most frequent complication of measles. It developed after the disappearance of the exanthema. What should occur in the skin—the elimination of the protein—must now be accomplished through the lungs. The exanthema appears in pneumonia as an enanthema of the lungs. It is obvious that the course by way of this organ is more dangerous than through the skin. Nevertheless, excretion and discharge can take place here as well.

In recent years, encephalitis has become more frequent as a complication of measles. Elimination is not possible in this case, as it is in the skin and lungs. The exanthematous reaction typical of this disease can no longer proceed "correctly," that is, with elimination; it must lead to severe disorders, often to death. It is characteristic and quite natural in view of the material presented that the encephalitis usually appears after the exanthema has gone. It would be rewarding to investigate to what extent encephalitis appears with a weak, "insufficient" exanthema, and how much it could be made to regress by means of a provocation of the skin, for example, by stimulation with a mustard compress. In any case, this proves to be a significant therapeutic measure. In general, in accordance with what has been said, the most important prophylaxis against encephalitis would be to prevent anything that suppresses the fever and with it the exanthema. The interaction of fever and viruses is discussed in detail in the chapter on inflammation, on p. 171 ff.

Thus we have a progressive metamorphosis of the disease process from the skin to the lungs and then to the brain. This is also the order of increasing danger. Therefore, it is a therapeutic requirement to move the disease process in the reverse direction, in the sense of a regressive metamorphosis, allowing it to run its course at its proper site, the skin, as a harmless process.

Another example will show the significance for the brain of disease processes that are not allowed to run their course in the skin. When rabbits are infected with smallpox, and the disease symptoms on the skin are prevented, encephalitis results with great regularity.[13]

The present increase in encephalitis as a complication may be due to a cyclic change of the "genius epidemicus"; that is, temporal appearance and severity manifest an inner law (see chapter on infectious diseases, Vol. III). To what extent we are dealing not only with a displacement inwards but also with a real change of locus of the disease manifestations could be judged only by observation of undisturbed courses. There is an ever-increasing load and strain placed on the nervous system today, and this affects even infants through strong sense impressions. Therefore, it is not surprising that a continually overtaxed organ becomes more susceptible to disease.

The following observation shows what a profound influence sensory stimuli have in infants, and what an importance protective warmth has in this connection.

> Repeated loud noises produce fright reactions in infants with increased sympathicotonus lasting one minute. There is an increase in the peripheral circulatory resistance. With a longer period of noise, a tendency to increased general vasoconstriction is observed. An excessive counter-reaction can also be observed in the form of increased vasodilation. The reactions are dependent on the temperature of the environment and skin. Warmth appears to balance the strong noise load to a certain extent.[14]

Scarlet Fever

Without an initial stage, and after a short symptomless incubation lasting 1–9 days, scarlet fever begins abruptly with high fever, chills, vomiting, and sometimes diarrhea. Tonsillitis, also appearing immediately, is distinguished from other sore throats by its flaming red color. The exanthema begins on the neck and trunk after 12–24 hours. The face is not affected except by redness from the fever; the pale mouth-chin triangle stands out sharply. The rash consists of countless small spots, which seem to cover the body with a uniform scarlet red. The tongue is at first thick and coated with a white film, and on the third or fourth day presents the picture of the so-called "strawberry tongue," with its swollen, bright red papillae. On about the third day, the temperature begins to go down stepwise, reaching normal as the exanthema disappears, usually on the seventh day. Desquamation, sometimes appearing only after several weeks, assumes a lamellar form, especially on hands and feet.

It is noteworthy that the head is less affected by the exanthema (circumoral pallor) than the body. This indicates that the physical disposition to scarlet fever is different than for measles; this, of course, follows simply from the fact that most children have already had measles when they contract scarlet fever. Inherited etheric forces, which were too strongly active in the organism, have already been eliminated with measles. In particular, the etheric forces have already been freed in the region of the head. Here the astral body takes effect physiologically, producing consciousness. This is why the head area stays free of exanthema during scarlet fever. The complications appear in the area of the metabolic system. Despite its destructive tendency and large number of complications, scarlet fever is followed by meningitis more often than by encephalitis. On the one hand, this is because the astral body is involved in the disease in the same way that it is normally active in the nervous system but to an even greater extent; on the other hand, it is important that with scarlet fever—unlike mea-

sles—streptococci, that is, bacteria, play a part, tending to act
on the blood, while viruses are clearly neurotropic (see chapter
on infectious diseases in Vol. III).

The intense activity of the astral body is also manifested in
extreme eosinophilia, which is also observed in manifestations
of parasitic worms, asthma, and other allergic diseases, that
is to say, where there is penetration of foreign protein or foreign astrality (cf. p. 217). Here there is a confrontation with the
individual's own astrality, which accounts for the much more
dramatic course and the flaming redness.

In pictorial language, one can say that while measles has
been described as a more "watery" disease, scarlet fever clearly
has a "fiery" nature. A related fact is that scarlet fever is easily
provoked by burns or wounds (traumatic scarlatina). In both
cases the patient suffers a psychic shock and at the same time
an injury to his blood system; the ego is attacked from both
within and without, and astral forces try to assert themselves
excessively.

In contrast to measles, scarlet fever tends toward complications that appear either in the first days of the illness, or else,
quite often, in the second or third week as late complications.
We find these mainly in the metabolic system when the astral
body has a directly catabolic action, causing destruction typical of scarlet fever complications. The most dreaded of these is
nephritis, which occurs usually in the third week. Its occurrence is accounted for by the relation of the kidneys to the
astral body (see chapter on the kidney in Vol. III). In scarlet
fever nephritis, the astral body's action in "its" organ is no
longer excretory but catabolic in an uncontrolled way.

Other complications are endocarditis; the dangerous angina
scarlatinosa maligna (necrotica); otitis media, which easily
leads to necrosis of the auditory ossicles and the petrous bone,
with the resultant problems of all these. Such complications
stem from scarlet fever's tendency to destruction (penetrating
action of the astral body), to "breaking out of the substance,"
which also appears in lamellar desquamation. It is often by
this desquamation (especially on the hands and feet) that an
atypical course of scarlet fever is afterwards recognized.

Rheumatism is an occasional complication of scarlet fever (usually at the end of the first or during the second week) of symptomatological interest. There is swelling of the upper or lower extremity joints that is similar to that in polyarthritis, though not reaching the same proportions and intensity. At this age, the disposition to polyarthritis is simply not yet present.

For a general evaluation of scarlet fever, we must remember that its appearance is cyclic. Phases, years long, of relative frequency and severity alternate with those of infrequency or total harmlessness (see chapter on infectious diseases in Vol. III).

The disposition to scarlet fever is not as common as that to measles. While all children in a family usually get measles when there is an outbreak of it, this is by no means the case with scarlet fever. Furthermore, the same individuals can have scarlet fever more than once, especially after it has been arrested with antibiotics, and adults are also still susceptible to it. The almost general disposition to measles and its relatively harmless course can be understood when we apprehend the disease as a process of eliminating inherited etheric tendencies. The etheric body is of a relatively uniform nature in all human beings. In contrast, all the symptoms of scarlet fever show that it originates in the astral body, which is much more individual. The astral body is the source of the catabolic, destructive, pathogenic impulses, which are especially noticeable in scarlet fever's complications.

The fact that these illnesses are childhood diseases and that the inner impulse to them comes originally from the ego gives them common features. In measles, however, which proceeds in the etheric body, one has the sense that a "will to health" stands behind it; while scarlet fever, as an astral disease, manifests long-latent pathological dispositions of the astral body, which must be overcome through the disease and thus eliminated.

German Measles

German measles, like measles, is a typical childhood disease; it was first classified as an independent disease in 1881. Two thirds of the patients are between five and fourteen years old.

The course is quite harmless for the patients, and complications are extremely rare. Only after Gregg described embryopathia rubeolosa (congenital rubella) in 1941 was German measles represented as a "dangerous" disease.

Like scarlet fever and diphtheria, German measles has a cyclic course; every five to ten years an epidemic is registered. It also varies seasonally, favoring the months from March to May. The incubation time of fourteen to twenty-one days is remarkably long. Once again we encounter exanthema, usually beginning behind the ears, then spreading over the whole body in tiny pink spots. The catarrhal symptoms are not severe, unlike in measles, and the fever is relatively weak. Together with fifth disease (erythema infectiosum), where the exanthema lasts longer, and roseola infantum (exanthema subitum), in which the rash breaks out only after three days of high fever, we are dealing here with typical childhood diseases characterized by outward elimination (exanthema) in connection with fever, and by harmlessness of course.

How then can this disease, of so little consequence for the organism of the mother, cause such serious damage to the embryo during pregnancy? The morbidity for the fetus depends on the stage of pregnancy and also varies from epidemic to epidemic and from place to place. The morbidity risk cannot be found exactly, of course; it is estimated at 20–80% for the first two months of gestation. Thus, the infection does not always cause damage to the embryo. The probability of delivering a live but damaged child is put at 12–15%.

In order to understand this strange result, we must remember that the formative forces of the head are predominant in the embryo; at the beginning, at least, it is almost all head. Into this situation comes the virus. As shown in the chapter on infectious diseases, all viruses, in contrast to bacteria, are neurotropic. Thus, their primary culture medium is nerve tissue, though also other organs of ectodermal origin such as skin. In gestation, however, the formative forces of the embryonic organism (form pole) pervade the nervous system. If they are hindered in their activity because the nervous system is disturbed or damaged, then disturbances in formation must result. This is why embryopathies occur only with viral diseases and never with bacterial infections. Embryonic damage quite similar to that after German measles can also result if the mother contracts, up to the twelfth week of pregnancy, measles, chicken pox, herpes, mumps, viral hepatitis, poliomyelitis, or influenza. The probability and severity of damage, however, are less with these diseases.

Fetopathies (damage to the embryo after the third month of pregnancy) are also possible with viral infections. If the mother falls ill with measles, chicken pox, or smallpox at the end of pregnancy, the child may be born with exanthema but without any resultant damage. Fetopathies are rare after infections with hepatitis, ECHO, and parotitis viruses. If the mother is immunized against smallpox toward the end of pregnancy, however, the fetus may show, besides exanthema, a serious sickness, the so-called generalized inclusion-body necrosis.

Here, again, it can be seen that damage is caused particularly by those viruses that evoke skin symptoms. Once again we point out the connection, mentioned above and in the section on measles, of viruses to the skin and brain. When there is a disease with a relation to the skin, and it cannot (or can only weakly) appear in the skin, then it is displaced inward with encephalitis a final result. For the embryo, this means damage to the developing nerve-sense system, resulting in a general hindering of the activity of the formative forces. This explains why the rubella virus causes damage above all to the sense organs—the eye (cataracts) and the ear (deafness from inner ear defects). In addition, however, microcephaly and deformities of the heart region, as well as defects of the milk teeth, can result.

The question remains whether or not there was embryopathy from German measles earlier, and this was only discovered in 1941, or if the fetopathy is something truly new that could not have been noticed earlier. The latter is more probable. A further question is to what extent damage to the nervous system increases in frequency with, or is at least encouraged by, the customary, and inappropriate, use of antipyretic measures; these prevent the breaking out of the skin, which is connected with the fever that is already weak in German measles.

Diphtheria

Today, diphtheria is a practically extinct disease, as well as a relatively harmless one. A few decades ago this was not the case. As we will illustrate in detail in the chapter on infectious diseases (Vol. III), diphtheria is a disease with a clearly cyclical course. Questions relating to this pathomorphosis will be treated in detail in that chapter.

The peculiar localization of diphtheria gives us a clue to its essential nature. In diphtheria, unlike the typical childhood diseases, the characteristic direction of the disease process is not from the inside outward, discharging itself in the skin; rather, there is the tendency to penetrate from the pharynx inward to the organs of respiration and speech. This inward direction is the reason the disease is so dangerous. It causes not only croup but also toxin formation, while the typical harmless childhood diseases show the tendency to discharge outward through the skin.

The membrane formation typical of diphtheria can be seen as an "inner skin," a tendency to internalization of the disease process; it is also an indication of the connection between diphtheria and the speech process. This relation, as Rudolf Steiner emphasized, is important for an understanding of the essence of diphtheria. It also illuminates the age disposition to diphtheria, which is greatest from the second to the fifth years since it is during this time that the child learns to speak. Therefore, we must examine the processes involved in learning to speak. To speak implies to break the natural rhythm of breathing, to learn, more or less unconsciously, to control the respiratory and laryngeal musculature with the will. The speaker stimulates a complicated metabolic process, the goal and culmination of which is in the organs of speech. But speech is not merely a metabolic process; the characteristic feature of it is that, to a greater extent than in other movements, it is a process controlled by the astral body through the nerve-sense system. It can be said of an arm movement that the will engages the metabolism in a rather external way; the movement is pictured as something external before it is executed. With speech it is different. The speaker's consciousness is inwardly bound up with the physical process. In speaking, we hear our own voice and continually modify our speech accordingly. The sequence of sounds that we bring forth shapes our organs of speech at the same time.

Thus, the metabolic process and the nerve-sense process are in continual and intense interaction in the speech organs. Now, if the metabolic process is dominant, as in exudative diathesis, this gives rise to a tendency to inflammatory diseases; if the nervous system is overtaxed—for example, in school or from frightening experiences, etc.—the result is crampedness, a tendency to stuttering, asthma, etc.

Here we must bring to mind everything we have said about the child's intimate capability for imitation. If those in his environment speak with strong emotion in their tone and rhythm, the child unconsciously imitates this, with the result that blood circulation is increased in the speech organs. It is known that all emotions, and even the mere thought of movement, cause increased blood flow to the particular organ. Naturally, we do not pretend to explain the origin of diphtheria by this train of thought; we are just indicating the direction through which one can arrive at an understanding of the appearance of the disease at a particular time of life and in a specific organ complex. In addition, one must consider the tender constitution of the child's organs and the dominance of the watery element at this age. The lymphatic constitution is also especially disposed to diphtheria. Furthermore, it must be realized that such "impulses to inflammation" of soul (astral) origin are at first held inactive in the etheric body until, when the tension is sufficient, an outer stimulus such as a sharp, cold wind sets off the disease process. Now we can also understand why diphtheria occurs so seldom in infants and then mostly as nasal diphtheria. At this age the disease process remains exterior, not reaching so deep into the organism as in later illness. The organism still has no inner relation to the diphtheria process, because the child does not speak yet. Also, the tiny infant is not yet truly separate from the mother and still possesses her antibodies.

Hence, we can see the essential difference between diphtheria and tonsillitis. In tonsillitis, there is a local purulent inflammation of the tonsils and pharynx with a febrile reaction of the entire organism; the disease process is resolved with elimination of the pus. In diphtheria, on the other hand, firm membranes develop on the tonsils; in severe cases, these can extend into the trachea and even the bronchi, forming a complete "mold" of these organs. Thus, the disease process is not resolved immediately, but forms a sort of double of the organs of speech; the disease partially develops a negative image of the organism.

Chapter III
The Second Epoch of Life:
From the Change of Teeth to Puberty

The Development and Shaping of the Child's Soul Life

With the change of teeth, important alterations take place in the supersensible organism of man. The etheric body, which at the beginning was closely connected with the surrounding etheric world and the physical body, is freed in the region of the head and becomes independent (see p. 31 f.). This event corresponds to a birth. In other words, the etheric body is born at the change of teeth in the same way that the physical body is born at physical birth. With its liberation from the etheric environment, the organism is also freer from surrounding influences, both natural and human. In this way, another precondition has been met for the development of the child's own soul life, which develops with increasing intensity from the second dentition on. The freed etheric forces now appear as forces of memory and intelligence. The child is ready to learn. The process is gradual, however, and it is important, particularly for the educator, to be aware of this, thus apportioning the amount of memory work so as to create the right relation between vitality and soul-spiritual development. The more memory work is demanded of the child, the more vitality is drawn from his organism. A pale appearance indicates too great a load while a rosy appearance and frolicsome behavior indicate too light a load placed on his memory.

To burden the child excessively and one-sidedly with memory work and thinking will have an injurious effect on him, which can appear in all kinds of "nervous" disturbances. Furthermore, in creating a constitutional imbalance, it will affect his entire life. If children at this age, between seven and fourteen, are made to think to the point of fatigue, the result will be that they will be subject to sclerosis relatively early. These circumstances make understandable an indication of Rudolf Steiner. Such consequences demand that we keep the whole person in view; in searching for causes of things we cannot look only at events immediately preceding them. The observation of these connections is of the greatest importance for a life hygiene. In fact, it is not only a question of a quantitative overloading of the child's memory and thinking; it is also important not to burden the child too early with rigid definitions. He should take in concepts that can grow. Content should be presented to children, especially younger ones, in the form of pictures. "Do not define, but characterize," was Rudolf Steiner's advice to teachers for the basic approach in teaching.

While in the first seven-year period of life the formative forces of the head predominate, in the second seven-year period the rhythmic system must be consolidated; in the third seven-year period the metabolic system is subjected to formation and characterization.

Age	Predominant Area of Formative Activity	Basis for Future Function
1– 7	Nerve-sense system	Thinking
7–14	Rhythmic system	Feeling
14–21	Metabolic system	Willing

A comprehensive development of the human faculties of thinking, feeling, and willing is thus also a matter of correct timing. For education to be "phase-appropriate," these physiological possibilities of development must be taken into account.

According to contemporary opinion, it is not possible to demonstrate the sequential character of child development. This may be because the present state of man is taken as the norm; the original human constitution is being increasingly altered by the process of acceleration and its consequences. What is needed is an idea of the essential "type" of human development, the archetypal image of man, and phasic development is a concept essential and intrinsic to this. Thus, the seven-year rhythm is the measure, not an average value.

In considering premature development, we must understand that whatever is to unfold at a higher stage must always be properly prepared for; otherwise, the full and necessary foundation for further development will be absent later. Premature development, which, by the way, is not quite synonymous with early maturity, interrupts the organic development process. When the developmental foundation is removed, the result may even be the phenomenon of an accelerated maturation that is forced through an emergency situation. This concept is known in biology.

In the second seven-year period, the child's organization constantly swings between a predominance of the nerve processes (pallor) and a predominance of the blood processes (flushing) expressing dominating metabolic activity. Therefore, it is the task of the educator to give his lesson a form calculated to bring these processes into equilibrium. Between these two poles, a new area is created in the rhythmic system (see chapter on the heart, Vol. III), a place for the development of what is properly human. The rhythmic system is prefigured in the organization of the human being, but only as a possibility; it can be developed to its full significance and independence only by the individual's own activity under the guidance of the educator. All education is really a process of "rhythmicizing" the organism in speaking, moving, and singing. Perhaps this is why the last children of a marriage are often the most musical.

In instruction, the rhythmic system is developed through an *artistic presentation* of educational material. If the teacher can form the material into an artistic picture, a dramatic event, this will appeal to the *feeling* dwelling in the rhythmic system. The child is enlivened by such instruction. It is crucial for the rest of the life that the rhythmic system be able to consolidate itself by producing this balance between thinking and willing in feeling, since feeling stands between thinking and willing. At this age the child is not yet in the position to use thought independently or to develop a real life of the will. Much abnormal development of soul life is caused by a premature appeal to thinking. Therefore, instruction must be suited to this stage of development and must respect the germinal character of feeling, from which the child can then develop thinking and willing *in inner freedom* later on.[1]

If a balance in the soul between thinking and willing is successfully established in this period, this will lead to a consolidation of the breathing and blood system; that is, to a correct unfolding of the rhythmic system. This will also provide the basis for a harmonious relation of pulse to respiration, which is a good index of health (see chapter on the heart, Vol. III).

Present-day science does not yet see the significance of the rhythmic system; it considers only the poles of the human organization, the nerve and metabolic systems. Only the development of the rhythmic system creates the basis for freedom and thus for what is properly human.

If the child is treated properly in this period of life, if he is not too burdened with school work, and if he has wholesome food and bodily movement, then he will be at his healthiest in this epoch. He experiences his existence in the rhythmic processes of breathing and heart activity, which cannot tire and which maintain their own rhythm if they are not disturbed. Diseases can originate in the nerve-sense or in the metabolic systems; the rhythmic system is affected secondarily. This is why the inner disposition to diseases is smallest in this period of life. Only toward the end of this epoch, when the organism is preparing for puberty, is there once again an inner disposition to disease. The inner tendency to health in this period of life can be seen in Halley's curve.

This curve expresses the probability of death with respect to age. It can be seen that the mortality is lowest around the tenth year of life, that is, in the second epoch. The mortality from tuberculosis also shows striking differences in different age groups, "with the lowest mortality of all among children from five to fifteen." Even in the famine of 1923 the mortality from tuberculosis in this age group was remarkably low.[2]

In order to understand the diseases characteristic of this period of life, we must remember that the struggle between the individual supersensible organization and the inherited corporeality should have ended with the change of teeth. It was mentioned above that a "watery-ethic remnant" can remain from

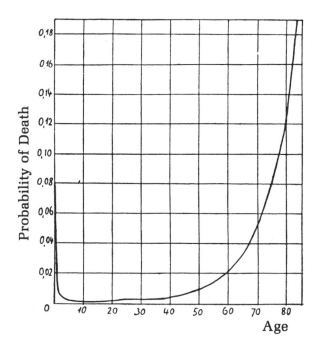

"Halley's Curve"

Probability of death for the German male population in the years 1932/34.

(From: Brock: *Biologische Daten für den Kinderarzt* Vol. III, page 314, Berlin 1939)

this confrontation; in the course of time, this moves further toward the heart, creating the disposition to pneumonia, pleuritis, and ultimately heart disease.

The Ninth Year of Life

With the ninth or tenth year, a new epoch begins in the development of the child.[3] It is at this time that the ego, whose forces have been penetrating the organism from the head until this time, is directly engaged—"coupled into the metabolic system," as Rudolf Steiner expressed it; thus, it is connected now with the *whole* organism. Man's soul-spiritual being begins for the first time to penetrate the entire organism to a certain extent.

The curve on the next page, based on the average values of blood sugar in childhood, reflects this more intense engagement of the ego around the ninth year. Sugar is a vehicle of the ego organization and shows this engagement of the ego in the metabolism, which is intense at the beginning of life but

Blood sugar in child-
hood. Average of 700
children classed in age
groups (J.B. Mayer).

(From: Brock, *Biolo-
gische Daten für den
Kinderarzt*, Vol. II, 2nd
edition, 1954).

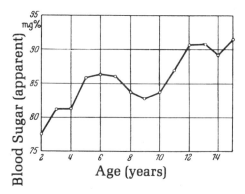

weakens with age, ultimately leading to the diabetes of old age, which is to a certain extent a physiological disease (see section on carbohydrate metabolism).

The "coupling of the ego into the metabolism" often involves difficulties. If it does not succeed, then sugar is not properly managed by the ego. This is why some children contract diabetes at this time; their ego organization cannot control the sugar process, which is so intimately connected with the experience of self. "It is also known that certain years are especially favorable to diabetes; its occurrence increases toward the eleventh year, after which the curve temporarily falls almost to zero."[4]

This new and intense connection of the ego with the whole organism also finds expression in the child's soul life. He has a certain sense of self-sufficiency amidst the world around him and may even experience strong feelings of loneliness. In this we can see a repetition and enhancement of the first occurrence of the ego experience around the second year; it occurs exactly seven years later. Pedagogy naturally must pay attention to this time of crisis in the child's development and consciously build up the relation of his ego to the surrounding world again. For example, the ninth year is a good time to begin animal studies and studies of local geography and history. Norse mythology is also appropriate for children at this time. They experience intensely the story of Thor bringing home his hammer, because this image fits their psychological situation at this time. Their egos have reached the metabolism and also support themselves now with the iron process (see below), through which the human being can act on the surrounding world and come back into himself. Therefore, in these years children play "cops and robbers"; they want to develop their courage and are thus most loud. The greatest insult to them is to be called a "scaredy cat."

From the Twelfth to the Fourteenth Year of Life

The ego having engaged itself in the metabolic system in the ninth or tenth year, merging deeply into the organism, in the following period it must master the whole human being from this central point of attack. Rudolf Steiner describes how this occurs first through the muscle system and then through the bone system. A manifestation of this process is the difficulty that children have at this age in gaining control of their limbs. Awkward movements are characteristic. The formerly unconscious process of motion must now be structured more consciously in a process of struggle.

With the conscious mastery of the skeletal system, the soul of the growing child also gains an understanding for the mechanical and inanimate processes of the outer world. For this age group, the Waldorf school curriculum provides physics (mechanics), chemistry, and mathematics. An understanding for abstract thought awakens. In school, a practical acquaintance with tools and utensils is introduced to balance the abstract mathematical instruction. The child grasps the tool and the concept at the same time in gardening and handicrafts.

The last step in the ego's mastery of the body is the confrontation with the bone system. Physiologically, this is expressed in the coalescence of the epiphysis and the shaft after puberty.

If a "watery-etheric" remnant is still present in this epoch (see p. 32), it forms the constitutional basis for two diseases, which we will discuss here: rheumatic fever and chorea minor (Sydenham's chorea).

Rheumatic Fever

The basis for rheumatic fever is created when the watery-etheric process is drawn into the typical tendency of the age group. Then it is subject to the dynamics of the confrontation with the muscle and bone system.

From this standpoint it can be seen why rheumatic fever occurs as a familial disease in about one-half of the cases, because the etheric realm is quite open to heredity (lymphatic constitution). It is also clear why the illness is absent in the tropics: warmth in the environment stimulates the organism more strongly to eliminate the watery-etheric element. If this were a disease caused only by infection (angina, granuloma, etc.), one would expect it to occur in the tropics as well.

The fact that the large joints (knee, ankle, elbow, and wrist) are primarily affected, points to the constitutional-functional connections described here. Even from the physical viewpoint, the larger joints offer a better opportunity for exudation, because their joint spaces are more closely connected with the water organism than are those of the small joints, which are relatively more affected by the formative forces of the periphery (astral body). The formative process radiating out from the head also protects the maxillary and cervical joints, so that these are rarely drawn into the disease. Further evidence that the inner purpose of the illness is really the elimination of the watery element is given by the fact that abundant, sour-smelling sweat is always secreted, even in mild cases. The acid character of the sweat is connected with the strong astral influence from the periphery. The fact that the inflammation often "jumps" from one joint to another is a further indication of the constitutional, total character of the disease. The individual joint is not diseased; rather, the disease, affecting the whole body, fluctuates in the individual joints.

The so-called focus (abscess, tonsils) is also nothing but an expression of the dynamic described above, which is especially strong at this time. The metabolic system begins to come into prominence; the appearance of acne at puberty points to this (see p. 73). The abscess is also a place where the metabolism is insufficiently formed and differentiated; for this reason, it is a place where toxins arise or bacteria thrive. It is most instructive that abscesses are found especially on the roots of the teeth, a place where life processes (periodontal membrane) must confront the most physical, hardest part of the human organism, the tooth. It is just this confrontation that we recognized as characteristic of the period before puberty, and the disturbance of which is the cause of rheumatic fever.

We know that it is often possible to eliminate an acute disease by removing the focus; it would, however, be wrong to draw the conclusion from this that the focus causes the illness, since we still do not know why one man gets an abscess and another does not. The focus merely indicates a disturbance in the sense of the processes described above. The tonsils may also frequently form a focus. After all, they are lymph organs and thus regions where the action of the etheric body is pronounced. They have the physiological task of serving as a protective wall against excessive penetration of the astral body. Therefore, the lymphatic organs retrogress as the etheric body dwindles with increasing age. The tonsils are thus also a place where, with insufficient formative force, protein disintegrates, and this can bring about, secondarily, further disturbances.

In the years before puberty, there are often diseases of the faucial tonsils (tonsillae palatinae), which hypertrophy as a result of the inflammations or due to constitutional disposition. Sore throats are also frequent in this period. Because such inflammations are often repeated and can endanger the entire organism by dispersing germs, attempts to remedy this problem are commonly made by means of adenoidectomy or tonsillectomy. It has been found that this (especially tonsillectomy) often promotes the child's growth. In young children the adenoids often regenerate quickly.

This fact shows that the tonsillar ring, as a glandular organ, is a particular collecting point of etheric forces. If the tonsils are removed too early and then grow back quickly, it is an indication of the locally active etheric forces. If at a later age removal of the tonsils leads to accelerated growth, it indicates that the etheric forces once confined in the gland can now be absorbed by the whole organism. Up to this time, the tonsillar ring has formed a sort of barrier, retaining the etheric forces flowing to the head, so that the head can develop according to its own inner laws. After puberty, the glandular organs undergo

slow evolution; they, like the thymus (see p. 25 ff.), are super-
seded by the entering astral body. Thus, these glands have
balancing functions to fulfill up to puberty; the physician will
have to take these functions, along with the child's age, into account before he can decide on their partial or total removal.

One of the most frequent complications of acute rheumatic
fever is endocarditis verrucosa, which typically affects the
mitral valve. The anatomical alterations on the valves exhibit
precipitated elements from the blood (erythrocytes, leukocytes,
platelets, fibrin). Thus, the individual components of the blood
have fallen out of the living whole. Why does this occur at the
mitral valve, where the blood passing through is rich in oxygen,
having just been revitalized in the lung? We can understand
this paradoxical phenomenon only when we realize that with
inspiration the astral body flows into the lung. Thus, the blood
in the pulmonary vein is the richest in oxygen, but it is
simultaneously the carrier of the strongest astral influences.
Since, as we have seen, the astral body is the essential vehicle
of pathogenic processes, the disposition of the mitral valve to
the inflammation is understandable; at this point the blood is
burning in the fire of astrality.

Chorea Minor (Sydenham's Chorea)

Another complication of rheumatic fever is chorea; it can
also occur independently, however. The disposition for the appearance of choreic symptoms is the same as for rheumatic
fever, that is, a predominance of etheric-watery processes that
could not be overcome at the right time. This explains the
symptoms of the sickness.

In rheumatic fever the fact that the astral body acts more
from the outside of the organism is expressed in the perspiration. In chorea, the astral impulses affect the muscles as well,
which is understandable given the connection of the bone and
muscle systems with rheumatic fever. The "accessory" movements occurring in chorea can be seen as the astral body's attempt to strengthen its efficacy in the organism by not quite
successfully engaging in the musculature, and thus to "encircle"
the disease. The disease can be precipitated by emotional up-

heavals, such as fright, anger, anxiety, and the like, that is, by all injuries to the astral body.

The beginning of the illness is often indicated by a change of the voice. The child becomes moody; that is, his mood no longer depends on his relation to the environment but is the expression of a physical disorder. The disease often begins with slight disturbances of respiration (gasping respiration) and of speech (the beginning of stuttering), with gesticulation and grimacing. Involuntary "broken" movements are characteristic of the disease. Since the essence of the illness is the astral body's desire to become active in the musculature without the mediation of consciousness, it is natural that the movements appear to express psychic contents, and that other people tend to see these disturbances as indications of clumsiness or bad manners. Therefore, they treat the sick child with severity, which only worsens his condition. Any strong emotion will have a harmful effect because of the very nature of the disease, since it will upset the astral body anew.

The fact that the uncontrolled movements stop during sleep is a clear indication that we are dealing with an overwhelming and inappropriate involvement of the astral body; the astral body is separated from the upper organism during sleep and operates directly in the metabolic system. Since the astral body is active in the muscular system without the mediation of consciousness, the patient does not get tired from the spasms, although they may affect a large part of the body's musculature.

Choreic symptoms can also appear in the first months of pregnancy. If we look at pregnancy from a purely dynamic-constitutional point of view, the entrance of a foreign etheric-watery organism into the mother's organism explains the motor reaction of the astral body.

There is less tendency to chorea minor in males, because the formative forces issuing from the nerve-sense system are stronger in them; according to our explanations, this is the same as a more intense involvement of the astral body and the ego organization. This also explains why the tendency to chorea minor has been essentially overcome after puberty.

Therapeutically, one uses copper and zinc as cuprum aceti-

cum D4/zincum valerianicum D4 in equal quantities. Copper
helps the organism accept the astral body into its metabolism
properly; this is the basis of its antispasmodic action. With the
therapeutic administration of zinc, one makes use of its calming, subduing, almost incapacitating property, which is enhanced by its association with valerian. These two metals complement one another in a most harmonious way and have also
proved valuable for other types of motor disturbance. They
can be supported additionally with Mygal compound, which
was composed along homeopathic lines by Dr. Noll, and has
proved itself especially in alternation with cuprum/zincum.
The etiology of the disease presented above also explains the
successful application of arsenic therapy, since arsenicization
is equivalent to astralization.

Chapter IV

The Third Epoch of Life:
From Puberty to the Twenty-first Year of Life

"Earth-Ripeness"

Just as the change of teeth is the outwardly visible conclusion of the first epoch of life, puberty stands at the end of the second epoch. Rudolf Steiner called it "earth-ripeness," because it represents the time when the human organism is sufficiently grown and formed so that the human being now begins to direct his gaze toward the outer world with a wider scope and to master his surroundings. This becomes possible as the astral body is released from its activity of organ formation and becomes free.

Beginning with the change of teeth, the astral body gradually breathes its forces through the organism with increasing strength, until it is "ripened," that is, ripe for the manifestation of the individual soul qualities. The changes appearing at this age in the soul and organism of the young person are related to this. It is only at this time that differentiation between the sexes begins in the proper sense. From about the tenth year on, the type of respiration is different in boys and girls. In girls, the costal type of respiration develops, while boys take on the characteristic male proportion of ⅔ chest and ⅓ diaphragm. This relative predominance of diaphragmatic breathing in the male expresses his deeper descent into the organism and therefore into matter; the lowering of the voice is another expression of this. In boys, the voice falls by a whole octave, while in girls it falls only a tone or so.

Anatomically, the breaking of the voice in boys is based on an enlargement of the larynx, particularly a lengthening of the vocal chords, but whoever contemplates the phenomenon of the deep voice in man will be able to sense that the whole organism vibrates, including the skeletal system. The resonating ground is simply different from that in women.

Another expression of a deeper incarnating process can be seen in the thinking of the man, which is directed more toward earthly things. The somewhat later entrance of the boy into puberty can also be seen in biological connection with this further developmental step.

The profound soul alterations in this period of development are unmistakable. At this time, the young person must learn for the first time to master the astral forces at his disposal. At first, there is an inability to cope with this new and unfamiliar force. The youth can no longer move his limbs so harmoniously, and he overshoots the mark in his movements and reactions. He presents the picture of thorough lack of control. Only gradually does he learn to control these astral forces and make a different, conscious use of them; only at the end of this period will the once unconsciously harmonious movements become consciously controlled, after a transitional stage of uncontrol.

We regard it as a characteristic moment of puberty when the gonads begin to give out mature germinal cells at the age of thirteen to fifteen in males and twelve to fourteen in females. The fact that this has occurred at an increasingly early age in recent centuries (the so-called acceleration) means that an ever stronger astralization is taking place—for the most part, however, in the sense of premature development. This will be explored more deeply in the chapter on the school physician.

Sperm and ovum formation is only the outer aspect of the gonadal activity; just as important—really of greater significance for the entire organism—is the internal hormonal secretion of the gonads, because this is connected with the blossoming of the organism during puberty.

This process, correctly described as blossoming, corresponds to blossom formation in the plant world, which is effected by astral influence. This impulse brings about a reversal or metamorphosis of the purely vegetative, anabolic, and assimilating forces in the plant. For this reason, we find a certain catabolism in the blossom, a transformation of anabolized substances into fragrant, lighter, volatile substances. The astral body represents the principle of ensoulment—for just this reason, blossoms and their scents appeal more than a purely vegetative leafy plant to the human soul—but it is connected by its very essence with a certain catabolism. This is how we have described the astral body throughout, but now we are confronted with an apparent contradiction. We see in puberty a clear astral impulse, yet this time it is not catabolism that stands in the foreground but growth, and this is connected with a great unfolding of force. In other words, we now see the astral body in a completely different dynamic, in which it works anabolically from below upward, while the catabolic impulse always is transmitted through the nervous system from above. A new activity of the astral body begins in the urogenital system now, which is just the reverse of what proceeds from the nerve-sense system. While the latter has a catabolic character, the astral impulses flowing through the urogenital system pass into the etheric body. That is, they are of an anabolic nature. In the chapter on the kidney (Vol. III) these connections are considered in detail (see also p. 264).

Comparison with animal development will bring this into relief. Here puberty signifies as well a certain decline. Besides the physical and etheric bodies, the animal possesses only the astral body, so that its development is practically concluded with puberty; in any case, nothing essentially new is added thereafter. In man, however, still another new phase of development begins at this time. The animal must always remain a group being, but in man the individual ego enters, whose phases of incorporation in the second and ninth years we have already discussed. But only at the end of this third epoch, at the age of twenty-one, does the ego become "free" in the same sense as the astral body does at fourteen and the etheric body at seven. Therefore, only at the age of twenty-one is the human being really "grown up." This is not simply a question of growth, because not until this time is the astral body enough under the control of the ego that the latter can make use of it. As with puberty, this process has also become generally accelerated of late; of this acceleration, what was said above concerning the acceleration of puberty also applies.

Understandably, the particular quality of this time of life must be taken into account in education. Rudolf Steiner gave the significant indication that the young person's interest is now most strongly directed toward the outer world, for which the soul yearns in its depths. The human being has become "earth-ripe," and he wishes to master the world for himself, if only in contemplation and understanding at first. For education to meet this healthy striving, the teacher must awaken interest in the outer world. If this does not happen, the young person becomes too occupied with himself, which, especially at this age, has the most unfavorable effects. Rudolf Steiner indicated that through this excessive attachment of the soul to the body, people yield either to eroticism or to the "itch for power," which appears to be on the increase in recent years, manifesting itself in the often cruel pranks of young people against school fellows, children and also teachers. Gottfried Keller gives a gruesome example of this in *Der grüne Heinrich*, which ends with the teacher's death. Also, the capacity for judgment, which really only begins at this age, should be extended to and exercised on matters relating to the world.

The Iron Process and Development

Following the construction of a human being's bodily nature in the individual time periods, we can see how he gradually leaves the cosmically closed sphere and penetrates into the earthly realm. In this process, definite forces or substances, in their interaction, play a crucial role for the individual epochs. We have seen that in the first seven-year period, the balance between fluorine and magnesium, which profoundly influences the child's constitution, must be correctly set. In the second seven years of life, there is a natural equilibrium. This is the epoch of greatest health. In the third epoch, the human being must come to terms with forces of iron and protein. With them is connected the process of all protein formation.

The fact that the relationship between these forces is endangered in puberty is shown by two typical diseases, acne and anemia, that frequently occur at exactly this time.

Acne vulgaris is a peripheral suppurative process. There is living protein in the periphery, but it is not sufficiently structured; thus, it offers a nutrient medium for bacteria. Protein (see p. 266 ff.) is the life and body substance of man and animal. The astral element often cannot be properly incorporated into the protein substance in this period of life, so that in a certain way it falls prey to foreign life, that is, bacteria. With mastery of the astral body at the end of this epoch, the acne usually disappears.

At this time, the human being must learn to manage not only his relationship with protein but also that with iron; for this, puberty also represents a time of crisis. Because the human being's relationship to iron is a direct index of the incarnation process, we will describe it in some detail.

We may regard hemoglobin as the primary form of iron through which the force of iron comes into action. Through the protein component, the relationship to the life process, to the watery-etheric element, is established. Porphyrin shows a clear relation to light, which is expressed in the heightened photosensitivity in porphyria, for example (see p. 297). It is iron that makes possible the correct assimilation and utilization of light.

Iron also shows a strong affinity to light. It is almost the only metal, apart from the rare earth metals, that forms sparks when struck; that is, the light locked in the substance is released in combustion. This capacity to store light is the basis for the role that iron plays in hemoglobin. It is known that copper (in hemocyanin) and vanadium can also be built into a porphyrin-protein framework; they perform the same respiratory function in lower animals as iron does in human hemoglobin. Because of their missing, or differing, relation to light, though, other metals are not in a position to assimilate and bear light in themselves. Light is the element that forms the "substance" of thought. Only a substance that is filled with light has the ability to set free the light in which the ego can be freely active. Hence, for man, only iron can fulfill this function. This is the reason why copper must be displaced by iron in phylogenesis.

The other metal having a similarly strong affinity for light is magnesium. In its light function it behaves in every way as a polar opposite to iron, as chlorophyll does to hemoglobin, reduction to oxidation, plant to human or animal. These relationships are presented in greater detail in the chapter on light metabolism.

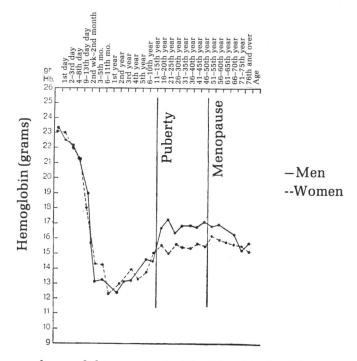

The mean hemoglobin content of the blood in healthy men and women with respect to age. (After Williamson.) Investigation conducted on 464 men and 455 women.

(From: L. Heilmeyer, *Die Eisentherapie und ihre Grundlage*, 2nd ed., Leipzig, 1944.)

This graph can be understood from what has been said above. As the curve shows, children have a lower hemoglobin content of the blood, if one disregards the first fourteen days of life, than adults. The hemoglobin content gradually increases until puberty. As we can see, the amount of iron then continues to rise in men, while it reaches a plateau in women.

This difference of the iron content in man and woman has been the subject of much puzzlement; it appears not only in hemoglobin but also in serum and even liver iron (see below). The most obvious explanation for it is blood loss through menstruation. This is still the belief of most authors today, although there are powerful reasons why this cannot be the decisive factor but is merely ancillary to an existing condition. That the lower hemoglobin and serum iron values among women are not just anemia from blood loss has been shown by the fact that no increase in the red cell count or the serum iron level can be induced with iron treatment; this speaks against an iron deficiency. Furthermore, we would expect that amenorrheic and postmenopausal women would show a rise in iron up to the value of men, while in fact just the opposite is true, as the curve shows; in old age, the hemoglobin value in men falls to that of women. For this reason K.H. Schäfer writes: "We must, therefore, admit for the present that we do not yet know the reasons for the described sex difference after puberty."[1] Throughout life the hemoglobin content in men, about 16 g in 100 ml of blood, is higher than the corresponding value of 14 g in women. The serum iron difference is 10–30γ%. How deeply this difference pervades the organs is shown by the curve of the liver iron as a function of age.

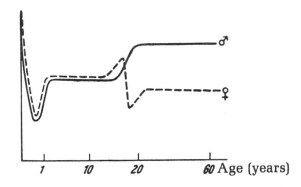

Vital Curve of Liver Iron

(From: *Erg. d. Inn. Med. und Kinderheilkd.*, Vol. 4, p. 773, 1953.)

Iron works above all in the metabolism, and this is seen most clearly in the chief metabolic organ, the liver. These differences become understandable only when seen in the light of iron's essential nature and higher function. Because of its light property, iron, and only iron, is in the position to take in something of man's spiritual being and allow this to penetrate into the organism, to incarnate. This connection of the soul-spiritual being and the body is stronger in man than in woman; hence, he is more earth-bound, as other values—for example, vital capacity—also indicate (see p. 179f.). Thus, with the help of iron, the man incarnates more deeply than the woman; in other words, after the differentiation of the sexes, the female organism remains more cosmic, while the male connects itself more deeply with corporeality and thereby with the earth. This occurs primarily by means of iron. It is *the* incarnation metal.

In the female there is a certain "physiologic anemia" but no iron deficiency. Her physiologically lower iron content, that is her "lighter" constitution, however, places the woman in greater danger of iron deficiency than the man. As we have said, this is not caused only by the physiological loss of blood, though it can be intensified by this. Therefore, relatively equal blood losses weigh more heavily on women than on men. The connections described will also serve to explain why the woman is more earthy, heavier, premenstrually, and can take on a strange quality then, while postmenstrually, she may feel lighter, more feminine, more cosmic.

A striking fact is the high iron value in newborns, in hemoglobin, serum, and the liver alike. Moreover, the serum iron, at $160\gamma\%$, is significantly higher than that of the mother. Thus, a considerable, active enrichment in iron takes place in the embryo. Naturally, all this can be "explained" by the altered embryonic respiration; in the light of the above explanation, however, one can see the sense of this peak of iron content around the time of birth as the equipping of the individual with the necessary incarnation substance for the physical incarnation at birth.

In contrast to the relatively stable hemoglobin, the serum iron is a much more labile and active form of iron, which reacts more quickly to a situation and therefore shows daily variations and alterations in the course of disease.

The high serum iron level of the morning hours falls off toward the end of the afternoon, showing a clear circadian rhythm. This variation is completely independent of food intake and erythropoietic activity. Rather, it is the expression of the daily renewal of the incarnation process. Therefore, this rhythm is reversed in night workers; since serum iron is a much more dynamic form of iron than the "cruder" hemoglobin, pathological changes in it can be followed more easily and rapidly. After concussion and cerebral diseases, the serum iron level falls; it does so as well one hour after electroshock treatment. Here one can clearly see the departure, the shocking out, of the higher members of being. (Depressed serum values can be easily recognized in water-clear serum, for example in a blood sedimentation test.)

Anemia

From the point of view presented here, the anemias appear in a new light. While in 1940 only about five forms of anemia were known, their number has climbed to over one hundred today without any basic change in the way the disease is understood. Actually, the chief forms of anemia are the same ones that have been known for practically half a century. To grasp the essence of the disease that stands behind the various forms it manifests, it is important to recognize the overriding factor.

The first and decisive indication of an anemia is provided by the clinical picture. This permits diagnosis in the great majority of cases. Laboratory tests should really only confirm the diagnosis and differentiate the type of anemia. The symptoms of an anemia or an iron deficiency are quite characteristic when taken together, although they are described as uncharacteristic in all textbooks and are, in fact, when taken singly. Weakness, fatigue, poor concentration, and pressure in the head can, of course, also occur in hypotension, since this is the consequence of too weak an incarnation process, just as iron deficiency can be understood as a lack of the incarnation metal.

The most obvious sign, the paleness of the skin and mucous membranes, reveals the deficiency of iron-containing hemoglobin. In addition, there are metabolic signs and symptoms: bloating, obstipation or diarrhea as an expression of dysfermentia, formation disturbances of the epithelium such as angular stomatitis, atrophy of the papillae of the tongue or glossitis, and mucosal atrophy of the stomach. Other typical signs are brittleness and spooning of the nails (koilonychia). The signs of atrophy and the defective formations clearly show the insufficient engagement of spirit and soul—ego and astral body—in the metabolism, which was described for iron above.

Anemic people characteristically have an increased need of warmth. This indicates a warmth organism that is too weakly developed. The warmth organism is, however, the dwelling place of the ego and with increased warmth the ego can penetrate the organism better. Thus, a process occurs that corresponds to the one we have seen with the iron process. The supply of warmth relieves the condition of the anemic patient; his whole physicality becomes more receptive to the higher members of being. Heat is thus an aid to incarnation, which in this case, of course, remains symptomatic.

There is another sign that is most instructive in evaluating the iron process operating in man, though it does not seem to be heeded at all: the voice of the patient. In puberty, not only the iron curve but also the voice register of man and woman diverges. The pitch of the voice gives a constitutional clue to a person's condition in regard to incarnation and iron. Of course, it is not meant that voice level and hemoglobin simply correspond to one another, but both are indications of how the human being handles iron and how he works actively with it. A man with a large chest and a bass voice is certainly not in danger of iron deficiency. A person who can hold his own in his environment with his voice does not have anemia!

Of course, one can say that voice pitch is "hormonally determined." The high voice of a man castrated before puberty, like the deepened voice of a woman treated with male hormones, demonstrates the hormonal factor. Interestingly, this change of voice in women is irreversible even after discontinuation of hormone treatment. In contrast, the use of estrogen in men does not raise the voice. We must, however, see the effective impulses in the hormones (see p. 263 f.); then, even through the structural formulas, we will be able to recognize the deeper connection of ego and astral body with the physical body in men (see p. 255).

The iron level, the voice, and the hormonal situation do not depend on one another; rather, all three are the expression of the soul-spiritual man working in them. This relation makes it seem as though one affects the other, for example, that anabolic or androgenic hormones affect the iron, or that iron deficiency causes potency disorders, and so forth. Rudolf Steiner repeatedly referred to the connection of the generative organs with the speech organs and to the future shift in their forces.

Starting in the sixteenth and seventeenth centuries, one form of anemia, the so-called chlorosis, played an important role. It was early recognized as anemia, but at that time more attention was given to the total structure of the patient. Thus, Sydenham (1624–89) connected chlorosis with hysteria, and others saw it as a neuropathic disorder. Likewise, in therapy they were not satisfied to administer "vinum chalybeatum" (Sydenham)—iron in wine—for the iron deficiency alone but expected this to "raise the life spirits that lay low before."

That chlorosis appeared in girls who had already begun to menstruate should be understandable in the light of our discussions. Since incarnation is weaker in women, puberty signifies a great burden and readjustment. Instead of turning toward the earth after "earth-ripeness," these human beings tend to withdraw, since they lack the power connected with iron to meet and manage the conditions of earth in freedom. Furthermore, essential hypochromic anemia virtually affects only women for the same reasons.

If nothing is heard or seen of chlorosis today, this is not just because diseases are differently designated; according to modern investigations, almost every second woman between the ages of sixteen and forty-five suffers from iron deffciency. Although we naturally have no hemoglobin determinations from the seventeenth century, there is general agreement that this severe syndrome of earlier times has disappeared. This is explained by the complete change of times. The human being (especially the woman) of today is better incarnated; the connection of spirit and soul with the body has, if anything, gone beyond the healthy state. For this reason, we quite rightly no longer make distinctions between man and woman in social life. One can surely agree with what Heilmeyer says regarding chlorosis: "Modern times have had a great therapeutic effect through the change in life style, as the present rarity of this disease shows, and it indicates the direction treatment must go." The differentiation of the individual factors here is secondary. Certainly more substantial nutrition plays a role, as does the life today that addresses the human being, especially the astral body, more strongly. Finally, there is the utterly changed relation to light.

There are forms of anemia, called "late chlorosis" by Alstedt, that appear predominantly in the winter and respond especially well to iron. They are certainly also related to insufficient light. Repeated mention has been made of iron's connection with light. Related is the striking fact that anemic people do not get sun-tanned; this reveals the absence of light transmission through iron. (Certainly this is the case in redheads, who by no means *must* be anemic but often are. According to Rudolf Steiner, the balance between iron and sulfur is displaced in favor of the latter in these people.)

An indirect effect of light evident in the seasons gives an important indication of man's relation to iron. Autumn is the "iron time" of the year. This begins with the meteor showers in August, when cosmic iron actually streams to the earth. The process of ripening in nature, in contrast to vegetative sprouting in spring, indicates a process becoming reality in the ensouled organism. Therefore, for diagnosis of the constitution, the time of year the patient feels best is an indispensable question. If iron is lacking (with or without anemia), then the patient feels best in the fall and worst in the spring when he is most susceptible to sickness.

It should be clear from what has been presented that iron deficiency does not consist *only* in the lack of a substance but is the expression of a general disease (if one differentiates between anemia and blood loss in which blood values will revert to normal sooner or later, with or without replacement therapy). Medical science, therefore, rightly speaks of iron deficiency with and without anemia—manifest and latent iron deficiency —but does not consider the integral personality, or it sees it as secondary. Only a knowledge of this and of the essential nature of iron, however, makes it possible to understand the whole phenomenon.

Hemoglobin values reveal a physiological difference not only between man and woman but also between individuals. In women one sometimes has the impression that a certain anemia is not an illness but an individual constitutional condition, an essential expression of the personality. For these people a lower hemoglobin value is simply their healthy level, just as for some constitutional hypotensives, low blood pressure is not pathological. Therefore, either the patients seem resistant to therapy, or else forced hemoglobin increases prove transient and bring no improvement in the general condition. It appears that for such people, the weaker connection with iron—and thus with the earth and the body—is a necessity of fate, which, though it forbids them some things, protects them from others and, in this way, gives their personality its characteristic stamp. In any case, we should beware, concerning hemoglobin content as well as blood pressure values, of taking normal values as altogether binding and of regarding all deviations as pathological.

Tumor anemia and the anemia of chronic infection belong to the hypochromic microcytic iron-deficiency anemias; they are special, however, in that the organism possesses sufficient iron that is "blocked" through binding in the reticuloendothelial system. Therefore, we also speak of an "internal iron deficiency." For this reason there is also increased resorption of iron. Thus, we can see that the substance iron as such is of no use to the organism if the latter does not have the capacity to transmit it to the hemoglobin, that is, to bring it to effective activity.

Iron is the instrument with which the higher members of being penetrate the organism, permeating it with light, even to the metabolic level; here they form and control the purely vegetative, hence, undifferentiated and proliferating, life, transforming it to a higher stage of life, that of ensouled and spirit-permeated life substance. Thus, in cancer, there is an inability to deal with iron, which is also manifested in the disturbed respiratory metabolism (hypoxia).

In infections the serum iron falls off, following the course of fever, while tissue iron increases. The iron goes from the "free" state of the serum, which is connected with outer daily activity, to a tissue-bound state, where it induces internal defense against bacteria, toxins, etc. This battle, involving self-assertion and active overcoming, is a typical iron process. Vitamin C also plays a large part in this connection, as one can recognize in it the iron process also, as was further elaborated elsewhere.[2] Anemia is especially familiar in pulmonary tuberculosis. Tuberculosis is not just an infection; it is a specific disease, characterized by "fleeing the earth," the insufficient connection with the earth (see chapter on the lung, Vol. III). Here, again, anemia is the expression of too weak an incarnation process.

In cases of anemia resistant to therapy, one should think of the relatively rare anemia of renal insufficiency, since erythropoiesis is often affected in pyelonephritis, which is common now. The kidney is the organ of the astral body, which acts on the metabolism through the kidney (see chapter on the kidney, Vol. III). In the anemia of renal insufficiency this happens inadequately. Another typical organ of the astral body is the thyroid gland (see pp. 250f., 255). This should help one to understand why hypothyroidism or myxedema brings anemia it, since this problem is a classic example of insufficient engagement of the astral body in the metabolism. This anemia improves even without iron replacement through treatment of the thyroid alone.

Thus, iron deficiency is not only a matter of a negative iron balance, as one can see particularly in the anemias accompanying malignancy and chronic infection. Resorption of iron depends on the body's need for iron and thus on the organism's handling of the substance. Bile and reducing substances promote iron resorption, especially the bivalent (ferrous) iron, the more "cosmic" form. (The higher valence, in this case the trivalent (ferric) form, has a basically more earthly character. This is not the place, however, to elaborate on this fundamental matter.) In general, one can add that food (especially grains, if they are not refined) contains sufficient iron. Thus, except in anemia resulting from blood loss, internal and not external factors induce anemia. Though it is possible to force iron into the organism by administering it in large amounts, especially intravenously, this still does not eliminate the original disorder, as is shown by the numerous recurrences after cessation of therapy and by the therapy-resistant cases. Conversely, we find that "among the great number of people with iron-poor diets, there are relatively few in whom iron deficiency becomes clinically manifest" (Stodtmeister/Büchmann). More important than administration of exogenous iron is the person's own relation to the metal, that is, his capacity to control the iron process. The aim, therefore, of a genuine therapy will be not only to replace lacking iron, but to strengthen the patient's ability to manage iron, that is, to aid resorption, distribution, utilization, availability, etc.

Of course, in manifest iron deficiency, replacement therapy —administration of utilizable iron—has its justification. This presupposes that the organism can accept the iron, which is probably always the case in manifest iron deficiency. The situation is different, for example, after resection of the stomach or small intestine, since an intact gastrointestinal system is naturally critical for absorption and resorption of iron.

More important for decisions about therapy is latent iron deficiency. As we have seen, this occurs with too weak an incarnation tendency and leads to inadequate management of iron and its resultant signs and symptoms, such as epithelial weakness in the regions of throat, stomach, and gut. Mere administration of exogenous iron is therefore insufficient; the organism must connect itself with the essence of iron, more with the process than with the mere substance or material. This stimulation of the iron process can be achieved, for example, by the use of a medication in which the material has been "transformed" into the iron process; this is therefore not replacement therapy. This transformation is accomplished through "vegetabilization" (see p. 311 f.), in which the substance is "unlocked" by means of a plant. Naturally, the plant best suited for this would be one that already possesses an iron impulse, for example, the stinging nettle. The preparation arising in this way is Ferrum per Urticam, which is given as a 1% dilution or as an injection. As an aid to incarnation, it is especially indicated in childhood, but also at the beginning of each session of iron therapy.

Anaemodoron addresses the iron forming process in a comprehensive way. It contains stinging nettle (Urtica dioica), which is intended to work not through its relatively high iron content, but through its capacity to handle iron especially well. It is complemented by the fruits of the wild strawberry, with which it is combined by a pharmaceutical process. The more vegetative iron process occurring in the leaf element of the stinging nettle crosses over to the animal side in the strawberry's formation of fruit. The involvement of astrality is recognizable in the catabolism accompanying ripening, in connection with reddening and sugar formation. These two natural processes reflect the polar functions of iron, its fluctuation between reduction and oxidation, anabolism and catabolism, cosmic and earthly action, which are united in the substance iron.

Anaemodoron is usefully complemented with gentian (Enzian-Anaemodoron), which addresses the stomach and intestines, whose importance for iron absorption in particular and for the whole blood formation (B_{12} synthesis, intrinsic factor) in general, is well-known. Actually, all bitters act on the stomach and intestines or metabolism and facilitate incarnation in this region. In this connection, one should also note the well-proven China-Anaemodoron.

Spinach in combination with sassafras is also useful as a medication for pernicious anemia, again not because of the plant's iron content, which is actually relatively small, but because of the process, that is, its inherent capacity for dealing with iron; this is what must be introduced into the organism. A decoction of the root is used in order to affect the nervous system and the disorder connected with it. In this way, one can bring the iron process back into the correct relation to the blood and nerves (Sassafras D2/Spinacia D2 aa ampules and dilution) (see also p. 352 f.).

A substance having a more comprehensive action than iron is scorodita, its natural arsenic compound. Arsenic appeals specifically to the astral body; arsenicization is synonymous with astralization according to Rudolf Steiner. Scorodite is indicated in cases of insufficient incarnation, especially of the astral body. This would be revealed psychologically by a feeling of general anxiety. It might also be seen in over-susceptibility to the influence of the weather (weather sensitivity), since our organism is connected with the atmospheric environment through the astral body and the less this is incarnated, the more susceptible we become.

A medication with a still more comprehensive, yet milder and more penetrating action is Levico, the curative water of a spring in northern Italy. Its essential contents are iron, copper, and arsenic in optimal proportions. Hence, it is superior to iron or arsenic alone. This water has been used for many decades for blood diseases. The dosage for this, however, indicated on the bottles in which it is dispensed, is too high if the water is to be used in its capacity for stimulating the incarnation process. As we have explained, in a latent or constitutional iron deficiency such stimulation is especially important and efficacious in the springtime. In addition, the same treatment is effective for constitutional hypertension, since this stems from the same difficulty in incarnating as latent iron deficiency. The following procedure has proven itself in the aforenamed conditions: Levico-strong-water is given with daily increases, beginning with 3 × 10–15 drops; after two weeks the dose has reached 3 × 30–60 drops (1 teaspoon), depending on the patient's age. This dosage is maintained two to four weeks, after which it is lowered to 3 × 10–15 drops for a two-week period. Doses should be taken with water and the higher ones preferably with food. Levico can also be used in potentized form, especially in D3 as a dilution or injection.

What is crucial in this process is not the immediate improvement of any particular symptom, but the deeper effects, from an improvement in the susceptibility to infections to a consolidation of the personality structure; that is, fundamentally, a better incarnation.

Once again the reader should note the relation of iron to light, which is also of therapeutic significance. Many cases of anemia that are resistant to therapy respond to medication only after the application of light, or even disappear without further treatment after treatment with light. Natural sunlight is the best, of course; otherwise, a light source approximating sunlight as closely as possible (arc-lamp, ultravitalux, etc.) should be used, but not one-sided ultra-violet.

The application of the rare earth metals should also be mentioned briefly here. As metals, they share much of the essence of iron, in particular a strong connection with light, which is otherwise found only in iron. Their spark formation is typical and also finds technical application in flint. Just as one can find individual properties of the seven planetary metals (see Vol. II) in isolated form in other metals, so can one recognize iron's affinity to light in the rare earth metals. The naturally occurring form of cerite is used in D6 as injection, D4 and D6 as powder. This has proven the most effective of the cerium compounds. The indication for this remedy is not primarily anemia but stimulation of the light metabolism (see p. 294).

A remedy of a special character is Carbo Betulae cum Methan.[3] The action of Carbo in potentized form goes through the kidneys and stimulates the anabolic processes (see chapter on the kidneys, Vol. III). Methane has a dull character, hence its strengthening action on the anabolic side of the metabolism. (In contrast to CH_4, CO_2 stands dynamically more on the catabolic, wakening side of the metabolism.)

The action of Carbo cum Methan is broad, though it is directed primarily toward blood formation. Therefore, it can be used for low vitality, that is, inadequate activity of the astral body, primarily "from below" through the kidney system. As we have seen, this weakness in engagement of the astral body is also present in anemia, both hypochromic and macrocytic.

Because of its comprehensive character, Carbo Betulae cum Methan is indicated in both forms of anemia, despite their oppositeness, when the blood is too weakly formed, coming into a state of "decay." Best results have been found with Carbo cum Methan D4, one knife-tip 3 × daily.

Anemia can also appear without even a latent iron deficiency. The prototype for this problem is pernicious anemia. The macrocytosis, as well as the elevated serum iron level, shows a relative over-saturation with iron. Thus there is no disturbance of the iron process; it is inadequately handled, however, as the defective erythropoiesis shows. As described in the chapter on the metals (Vol. II), copper provides the foundation that enables the activity of iron to unfold. In pernicious anemia the disorder is more on the side of the copper process than of the iron process. Copper prepares the site where iron will act. On the basis of this knowledge, spiritual-scientific medicine has long made use of copper in disorders of the iron metabolism, and not only in megaloblastic anemias. Copper simultaneously stimulates erythropoiesis and leukopoiesis. In addition, the inverse behavior of the iron and copper values in the serum indicates their polar relation. Copper always stands on the anabolic, nourishing side, while iron tends toward oxidative catabolism. By taking these facts into consideration, one will be able to decide when to use copper instead of iron in a particular case. For example, copper is used to stimulate the total protein metabolism, while iron controls it "from above." The use of spinach and sassafras has been mentioned above.

In dark-haired people especially, copper, rather than iron, is indicated, particularly when there is a qualitative nutritional disorder or a tendency to cramps. In early pregnancy it is also preferred to iron. Nevertheless, copper alone will not cure pernicious anemia, and this does not speak against the origin we have described for the disease. Cobalt, which is specifically active here in vitamin B_{12}, manifests part of the comprehensive nature of copper but also shows features of iron and can therefore help fulfill this specific function of vitamin B_{12} in erythropoiesis.

Finally, in certain cases of anemia, gold can also be indicated. This works in the widest sense on man's relation to extraterrestrial, cosmic forces of "lightness" (E. Lehrs) and to the earthly forces of gravity. For this reason, at low potency it can support incarnation when abortion is threatened and can be efficacious in anemic people when their earthly consciousness is not sufficiently developed.

Chapter V
The School Child
and the School Physician's Guidance

Prefatory Remarks

The contributions on school medicine come from two authors, whose chapters complement one another. H. Matthiolus speaks from the point of view of a school physician and describes the influence of instruction on health in reference to different types of children in Part 1. In Part 2, W. Holtzapfel characterizes the constitution of the school child and its therapeutic consequences.

Part 1.
Basic Elements of the School Physician's Activity

With the founding of Waldorf school pedagogy, a new occupation came into being in the medical field as well: the work of the school physician as a member of the staff. The school physician must know every child in the school and be informed about the circumstances of his development. He is the mediator between the child on the one side, and the teacher and parents on the other. With his exact knowledge of the child's health, he can help the teacher in the pedagogical treatment of the children entrusted to him and can advise the parents.

A fundamental fact that every teacher should continually keep in mind when working spiritually with children is that young people need not only to learn; they must also grow and mature organically. Each school child must accomplish this double task. We should help him to master the task "without suffering damage." Academic abilities and the powers of thought are liberated, transformed growth forces. After the change of teeth and the first structural metamorphosis, the young person needs and wishes to put these freed forces to use. This must occur, though, in the right way and measure. The child "wrests" the power to learn from a growing organism, one that is maturing in its individual organs. This is a "wresting away," because growth, anabolism and vitality stand in a polar relation to the formation of consciousness, which is always based on the catabolism of bodily substance, as was illustrated in detail in the preceding chapters. Growth is not simply a matter of increasing in size; it is a structural and essential metamorphosis occurring in definite phases. The incarnating human being, whose individuality is at first mainly occupied in building up and forming the physical body, manifests himself most clearly in the molding and remolding of his body. His physical make-up and structural metamorphosis are the visible stages in his inner course of becoming. While the structural form develops quite individually in each person's life history, it goes through quite typical phases in general. Here again we find that the child and adolescent are subject to entirely different laws from adults.

The type of bodily form found in each stage of human development is quite aptly described in common language usage. We distinguish the premature baby, the newborn, the infant, the crawler, the toddler, and the kindergartener. Up to this stage, in accordance with this sexually neutral phase of human development, the names do not indicate sex. Only with the first structural metamorphosis, from the beginning of school, do we begin to differentiate linguistically between masculine and feminine. Now we begin to speak of boys and girls. The French call a girl who is no longer a child but who is still not mature, "enfantine." In old age, sexual differences practically disappear again; they are effaced and lose their significance.

In the first chapter of this book, we have already characterized the structural forms typical of infants and small, preschool children. Now we turn to the time of the first structural metamorphosis, which begins in the sixth year of life and lasts until the seventh. In this phase of radical change, the small child becomes a "school child." This change is most clearly visible in the growing person's appearance as a whole and less so

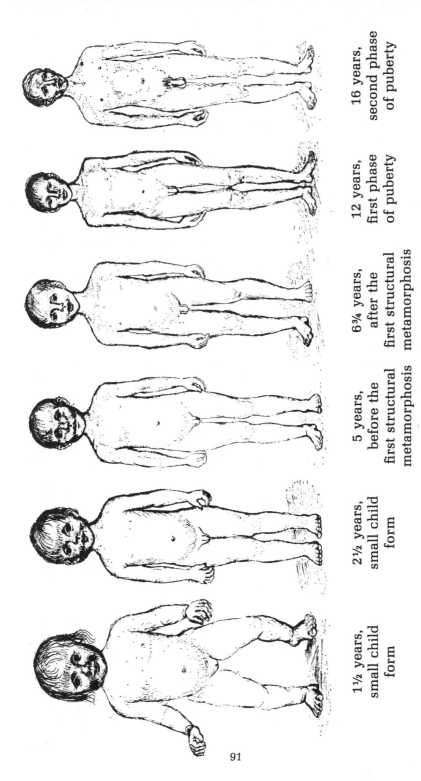

1½ years, small child form

2½ years, small child form

5 years, before the first structural metamorphosis

6¾ years, after the first structural metamorphosis

12 years, first phase of puberty

16 years, second phase of puberty

Drawings: Manfred Welzel

91

in psychological tests, which can show only subordinate characteristics (see drawings).

Here the structural form is subjected for the first time to a definite remolding process from head to foot. Its culmination is at the beginning of the change of teeth, in which old substance and form are not only remolded, but visibly replaced. A temporary terminal point of development has been reached. The etheric formative forces, which until this point have been at work deep in the organic, are now free from a point of their organ-molding activity and come, especially in the head region, to be metamorphosed into capacities for memory and ideation, forces of intelligence. The formative forces, which formed the body and organs, become formers, sculptors, of ideas, once the inherited "model body" has been thoroughly refashioned into an "individual body."

This "freeing" is a slow, rhythmical process, like an ever more frequent and ever greater emergence from a stream. Even in their purely outward aspect, the children look different at this age. They lose the more rounded shape, becoming lean and relatively thin. The fatty pads on the arms and legs recede, and the muscular profile becomes clearer because of this, and also simply from increased muscle growth. The joints stand out more from the whole contour of the limbs. The drum-shaped, protruding belly of the small child flattens out. Everything rounded, plump, and soft is lost.

Muscles and ribs become more visible individually; the waist begins to be defined, as do the curves in the vertebral column, the convexity of the chest, and the concavity of the lumbar spine. The breadth of the shoulders is greater than that of the pelvis, so that the trunk tapers downward.

In the head region, the mid-face grows primarily, but the lower face also undergoes a characteristic transformation. The forehead and eye portion recedes somewhat in its total impression and becomes relatively smaller. The child's look becomes more distanced, more reserved, more "critical."

The form of movement is also new. Now the children prefer to hop and jump to and fro, and take great joy in accelerating and braking a motion. The movements are rapid, harmonious, and of supple lightness. Everything is effortless and graceful; up and down, back and forth, a continual swinging, constant repetition of identical movement forms. Through this rhythmic practice, the limbs grow into new functions.

In his soul development, the child at this age turns increasingly toward the group. He participates in communal games with greater purpose and concentration. The children are no longer so easily distracted by every event taking place around them. Their play is more goal-directed. They have a need for rhythmic activity and like to help in the group or family. They will take on shopping and little jobs in the household, such as rinsing or drying the dishes, sometimes with enthusiasm and a certain perseverence. They begin to be interested in numbers and letters. Disregarding their possession by the demon of question-asking, they now say remarkable things: "Now I can do something that you can't see or hear; I can count in my head." Or the child notices a striking man on the street and perhaps looks at him quite closely. In the evening he says to his mother, "I can still picture the man. When I want, I can close my eyes and see him." Such a statement certainly comes from a child who is ready for school. One who is not ready, in contrast, would seem to be the little girl who is asked at her school admission interview what the windows in a house are for, and who answers spontaneously, "For cleaning!" This answer honors the domestic industry of her mother; the child quite obviously has imitatively learned that her mother uses the windows mainly for cleaning them. The child still lives so much in imitation of her mother's actions that this is what seems to her the most important thing about a window.

The first freeing and availability of the hitherto organ-bound etheric forces is a gradual process that the child's teacher must know well. These newly emerging forces are to be used prudently. Earlier, they were active in an artistically forming, plastic manner, and now they must be activated artistically in their new form as well. Everything, therefore, that the child is to accomplish in the beginning of school and through the first years must be breathed through with beauty.

Interestingly, the recently discovered reading and writing

center of the brain matures around the time of the first structural metamorphosis. This is another indication that to push
reading and writing into the early years of childhood is in open
contradiction of natural development. We cannot make a good
runner by prematurely training a child to stand and walk; this
will only give him crooked legs. Similarly, early reading and
writing only create hindrances for the correct development of
the spiritual faculties.

The shaping of the human form in the time of puberty presents the greatest conceivable contrast to the forces of growth
and forming that have been described in early childhood. In
the first phase of puberty, before the onset of "earth-ripeness,"
we no longer see the head as the focal point of development,
the pole of growth and forming; at this age, it is the feet in
which the first spurt of growth is seen. Following them are the
lower leg and thigh, while a parallel process occurs in the upper
extremities (hands and arms); thus, there is a peripheral growth
from the outer points to the center. In the growth spurt of the
first phase of puberty, the extremities are seen not to be pushed
outward from the center of the body but to grow from the
periphery inward to the center, if we attend to the course of
the growth spurts. At this time the trunk is not yet affected by
the lengthwise growth that is proceeding from the foot,
through the lower leg, up to the thigh. In this way, a dispropor-
tion arises between the length of the legs and that of the trunk.
At the moment of the greatest relative leg length and shortest
relative trunk length, that is, at the moment when the center of
gravity is at its lowest (most caudal), is the time when sexual
maturity sets in. In the course of development, the center of
gravity migrates from the second cervical vertebra down to the
sacral region.

In the first phase of puberty, the frequency relation between
pulse and respiration is strongly in favor of the pulse, and
hence of the blood. In the small child and the infant, the respiratory side predominates, so that the pulse-respiration quotient at this age is under four. In contrast to the warm, short,
round little hand of the pre-school child, that of the adolescent

is long, sinewy, and well-defined; in boys, it is usually some-what ungainly, coarse, and heavily built. Often there is a hint of acrocyanosis—a sign of labile circulatory and vascular dis-turbances—and strong perspiration. The hands and feet are clumsy and their fine motor control is not yet sufficiently developed. The arms and legs are well-segmented, primarily in the jointed parts, and have taken definite shape from the mus-cles; this is naturally more pronounced in boys. The arch of the foot attains its full span; heel and leg stand out more clear-ly. Many deformities can already be detected at this age and are sometimes already pronounced. The span of the pelvis in the lumbar region corresponds to that of the arch of the foot. The curves of the spine, which begin to be visible with the first structural metamorphosis, are now fully formed; the waist is narrow and belted. In contrast to the small child's round, cylin-drical trunk and jolly little belly, we now see the "wasp" waist as the formative tendency and naturally also as an artificial result. What is segmented, membered, is now further drawn in with a belt and thus emphasized. This shows that the con-sciousness and sense of life also lie in separation and member-ing. The costal margins become sharper; thorax and abdomen flatten out in a frontal plane, and the separate, dynamically operating muscle systems become increasingly visible under the skin. Primarily in boys, the skin becomes darker and firmer. In girls, there is particularly solid hip development.

The kind of movement typical at this age takes its character from the overly long legs that cannot quite be accommodated in the course of motion. The youngsters trip over their own legs; the movements are ungainly, uncontrolled, and often hap-hazard and abrupt. Soft suppleness and harmonious motion are gone. The form of movement is angular and sharp, over-shooting the mark linearly. Idleness alternates with an exces-sive urge to move. The movement now begins with greater in-tensity and acceleration but is broken off, braked, stopped. The young person experiences himself in a luxury of movements; activity and motion themselves are the important thing, rather than the goal of activity. In walking, the heel is often set down with emphasis and the play of movements is directed, initiated, and experienced from the hip. Swinging, rocking, and gliding motions are now carried out with the hips.

In the second phase of puberty, during the post-pubertal growth spurt that is so typical for the human being, movements and the structural form of the body are reharmonized. The step becomes sure, strong, and supple.

Formerly, there was a notion, in part quite well-founded, that many disorders and pathological tendencies disappear in puberty. Mothers were advised to wait until this time of development in their children; then, many weaknesses and deficiencies would disappear of themselves. Puberty was felt to be a time when the organism has a heightened capacity for self-healing. Today, however, the boundaries of puberty have become blurred. It remains true, however, that the phase of puberty marks a new beginning. The body's structural form undergoes a metamorphosis; the functions change; new centers of gravity are set. It is like moving within one's own house; everything gets a new place, a different value and significance.

This reconstruction has definite traits; through it, the human being's own soul characteristics come into being. The young person has the feeling of being pushed into a stormy sea of uncertainties and loneliness. Hitherto, the soul has sailed only in inland waters; now, however, it comes into the high sea, and its own little ship is exposed to utterly unknown dangers. Only much later, and with great effort, will the core of the being, the ego, be able to steer surely and steadily through all perils.

Puberty is the time of the first deeply felt life-encounters, of young friendships, of first love. It is also the time when one's own aims in life and vocational direction become conscious.

At puberty, striking changes take place in the circulatory and respiratory systems. Pulse and breathing, heart and lungs now clearly enter consciousness. The young person experiences this reorganization of the rhythmic system; in this age group, we find increased respiratory arrhythmia, palpitations, and tachycardia, as well as a tendency to collapse. At this age, such disturbances are felt intensely, while a child beneath the age of nine or ten never mentions the heart or circulation.

The whole pneumatization, the internal aeration, presents a new picture. The sinuses of the head are now completely formed and pneumatized. Through the growth of the vocal chords and the entire larynx, the voice has become deeper—only slightly in girls, but appreciably, by a whole octave, in boys (see pp. 69, 78). The vital capacity is considerably increased, as are air circulation and ventilation. The process of breathing penetrates to the depths of the organism. Primarily in boys, pronounced diaphragmatic and flank breathing appears as a new type of respiration, though it has been in gradual preparation since the ages of nine to eleven. In girls, costal respiration remains predominant and the respiratory curve runs in harmonious waves. In boys, we begin to see a less placid respiratory curve. Further phenomena related to stronger astralization now appear; juvenile struma, heightened gastric acid values, the increase in 17-ketosteroids, and the altered body odor. Now the young people smell differently and suddenly "can no longer smell themselves."

The third seven-year period—the period of development after "earth-ripeness"—is characterized by segmentation, bifurcation, splitting, and separation. At the beginning, there is the separation of the sexes, which assumes its actual significance when the stage of sexual functioning has been reached. The separation of the sexes was naturally present before, anatomically and morphologically, but not functionally or in terms of soul life.

The so-called "infantile sexuality" described by Freud and his followers is utterly foreign to the essential being of the child. The observations of Freud and his disciples simply pass by what is most essential: the asexuality of the human being before this point of development. This long phase of human juvenile development held free of all real sexuality is a unique privilege of the human being, the basis of his cultural creativity and his inner freedom. What is typical for the human being is not domination by his drives, but the possibility of freedom from his drives in childhood and youth and the mastery of his drives in later youth and adulthood.

The experience of the inner space of one's own soul is at this time in contrast with an increased interest in the world, and an exaggerated feeling of self-worth alternates with periods of a definite sense of inferiority. Wild affirmation of life and joyfulness turn into deep sadness and *Weltschmerz*. For the first time there is a danger of suicide. Typically, black is often chosen as the favorite color at this age—a choice that no healthy child could make. An exaggerated dynamism alternates with lack of movement, even torpidity. The "dance of death" is a fitting image for this time of life. The diseases of this epoch reflect separation, displacement, polarity; we need only think of such opposite syndromes as pubertal emaciation and obesity.

Acceleration

The study of human growth leads to still other results. If we compare the stature of human beings of previous centuries with that of contemporary people, we find a striking difference in height. Human beings have grown considerably and are continuing to grow. This process has been taking place for about one and a half centuries. The average measure for Wilhelm I's guard was 170 cm, which would occur in the lower third of a normal company today. Old armor also gives a clear indication of the significantly increased stature; no Central European of normal size could fit in such armor today. As recently as the last century, C.G. Carus felt that 165 cm represented the measure of beauty for an ideal human stature, disregarding sexual differences; to greater statures he attributed a more masculine character, to lesser ones, a more feminine character. The greater final height of men and women observed today is reached at an earlier age than was the earlier normal height. Today, boys are fully grown at seventeen or eighteen at the latest, and girls at sixteen. Unlike former times, apprentices today reach their final height by the end of apprenticeship. This acceleration applies not only to growth size alone; it characterizes the whole of human development.

Infants are now heavier and longer than formerly.

The milk teeth come in earlier and can sometimes be present at birth!

The permanent teeth also appear considerably earlier than

fifty years ago. In 1928, they appeared at 7.4 years; in 1937, at 6.4; and today at 5.66.

In the first seven-year period there is already a clear increase in size compared to earlier measurements of that age; the rates of increase in the first two years are especially striking.

Physiologic myopia sets in about two years earlier than previously.

Typical childhood diseases come earlier.

The pubertal growth spurt comes earlier by about three months per decade; it now begins at about ten in girls.

Puberty arrives earlier by about three months per decade; the onset of menstruation in Bavaria in 1968 occurred at 12.6 years, while in Germany in 1920, at 14.6 years.

Menopause arrives earlier.

Shortening of the growth period has been noted, with masculine development now ending at seventeen or eighteen years and feminine usually at sixteen.

There has been an increase in final height by 1 cm per decade since the last third of the nineteenth century. The final height of men averages 177 cm; of women, 165 cm. Use of hormonal contraceptives before eleven can lower the height in women. Use of birth control pills at this age suppresses the post-pubertal growth spurt, which occurs only in humans.

The time of lowest mortality, that is, of greatest health, has moved back from age eleven to twelve to age ten to eleven.

The length of pregnancy has not yet been involved in the acceleration process, unlike the development of the embryo, which, as we have mentioned, is born larger and heavier today than formerly.

There have been many attempts to explain these phenomena, which are probably unique in the history of mankind, involving as they do such a fundamental alteration of the outer form and its developmental rhythms in so short a time. The picture of this acceleration was first presented with clarity and in detail in 1935 by Koch, the medical officer of Leipzig. These remarkable phenomena, difficult to explain through external factors, have received many interpretations.

The altered and increased light metabolism since the inven-

tion of the incandescent light in 1879 has repeatedly been
named as the cause, and the impact of artificial light on the
carbohydrate and oxygen metabolism and on biological functions in man has also been noted (see p. 291).

The observation that the total acceleration is more clearly
visible and pronounced in cities than in the country led to the
assumption that an urbanization trauma must be the hidden
cause of this phenomenon. The pediatrician de Rudder is the
primary proponent of this theory. He writes:

> Almost all affects, even attentiveness, mental stimulation, dis-
> turbance, noise, sport activity, baths, and irradiation with artifi-
> cial ultraviolet lamps all have one thing in common: They all
> act sympathicotonically. That is not theory but measurable phy-
> siological fact. Therefore, they must all represent growth stim-
> uli. . . . A child's (or adult's) existence in present-day civilization,
> especially in its more pronounced, metropolitan form in which
> a quarter of the inhabitants of Germany already live, is nothing
> but an enormous accumulation of such sympathicotonic stimuli.

As obvious as the theory of urbanization trauma appears at first
sight, the fact is that the trend of acceleration is found today
not only in areas of urban conglomeration, but also in the
country. In the face of the general trend of acceleration, the
differences between city and country are decreasing, though
they can still be detected, of course. It is true that country life
is becoming similar to city life. Technology and a scientific, intellectual approach to life are penetrating rural areas as well.
The natural rhythm is yielding to the arrhythmia of modern
life. An interpretation of the effects of urbanization was under-
taken by the well-known Munich child clinician, von Pfaundler,
among others. It was an attempt to explain these phenomena
in terms of social standing. Specifically, detailed investigations
of the urban population showed that those who were in a
higher social position and were more intellectually developed
grew faster and taller; in the face of the general diffusion of the
phenomenon, however, this viewpoint no longer seems fully
satisfactory.

Again and again, mention is made of the improved nutrition
of contemporary man. Experiments have shown that a more

nourishing diet brings about increased weight, but no increase in final height. Nutritional experiments in times of war, post-war, and famine have proven that although the undernourished organism shows an interesting ability to make up growth later when given better nourishment, this growth does not exceed a certain limit. After this limit, additional improvement of the diet has no further effect on final height. This dramatic ability to make up growth, which also occurs after long and severe illness, is a most interesting phenomenon, but it cannot explain acceleration.

If nutrition has a bearing on this question, then it is more likely to be a qualitative problem. Certainly the basic diet is more plentiful today than centuries ago, since more provisions are available. The food value of these provisions has fallen considerably, however, through unwholesome chemical interference in the form of pesticides, artificial fertilizers, preservatives and colorants, inappropriate processing, etc. We will leave open the question as to what extent the one-sided decrease in food quality in favor of increased quantity plays a part in the acceleration.

The part played by individual food components would seem to be more significant. A high-protein diet leads to an acceleration of growth, as can be shown in comparing the time of human development with that of various mammals, referring to the composition of the milk (detailed exposition on p. 230). Accordingly, the relatively high protein consumption usual today should also contribute to the acceleration of development, primarily in infancy. Zeigler[1] showed in his monograph on acceleration that not a generally better diet, but an over-consumption of sugar has a clear effect on growth. Given the essential nature of sugar as the vehicle of the ego organization, and a firmer anchoring of the latter in the metabolism, an effect in the direction of acceleration would be quite understandable (see pp. 227 and 233).

Similar circumstances are present in man's relation to movement, which is likewise held responsible for acceleration. True, people participate more than formerly in sports; almost everyone, however, suffers from sedentariness in the normal course of daily life. The technologizing and mechanizing of the place of work and the household create an alarming deficiency of movement and a monotonous life for most people. The average citizen of our day, with fat belly and thin legs, is eloquent testimony to the decrease and monotony of movement. Thus, we certainly cannot hold increased physical activity responsible for acceleration.

Nold has elaborated an interesting theory.[2] Starting with the notion of the "luxuriance of hybrids," which can be observed in certain species of plants and animals, he came to believe that the greater final height of contemporary man should be attributed to the fact that originally isolated groups of people are increasingly being mixed through marriage of people of different origins. This has increased considerably in recent decades, especially since the end of the last century. This theory chiefly provides a good explanation for the increased size and weight of humans at birth.

All of these exogenous factors no doubt play a part in the genesis of acceleration but are not its original cause. These factors meet with a changed human type, whose formative forces stand in a different relationship to his body than formerly. It is only this new endogenous situation that permits the exogenous factors to take effect. The inner structure of the organization of the members of man's being has changed in recent times; this is the real source of the increased growth observable today, independent of all exogenous reinforcing influences.

Also of great importance is the influence of the upbringing, or the psychological approach in, and type of, education, in the widest sense, given the child; their influence on growth is evident. A one-sided load on intellect and memory seems to force acceleration and longitudinal growth, while a more artistic form of instruction, appealing to all the young person's gifts and capacities, promotes a more harmonious development. Wherever the intellect is highly cultivated, the final heights rise and the inner rhythms are cut short. The haste and hurry, the impatient unrest become organic, disturbing the equilibrium of the endogenous developmental rhythms. Rudolf Steiner indicated that the teacher can have a deep effect through the manner of his teaching, reaching as far as the growth forces, that is, the formative forces, of the child. Warm and imaginative instruction enlivens the blood forces and tends to keep the stature small, while overloading with memory material makes for a thin, tall body. Thus, it is specifically indicated how soul activity influences the growth forces. The true significance of this will be seen only in later decades.

A phenomenon just as clear as physical acceleration is the displacement of the inner developmental phases to an earlier age; an example is menarche. It is of special interest for teachers and school doctors, and also for physicians in general, to see how this inner rhythmic process takes place in two different types of schools. Female pupils at the Waldorf school in Stuttgart were compared with pupils at state schools with respect to age of menarche. Noting all instances of menarche in classes 10–13, comprising 207 students, we arrived at the average age of 13.4 for girls who had attended the Waldorf school from the first class on. This figure is based on 122 pupils. In 58 others, who had attended the Waldorf school since the fifth class, the age of menarche was the same, 13.4. Girls who had entered the school after the beginning of the fifth class, however, and therefore had not had this sort of schooling before, showed a lower average age of menarche, that is, 13.0. Compared with the figures from the latest survey in the Federal Republic (taken in Bavaria), both these values were above the average age of menarche, which was reported at 12.6 years. In order to have an exact comparison of students of the same city and the same age, we made a further comparison of the seventh class of a public school with a seventh class of the Waldorf school. Forty-three public school pupils were compared with 40 Waldorf pupils. Both groups were interviewed at the same time of the year, in February. The average age of the state school girls was 12.60; that of the Waldorf girls was 12.59. Thus, the two groups were quite comparable and of practically the same age. Of the state school pupils, 22, or about half of them, had begun to menstruate and 21 had not. Of the Waldorf school pupils, only a third, that is 14 of them, menstruated and 26 did not. Both studies indicate that the onset of menstruation

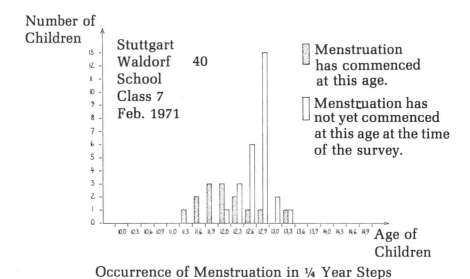

Occurrence of Menstruation in ¼ Year Steps

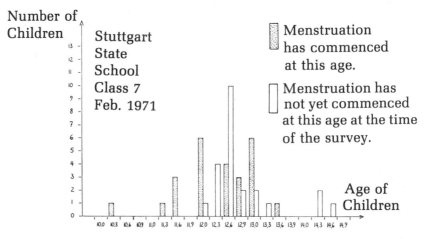

Occurrence of Menstruation in ¼ Year Steps

in the Waldorf school comes significantly later than in a comparable group of young girls who have gone to public school.

The significance and influence on man of the change in human stature and the alteration and acceleration of the developmental rhythms are hard to evaluate. It is certain that the long period of youth and childhood is a privilege of the human being, and that our creative powers and freedom to unfold are based on this slow maturation. Any shortening of this period poses a threat to the specifically human qualities. The faster a developmental process comes to an end, the more rigid the foundation for a certain form of behavior, as we are continually taught anew in the animal kingdom. Throughout the education and care of children, this point of view should stand foremost, that the more nobility and perfection are fostered in an organism, the longer its development and completion will take. This was pointed out by Schopenhauer as well. Slow unfolding is the prerequisite for higher development.[3]

The Constitution: Large-headed–Small-headed

If one wishes to learn something essential from the child's structural form, there is little help in the currently employed orthodox views of constitutional types. Thus, in every health examination, school children are classified according to Kretschmer's categories into leptosomic, athletic, and pyknic types. To an experienced observer, however, these concepts are a scientific Procrustean bed, at least when applied to children and adolescents. Who has ever seen an athletic first-grader? These are non-concepts concerning this age. If Kretschmer's categories have any meaning, it is for adult males; an athletic adult woman is also unnatural.

In the conference of June 2, 1923 at the first Waldorf school, Rudolf Steiner and the teachers considered two types of children, and their descriptive sketches can serve as a starting point for a new theory of constitution in youth. He pointed out that two constitutional types may stand out in a class: the large-headed and the small-headed.

The large-headed type is characterized by the preponderance of the head in relation to the rest of the organism, like the structural type seen in early childhood. The head is striking not only in its size but also in the high, noble curve of the forehead and crown, the strong definition of the cranium, and the childish form of the face. The facial skin shows plentiful circulation. Not only the facial features but also the whole form of the body shows a childlike stamp. These large-headed children are in repose in themselves; they are not easily distracted and have good concentration. They demonstrate a warm sensibility; their fantasy life is strong and richly developed, as is the power of synthetic, constructive imagination. Children of this type have the capacity to symbolize, to see things easily in pictures; they also have a tendency to dream, however, and often lull themselves in illusions. They can also fall uncontrollably into the realm of fancy. Their capacity for analytic thinking is small and poorly developed; they throw everything together and have trouble in making distinctions. In art instruction they produce original works and often find surprising solutions, while their performance in arithmetic and grammar is often weak. For such children, Rudolf Steiner recommends not only pedagogical measures but, in pronounced cases, also dietetic, hydrotherapeutic, and medicinal treatment. Of course, these all must be prescribed by a physician.

These physical measures are necessary in order to make the physical instrument more suited for spiritual functions; conversely, spiritual measures are applied to alter the physicality.

The following therapeutic measures are described by Rudolf Steiner. The head should be washed in cold water in the morning; the child should be given salt. Often a diet of root vegetables is enough, since these have a high content of salty substances. Naturally, great care must be taken in the use of salt. At the final stage, the medicinal application of lead in potentized form is considered. Lead is related to the head forces and stimulates the aging process, which in this case is retarded.

Diametrically opposed to the type of child just described is the type that Rudolf Steiner called small-headed. When the teacher brings such a child into the doctor's office, a thin, pale student stands in front of him. His head is quite small in relation to the rest of the body; especially striking is the small

cranium with its often flat occipital region. The forehead is
low and often receding; the face is better defined. The entire
head-pole gives a solid, hard impression. The frame is already
reminiscent of a later age; the limbs stand out in the whole
appearance.

The teacher reports that the child lacks the ability to concentrate, letting every sense impression distract him. His consciousness is too absorbed by his surroundings so that he gives
an impression of restlessness. The teacher is especially struck
by the child's weak powers of fantasy. In drawing, he usually
produces only little stick figures and cars. In painting, he is
helpless; the colors are put next to one another without relation
and without much inner feeling, and they are usually smeared.
Similarly, in the other artistic subjects, the teacher reports a
lack of talent and imagination. In arithmetic, reading, and
spelling, the teacher notices no deficiencies; the child tends to
perform well in these. Writing assignments, however, regularly
come out poorly; they are pedantic and dry and exhaust themselves in bloodless enumerations.

The small-headed child has a tendency, on the one hand, to
brood and, on the other, to lose himself in his surroundings.
This is a matter of his particular constitution. He is too greatly
stimulated from the outside. He is not a stranger in the world,
like the large-headed child, but he is simply easily distracted.
The reason for this, as Rudolf Steiner describes it, is that the
metabolic-limb system is too isolated. The metabolism is not
spread sufficiently through the whole body, through the whole
being. By this we mean not that there is insufficient metabolism
but that the ego does not take hold of and transform the metabolism sufficiently. In these children there is also a deficiency of
"cosmic nourishment." The body is quite saturated with ali-
mentary processes that have not been fully overcome. Here, we
are dealing on the one hand with a slight poisoning, and on the
other with a hardening, a solidification. The metabolism does
not "blossom" into the brain; it does not warm it enough. The
brain, the entire head, becomes too solid and stays too small
because of this. The adult "type" appears too early. The child
has succumbed too much to gravity. Rudolf Steiner indicated

that the forces of heredity take on too much weight in these children so that the line of the individuality cannot assert itself sufficiently.

A factor contributing to the development of this type of constitution is the administration of isolated or synthetic vitamin D, which is given indiscriminately for rickets prophylaxis. It is easy to see how this would promote the already present mineralizing tendency in the sense of a further "cerebralization" (see pp. 39 and 258).

As an expression of their being weighed down by the earth, small-headed children have a melancholic trait of character, while in large-headed children we occasionally detect a phlegmatic note, since the head is retarded. Nowadays, small-headed children are numerically predominant; this is understandable, since the present life situation promotes precisely their characteristics.

As therapy, Rudolf Steiner referred again to hydrotherapeutic, dietetic, and medicinal possibilities. The child should receive warm applications on the abdomen in the evening. Absorption and blood circulation must be promoted in the abdominal region; the entire metabolic-limb system must be kept in continual activity. The children should be given more sugar. Here, again, just as with the increase of salt for large-headed children, one must proceed with care, since these measures can have negative aspects as well. Sugar, for example, promotes tooth decay and the phenomenon of acceleration. In this case, it will be necessary not only to attend to dental care, but to administer sugar well. This might be given in the form of sweet fruits, figs, dates, honey, etc. The choice and amount of sugar will depend on the given situation. This is another case where the same substance in the same amount can be a remedy for one child but have quite a negative effect on another. Any schematizing is a danger—more so for children than at other times of life. As for the medicinal treatment of small-headed children, silver is of use in bringing about a better incarnation in the metabolism.

The warmth organism needs to be activated in small-headed children; likewise, the circulation and the streaming of fluids. In particular, the life forces in the head region must be stimulated.

Both the small-headed and the large-headed child are healthy school children, but each shows in his development a particular one-sidedness that can lead to definite dangers if left untreated.

According to Rudolf Steiner, these concepts of large- and small-headedness apply until the sixteenth to eighteenth years of life. Thus it is a theory of constitutional types for childhood and youth.

In spite of the disadvantages of a schema, let us compare the characterization of the two constitutional types:

Large-headed	*Small-headed*
Preponderance of the head over the rest of the frame; rather short-limbed.	Head small in relation to the body; preponderance of the limbs.
"Vital" head-pole; weak salt process; insufficient circulation in the extremities.	Head-pole solid, dry, dense; pallor; rather poor circulation in the head.
Retention of childhood type; delayed development.	Early development of adult type; prematurity.
Latent divergent strabismus.	Latent convergent strabismus.
Good concentration; introverted; reposing in self, not easily distracted, warm sensibility.	Poor concentration; extroverted; "brooding"; distracted easily by sense impressions, stimulated by the surroundings.
Strong powers of fantasy, dreamy, not very object-oriented, hence often flighty; synthetic, constructive imagination, capacity for symbolization.	Weak fantasy; awake, sober, object-oriented; analytic, "bloodless" imagination.
Marked artistic tendency and talent.	Not primarily gifted artistically; "in art, a sort of primitive."

Large-headed	Small-headed
Ego and astral body are diverted from the nerve-sense organization; their action here is as in the small (pre-school) child.	Ego and astral body do not engage properly in the metabolic-limb organization.
Salt is not processed sufficiently; low capacity for salt intake and assimilation.	The organism processes relatively too little sugar. Melancholic-choleric tendency.
Phlegmatic-sanguinic tendency.	
Therapy: Cold; salt; lead.	*Therapy:* Warmth; sugar; silver.

The classification "large-headed/small-headed" represents the principal leitmotif of a constitutional theory appropriate for childhood; Rudolf Steiner extends it with the polarity cosmic/earthly.

Cosmic children show features similar to those of the large-headed children, but the cosmic parts of their organization predominate even more clearly; that is, the neurocranium is quite pronounced, beautifully domed and well-defined; the face receding and delicate. One is reminded of Goethe's words from his fragments on physiognomy:

The way our skull is domed,	Wie unser Schädel sich wölbt,
it is like the sky above us,	gleicht er dem Himmel über uns,
so that the pure image	damit das reine Bild der
of the eternal spheres	ewigen Sphären drinnen
might revolve within it.	kreisen könne.

As the cosmic type of child represents a further one-sided development of the large-headed type, so in the opposite direction, the earthly child is an exaggeration of the small-headed type; that is, the limbs and the whole body are strongly penetrated by the forces of heredity. In these children we find a "melancholic streak," and we particularly note a preponderance of the facial structure over the cranium. The lower face is often strongly cast, protruding far in relation to the neurocranium. It is often a striking face, occasionally a somewhat coarse one.

These constitutional types, the large-headed and small-headed, the cosmic and earthly, give a clear indication of how the activities of the doctor and teacher can and must go hand in hand. The doctor shows the teacher where there are hindrances and obstructions in the physical instrument and bodily organism that stand in the way of the child's soul-spiritual development. These difficulties and deficiencies often can be solved only by medical means, that is, by the right medication, by appropriate curative eurythmic exercises, through individually suited diet, physical therapeutic measures, and much besides.

So the doctor becomes an educator. All instruction, both good and bad, has the greatest conceivable influence on the health of children and young people. Not just the material presented but especially the manner of its transmission is crucial. Whether a historical event touches the growing person in the depths of the soul, awakening life aims, or is simply loaded on his memory as dry fact or figure, depends on the teacher's ability to describe and experience it in front of the students. Today, too much is demanded of children intellectually, while they are emotionally unresponsive; in the depths of their will, they are not stirred, much less enthusiastic. Their learning does not go beyond the simple assimilation of facts. But as the intellect responds quickly, so the emotions respond slowly, and the will response matures slowly. The response time of the individual soul-spiritual faculties are simply different. The present manner of teaching separates the head from the rest of the organism, from the whole person; the latter languishes and falls ill. The spiritual impulses building up and molding the organs do not reach the person. Thus, Rudolf Steiner attributes the occurrence of abdominal disturbances and diseases in later life to boring grammar lessons.

In contrast, a history lesson that touches the depths of the soul, in which the pupils are involved with the whole of themselves, taking sides by choosing their heroes and villains, not only awakens in them ideals with will character, but also engages the blood and metabolic activity with a health-giving effect. The fire kindled in the child's soul by great deeds and life histories is transformed into the ability to *do* with decisiveness and efficacy in later life; it makes the genuine goals of life shine more clearly, and also enables the child to grasp his own organic depths better. Not only an artistic conducting of the class is needed to promote the child's ability to attune himself emotionally and to anchor himself with his will; rhythm and timing also play an essential role here. The Waldorf school curriculum provides good conditions for this. The morning begins with the two-hour main lesson, enough time to build up the lesson's theme, reach the climax, and bring it to a conclusion. The study of epochs, lasting several weeks, is interrupted by periods for creative forgetting. Furthermore, the school day is rhythmically divided into scientific subjects, art instruction, artistic exercises of the most varied sort, physical exercises, manual crafts, and gardening. Special mention should be made of eurythmy here.

The subjects are like instruments in an orchestra. They must make their entrance at the right time; their beneficial action comes about in playing together. The individual voices of this orchestra—the canon of subjects—have quite specific actions penetrating into the physical body, into the anabolic, health-promoting forces or the catabolic, disease-causing forces. The soul-spiritual level of the whole of the rhythmically membered and structured instruction echoes to the organic depths of the child. From this soul-spiritual plane, a second and higher health is built up in subtle form. The freed formative forces, transformed into the power of thought and ideation, should then be able to radiate back from the spirit-soul plane and once again work at building up the body, giving form. The process of forming the spirit turns back and becomes the forming of the body. If this process is promoted correctly and intelligently by the teacher, then a new, higher health will arise in the pupil. To be sure, this effect of higher spiritual formation will become fully manifest only when the thoughts and methods behind instruction are the result of meditative work. The efforts of the teacher to attain spiritual originality on the basis of a total educational plan conceived from the spiritual world reach these health-giving forces in the child. In this way, education becomes a second sun, warming and streaming through the whole of the human organism.

The particular demands we make on the student's mind have quite different effects on his bodily organization. For example, if the lesson places too great a burden on the memory, if the children are given a great deal of memory material, then they tend to become pale; in extreme cases the teacher is promoting unhealthy increases in height. If the instruction enlivens the fantasy too strongly, if it stimulates the emotions strongly, then it works in the direction of increased blood flow in the head; the organism will be rather retarded in growth, since the retarding forces of the head-pole are strongly stimulated. The healthy mean lies in a well-balanced alternation between stimulating fantasy activity and deft exercising of the memory. The teacher must create this balance; he must also be able to make up exercises that are appropriate in this sense for an individual child. The lesson must be expressly tailored to the changing states of the class and of each pupil, not taken "ready-made from the pedagogical rack." It is necessary for the teacher to study individually the destiny of each child—his mental abilities, his emotional strengths, his constitution and health, etc. Only in this way can a real meeting between teacher and pupil come about. The teacher must take the responsibility to study conditions and requirements relating to the pupil's destiny, not just books. He must know how and to whom he wishes to present a subject; not just his knowledge but also his grasp of the individual child in front of him is a prerequisite for successful instruction. It has already been mentioned that the alarming preponderance of abstract material, memorized connections, dead formulas, and schematic instruction is related in a significant way to the present-day acceleration syndrome.

Not only the individual spiritual disciplines, but also the personality of the teacher has an effect on the whole of the growing human being. The important consideration for him is that education must, above all, be self-education. Ready-made knowledge does not benefit the child any more than it helps the teacher to have a living contact with the pupil. What gives him the right to come before the pupils is not that he is ahead of them in knowledge, but that he has worked on and, more important, is continuing to work on his personality.

The teacher who lets himself go, who gives free rein to his choleric temperament, for example, is not only in the wrong in the soul realm; the wrong he does penetrates into the depths of the child's organism. The consequence of his unbridled choler will be metabolic and circulatory disorders in the later life of the child. An example will demonstrate this. As I was conducting a thorough examination of a child's heart, circulatory, and respiratory processes with recording devices, his class teacher came in. He wanted "to settle an account" with the child. The teacher's anger was short but effective. Just how effective, the teacher could be convinced of right on the spot; I had left the recording apparatus on the whole time. Afterward, I gave the teacher part of the curves so he could take the effect home with him in black and white. It was quite impressive how the respiration and circulation curves were disturbed and "pathologically" altered for a considerable time, even long after the teacher's anger had passed.

The teacher, whose anger had been justified and brief, had caused a "miniature sickness," which naturally remained only a slight disturbance. But when we think of the not uncommon situations in which a child is continually exposed to the outbreaks of anger and fits of rage of an instructor, then we understand well Rudolf Steiner's reference to lasting disturbances in the metabolic and circulatory systems.

The phlegmatic teacher produces a nervous component in the child; when the effect is strong, neurasthenic conditions can appear. The melancholic teacher tends through his temperament to cause disturbances in the child's respiratory system; the circulatory system can also be affected. If the teacher allows his sanguinic temperament free rein, a lack of vitality, energy, and joy in life will result in the pupil. These consequences usually will not appear in the child immediately but as after-effects later in life. The teacher's attitude of soul in interaction with the child will have repercussions even for the constitution and health in later phases of the child's life. What takes place in the school room in the soul realm of a child will have a later echo in the physical-etheric region in this human being.

Many such connections were discussed by Rudolf Steiner with the teachers. He advised them to see the success of their activity not in the achievement of certain scholastic aims, but in a higher health of the student. He showed them, for example, how the instruction can have a beneficial effect on breathing, sleep, and the circulatory system. He spoke of many other possibilities for creating a healthful influence. Breathing, sleep, and the circulation of the blood are given only as examples.

The Temperaments

At this point we shall touch briefly on the theme of the childhood temperaments. In the lower grades, the temperaments of the children often play a decisive role and are given special pedagogical attention. The medical view, however, can also contribute significantly to the balance and harmonizing of the temperamental disposition.

The best way to be cured of a particular temperament is to perceive it in all its one-sidedness. The child experiences such a conscious awakening to the particularities of a certain temperament most strongly when he sees them in another child of the same temperament; he is plagued and bothered by the very same things to which he subjects those around him. A classmate of the same temperament, sitting on the same bench with one, is a mirror of one's own soul. The temperaments become apparent in the children's behavior.

The choleric child experiences everything strongly and expresses his will decisively and vehemently, often in a sort of frenzy. He acts quickly and aggressively and sometimes passionately. His step is firm and energetic. The blood tends to rush to his head, especially when his temperament accompanies him in a rage. These characteristics appear most clearly in play with other children on whom he imposes himself. At the extreme, this temperament can appear as violent anger and raving. The physician should give the mother primarily dietetic indications and advise her to avoid all hot, fiery, sharp foods. Spices should be used carefully and sparingly; often they should be entirely left out of the diet for a time. As medicinal treatment, Levisticum Flos (D2) can be used.

The sanguine child will lend his interest to the nearest object; his inner contact with things is flighty. He cannot stick to any one thing because the next one already interests him more; he is desultory. His attention is directed at a certain situation only for a short time; he then withdraws his involvement, only to turn it to the next situation. These children change toys and activities quickly. The sanguinic often has a merry look and is happy. In walking, he does not set his feet firmly on the ground. At the extreme, this temperament reaches flightiness and carelessness. Here the main dietary advice is that the child should have "hard nuts to crack." All sugar and sweet things should be avoided. The child needs root vegetables; that is, food that presents a challenge and requires hard work to eat. The sanguinic's boat, so to speak, has too little draught; it is tossed on the waves. The therapy consists in giving it some ballast so that it sits deeper and more calmly in the water. In dietary terms, this means giving foods that demand a little effort to deal with, like the root vegetables mentioned, or perhaps a diet of raw vegetables.

The melancholic child tends to brood. One has the impression that he is occupied with himself, but he does not express himself enough and can be sullen and stand-offish, even contemptuous. He holds on to the past, and cannot let go of what is over and done with. He struggles in vain against inner and outer difficulties—homework, for example, exhausts him—and all this produces a melancholy mood in him. The melancholic is often sorry for himself and very touchy; he keeps and cherishes his experience of pain and injury. At the extreme, this temperament leads to gloom and sadness. The melancholic needs to be encouraged. He should eat foods that have ripened in the sun and that flourish high above the earth. The melancholic child needs sugar in his diet such as is contained in naturally sweet fruits.

The phlegmatic child is not occupied inwardly and manifests little interest outwardly. He is not easily impressionable and is often lame in his reactions. Once his interest has definitely taken root somewhere, however, he is steady and consistent in carrying through. His gait is somewhat wobbly and trudging. He does not step energetically. All of his movements can occasionally be alarmingly retarded. He is also frequently lazy. In extreme cases, stupidity is apparent. Dietetically, stimulating foods are recommended, but preferably nothing that grows under the earth, and plenty of stimulating spices.

The care of the rhythmic organs is of special importance in childhood and youth. At the beginning of life, at the beginning of every human existence, is a rhythmic interaction between the microcosm, man, and the macrocosmic world forces from which he was created. This rhythmic harmony creates strength and life energy; the healthy building up of the human organism takes place in these life currents. The younger and more delicate an organism is, the more dependent it is on adherence to the naturally given rhythms for it to grow and thrive as it really should. Any disturbance, any arrhythmia, has an effect that is hostile to life. Today an adult must often, all too often, bring about such disturbances. The growing person should be spared them as much as possible. Every rhythm is interwoven with other rhythmic processes; none exists for itself alone. For the most part, whole-numbered, harmonious conditions prevail; there is a harmonious hierarchic order. When we look at single rhythmic processes, we find it to be a law that childhood and youth are much more strongly impressed with the element of rhythm than adulthood or old age.

Turning our attention to the end of pregnancy, let us consider the amniotic fluid, in which the human embryo lives before its birth as in a private ocean with its wonderful, strong currents such as the ocean itself contains. We do not realize with sufficient clarity the significance of the fact that the entire amniotic fluid is exchanged every three hours, eight times a day. Into this mighty streaming, arising, forming, and disappearing of fluid, into these unsuspectedly many levels of flow, the etheric body engages itself powerfully. Just how clearly we are dealing here with an engagement of the etheric body, of the formative principle, is shown by the most recent research, which reports deformities and even embryonic death when these currents do not flow rhythmically. We see here a cosmos of currents and a deep, pervasive engagement of the etheric forces. The embryo is enclosed in the embryonic sheaths and surrounded by the warmth of the mother's blood, while the ocean of the amniotic fluid encircles it with flowing currents.

The child's polyphasic need for sleep is to be understood in much the same sense, as an ever renewed immersion in the spiritual world. The child does not sleep because it is tired, but is tired because it wants to sleep. Also, the child's lightness and untiringness are a direct result of this rhythmic association.

Like the entire human form, the respiratory and circulatory systems undergo many transformations during the time of growth. For instance, the chief blood-pole of the small child was located in the head region; this situation is gradually reversed in the time before puberty. At this time, the main concentration of blood is in the abdominal organs. In this period, the head-pole is often inadequately supplied with blood, which explains the tendency to states of collapse and to orthostatic reactions, which are especially common at this age. In preschool children, the respiration-pulse relation is displaced in favor of respiration; the pulse-respiration quotient is low (under 4). In puberty we find the opposite; the pulse clearly prevails over the respiration; pulse rates can be extremely high and breathing relatively slow. An increase in the pulse-respiration quotient is always found during phases of metamorphosis and remolding in human development, namely, in the processes of the ninth and tenth years, in prepuberty and puberty. The particular growth phases in human development are clearly correlated with a high pulse-respiration quotient. Again and again we are taught that the child is far more bound to and formed by rhythm than the adult. Among adults, the female organism again proves more rhythmically anchored and bound than the male.

All education, all learning must be a process of giving form with rhythm. This applies especially to the nurturing of memory, the capacity for remembering. The child is to be understood in terms of rhythm—the connection to the spiritual world

—and is to be educated in accordance with his rhythms. In order to achieve this, we must penetrate into the human being's temporal form, the harmony of his rhythms. The more these rhythms are disordered, the more they disintegrate—as can be observed everywhere in our times—the more the human being is invaded by chaos. Here we see one of the principal tasks of education: to be an ordering and reharmonizing influence. Through this struggle for understanding and knowledge of man's rhythmic temporal form and separate stages of life, we fulfill a task that the spirit of our times places on us. We fulfill a task of Waldorf school pedagogy in particular. Today, healthy development must be built on the basis of higher understanding and insight into the spiritual nature of man. It can no longer be taken for granted, as formerly, that a healthy spirit lives in a healthy body. Education carried out on the basis of a higher, broadened image of man consciously works not only on a healthy mind but also on a healthy body. The art of education that originated from supersensible knowledge acts on the human being into the depths of his organism, where it produces the new and higher health of which we have spoken.

We have seen that care and healthful treatment of the physical body is a prerequisite for meaningful pedagogical activity and that in this way the physician becomes an educator, a helper in the pedagogical field. On the other hand, it is also true that pedagogical influences and measures can be seen to have a strong effect on the organism when we have gained insight into the various kinds of influences that the different spiritual disciplines have. Then spiritual education and discipline truly become a cornerstone of the whole human being, even in his physical organization. This physical organization is the field for implementing our individual destinies. Here, it is decided how the forces and capacities from past lives on earth are realized and manifested in the present life, and how they can develop further. The teacher who has not only recognized the law of body-soul and body-spirit interaction, but also knows how to apply this knowledge in detail to the benefit of the pupil, also becomes a therapist. He engages himself in the stream of formation in the inner organism; he appeals to the "inward doctor" (described by Paracelsus) in us. Here educating simultaneously becomes healing.

The sphere of activities and duties of the Waldorf school doctor aims especially at promoting the inner forces of health in the student. With an insight into the health forces and disease tendencies inherent in human nature, one can direct the development even in early youth in such a way that diseases are avoided ever after, or at least they will have a mild course. The physician who treats and cares for the growing person will take the latent disease tendencies into account when he advises.

In order to perform such counseling, it is imperative that the doctor knows of the influence of soul experiences on later physical functioning. Thus, the sphere of activities of the school physician can be seen as the starting point for a new field, that of hygienic occultism.

Part 2.
Aspects of Diagnosis and Therapy
for the School Physician

The pediatrician differs from most other specialists in that he does not specialize in a particular organ system but in a certain time of life. The school doctor goes a step further and selects a section of time from the period of childhood. Because school is bound up in such a varied and unique way with the child's health (see part 1), and because the school doctor— through his involvement in the instruction and advice to the teachers—can also make use of instruction as a form of therapy, the activity of the school physician represents a unique form of medical practice.

When a child enters school, not only the outer circumstances of life change for him; the child is himself transformed and in this way opened to the new influences that begin at this time.

The small child lives—or certainly ought to live—sheltered within the envelope of motherly influences. He needs this shelter; without it he would certainly waste away in body and soul. These supportive forces have largely abandoned the school child, but he still cannot quite stand on his own like an adult.

He is a being in transition, constantly swinging back and forth between one state, in which he is still carried by a supportive environment, and another, in which he is already testing his independence. The transitional situation of the school child is reflected symbolically in a physical sign in the change of teeth. The child's face with gaps between the teeth tells us that the old (the milk teeth) is giving way, while the new (the permanent teeth) has not yet fully appeared.

The "gap" between "no longer" and "not yet" forms a sort of signature for this age. We meet with it again and again on different levels. Physically, it confronts us in the change of teeth, for example. In the field of the soul, we have seen the gap arise between the maternal, supportive surrounding forces and the incompletely awakened independence. In the spirit, this unbalanced situation is caused by a reorientation in the engagement of man's central member of being; Rudolf Steiner speaks of an altered "coupling" of the ego.[4]

The ego of the small child approaches his physical organization from above, increasingly taking hold of and forming it. "From above" can also be taken literally because we see the development of the small child progress from the head to the limbs. This is also true of the shaping of the body, which is expressed in its changing proportions, and of the motor process, which unfolds as directed movement from above to below.

In the school child, this direction of development is gradually cut off by another one arising from below, out of the metabolic region. From this central point, the ego must gradually gain the strength to process everything that comes into the child from the outside. Not only food must be digested and processed but, in a finer way, so must the sense impressions and soul experiences to which the child is now exposed.

On entering school, there is a flood of new impressions and experiences for the child. There is not only the teacher with his pedagogical measures; there are also the various influences coming from the class and school community and from the individual classmates. In homework assignments, the influence of school extends into the home as well. The way to school often poses a great burden because of traffic, noise, advertisements, the temptations of store window displays, supermarkets, etc.

All this must be coped with, and the school child, in his unstable condition, is not always up to it. True, externally he will generally meet the demands made on him. Inside, however, much remains undigested. This leads to the health disorders typical of school children, which we collectively call "school sickness."

School Sickness

The children complain of head and stomach aches, of sickness and nausea, palpitations and other troubles of the heart (tachycardia, extrasystoles, respiratory arrhythmia), respiratory disturbances ("tightness," shortness of breath), dizziness, weakness. Occasionally, short attacks of fever arise without apparent reason. Sometimes there are attacks of anxiety, faintness, or fainting. The mother reports the paleness and generally poor appearance of the child: the shadows under the eyes, lack of appetite, nervousness, tiredness, and poor sleep. The teacher notices that the child tires quickly and that his concentration is weakening.

These symptoms, of which just one or a few will appear in a particular case, are characterized by a variable course, and in this they fit in with the general character of this period of life from about age seven to fourteen. They come and go; they replace one another. The same child who suffers from a headache today comes back later complaining of a stomach ache, and so on. Yet, all these different symptoms are really just variations on the same theme. One little girl said, appropriately, "Now I have my headache in my belly."

The treatment is guided by two principles. First, the child must be strengthened from the inside so that he can deal with all the demands and burdens pressing on him. Then, the overwhelming influence of this load must be minimized.

This inner strengthening comes to the child through his trust in the adult who leads him as teacher, father, mother, etc. In the inner support that the well-founded authority of the educator gives to the child, there is a paternal element, even if it may come from the mother or a female teacher.[5] This paternal element also works in the direction of the child's awakening forces of independence ("I and the father are one"). The physician provides the same support on the level of substance, as medicine. Chiefly medications containing iron are considered. Iron, which bears a definite relation to the masculine-paternal element[6] (see p. 76), can be used in various modifications suited to the given symptom.

In childrens' metabolic disorders, iron carbonate is the form that is "like a crutch to the crippled," to use Rudolf Steiner's phrase.[7] Siderit (nat. Ferrum carbonicum) D3 to D6 is indicated here. Ferrum muriaticum D6 is effective in the heart and circulatory disturbances mentioned. In connection with plant acid, as Ferrum citricum D8, the action of iron is extended to the respiratory process. The pure metal, preferably as Ferrum praeparatum D12 to D30, is an effective remedy for the "school" headache.

Other iron remedies like Kephalodoron (Biodoron), Solutio Ferri cp., and Urtica dioica, can also be used. In general, however, the four we have indicated are sufficient. It is imperative for parents and teachers to see that the children get enough rest during treatment. School work may have to be limited for a time. The most important dietetic measure is to avoid burdening the children with too much food. Parents tend to overfeed children because of their sickly appearance.

Von Pfaundler summed up the main symptoms of "school sickness" under the name of "mock anemia."[8] With this, he hit on a fitting concept that points from the clinical observation directly to the therapeutic iron process. Since this is a disturbance in the iron "process," however, which does not necessarily manifest as a material iron deficiency, this therapeutic conclusion was generally not drawn. Today, the symptoms described are thought to indicate a pre-latent or latent iron deficiency. "It is not impossible that the lack of an as yet unidentified iron-containing substance shares in the responsibility for the pre-latent and latent iron deficiency.[9] This formulation comes quite close to the concept of the iron process.

A manifest iron deficiency is also not uncommon, especially

in the first four years of school. In one study, an iron-deficiency anemia was found in 15% of the boys and girls between the ages of seven and ten.[10]

Of course, the symptoms appearing in "school sickness," such as abdominal pain and vomiting, may also conceal appendicitis, the more so as it occurs most frequently at this age.[11] One must also think of parasites and mesenteric adenitis.

Some of the stressful conditions related to "school sickness" are practically unavoidable, for example, those encountered on the way to school. There are, however, some that can be avoided. One problem that deserves special care is the assignment of homework. If this consists in asking the child to go over and summarize material that he has already assimilated in class, then this is within his capacity. Yet, he still must be given enough time for play and for his own interests. If he is confronted with new material, however, or an assignment to be mastered alone, then too much is being asked, and the child will react with the health disorders we have described. It is simply not in accordance with the essence of this time of life to confront the world independently.

Much can be accomplished in this direction if the schedule can be arranged to take into account the daily variations in the childrens' capacity for work.[12] Every time of day has its own quality, and different times of day are suited for different kinds of instruction. Attention must be given to the midday low point; lessons between noon and three o'clock are uneconomical, since the efficiency of both pupil and teacher is impaired at this time.

In the labile, transitional situation of the school child, who is swinging between "not yet" and "no longer," iron stands on the side of the forces of independence, which need to be strengthened. With the therapeutic administration of iron, we are following nature's model, since the iron level in the blood (both hemoglobin and serum iron) arises continuously until puberty (see p. 74).

Just as iron is connected with the child's awakening independence, so is copper connected with the waning supportive environmental forces, which we characterized as a maternal element. The copper-iron relation is shifted in favor of iron in men's blood, and in favor of copper in women's blood. While the iron level in the school child is rising, the serum copper level falls from year to year. The relation of copper to the feminine-maternal element is shown by the uniquely high serum copper level during pregnancy, the time of the greatest increase of the organic-maternal forces. "During pregnancy, there is regularly a rise in the serum copper, to be precise, a continuous rise from the beginning to the end of pregnancy, the increase affecting primarily the serum copper (269.2^g%), while the copper content of the erythrocytes corresponds to the norm. Here again we see a mirror-image relationship of Cu and Fe; serum iron tends to decrease appreciably toward the end of pregnancy."[13]

Thus in "school sickness," besides our chief remedy of iron, we can also get help from the other side with copper, especially when the supporting maternal forces give way too early. This is frequently the case with the increasing helplessness and lack of instinct of young mothers, and with the disintegration of the family. For symptoms appearing in the area of the digestive system, we might complement the ferrum-carbonicum therapy with the application of copper salve on the abdomen.

Copper is especially indicated for nocturnal tossing of the head in children, jactatio capitis nocturna, which is known often to be associated with the lack of maternal warmth. Besides Zincum D12-D30 and Agaricus muscar. D6-D15, Cuprum is also useful here, preferably as Cuprum per Chamomillam 1% dil.

Like jactatio capitis nocturna, some childhood diseases involving cramps and seizures manifest a relation to copper in the fact that peaceful, supportive influences alone have a healing effect on them. "Anxious, troubled behavior in the environment aggravates the attacks, and calm behavior favors healing," writes Feer[14] regarding whooping cough, for which the efficacy of copper is known (Cuprum aceticum D3).

In chorea minor and various tics, the influence of the environment is even more decisive, which is why a change of surroundings is often helpful; a child with chorea must, without fail, stay out of school for a time. Here, as well, copper has a beneficial effect (especially as Cuprum aceticum/Zincum val. aa.; this mixture is complemented well by Mygale comp. for treating chorea).

"School sickness," as the expression of a transitional situation in grammar school children, is almost obligatory; nearly every child, "unless he is from the staunchest peasant stock,"[15] goes through it more or less severely. The intensity of the symptoms can vary widely, from conditions requiring prolonged bed rest to those whose transient symptoms are scarcely noticed. As a general rule, the symptoms disappear with puberty. It would be wrong, however, to assume that they can be left untreated because of their transitory nature. If they are not given attention, "the ailments of this time of life will leave behind all kinds of pathological dispositions for the entire lifetime."[16]

Puberty

Puberty will be considered here primarily in relation to the heart and blood circulation. The common circulatory problems of the extremities are manifested by cold, blue, sweaty hands and feet. In transitory pubertal hypertension, which is frequently discovered during regular blood pressure measurements, systolic values up to 150 mm Hg are reached, unaccompanied by other pathological symptoms. Heart defects that formerly were compensated to a certain extent frequently lead to heart failure in puberty. This is true particularly of congenital heart defects, especially of Fallot's teratology. Even with an apparently healthy heart, however, sudden death can occur at this time of life, from a shock or great excitement. All of these phenomena, which point to a certain lability of the heart and circulatory system, stem from a transitional state in the supersensible structure of the heart. Rudolf Steiner characterized this condition in the following words:

> The inherited etheric heart, which we have until puberty, is now expelled, and we get an etheric heart of our own. . . . In an

invisible manner, our etheric heart is given over to decay at puberty, and we receive a sort of permanent heart, a sort of ether-heart.[17]

Therapeutically, Aurum praeparatum D15 has proven itself as a basic remedy in puberty, especially for heart and circulatory disorders.

While "school sickness" and puberty require the school doctor to monitor the situation in a particular period of life, the characteristic constitutional peculiarities of childhood confront him with another task, that of balancing a one-sided direction of development. School-age children are still pliable, so that it is at least possible to prevent such a one-sidedness from going to the extreme.

On p. 105 ff. the essential type and characteristic appearance of the large-headed and the small-headed child were presented. Rudolf Steiner indicated that the large-headed child needs more salt and root vegetables. This becomes understandable when we recognize that an inadequate "salt process" stands behind the physical and psychological characteristics described. We must strengthen that process that leads to form, solidity, and contoured articulation. Physically, this process is seen in the way that the limbs become more and more articulated into separate parts toward the periphery; in soul life, it forms the foundation for analytical thought. Therapeutic stimulation of the salt process is achieved with lead (Plumbum praeparatum D20). Once lead has been given for a time, the effect it has initiated must be "healed over" by means of copper (Cupr. sulf. D6).[18] A good plan is to give lead for five weeks, then copper for two; after this, repeat the sequence.

Correspondingly, in small-headed children we must stimulate the sugar process, which influences the functioning of the brain through the blood. This is done by sweetening the food with honey and fruits. Therapeutically, silver is indicated (for example, Argenit D6), which is "healed over" with iron (Ferrum praep. D8).

This alternation between two metals creates a rhythm, which prevents the treatment from becoming set in a one-sided direction. The sequence of the metals—copper after lead, iron after silver—is determined by their arrangement in planetary order.

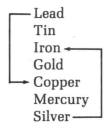

As this arrangement shows, the treatment is begun with one of the metals standing at the endpoints, followed by the metal that is one degree beyond the middle of the row from it. This provides a counterweight, but one that does not completely neutralize the primary effect.

Besides dietetic and therapeutic indications, Rudolf Steiner also recommended simple hydrotherapeutic measures. Large-headed children should receive a cool rinsing of the head in the morning, and small-headed children should be given a warm abdominal compress in the evening twice a week. It is obvious that with these measures, we are producing an awakening effect on the large-headed children, while we are stimulating the increasing blood circulation from the metabolism in the small-headed children. These simple applications of water take on an unsuspected weight, however, when we consider their placement in the course of the day. In this we benefit from results of research on rhythm that had not yet been carried out in Rudolf Steiner's time: independent of the influences of work, food assimilation, and sleep, there are rhythmically alternating processes of anabolism and catabolism pervading the organism. At three o'clock in the morning, a phase of catabolism, of emptying and of secretion (of bile, urine, etc.) begins. From six to nine a.m., it undergoes a sharp intensification (the so-called "morning flood"), and continues on until three p.m. Then a phase of anabolism, of deposition of substance, of resorption and increased blood circulation sets in, intensifying in the evening from six to eleven p.m., and lasting until three a.m.

Into this powerful rhythm we enter with our water treatments. We enhance the morning phase of catabolism and elimination by the use of the cool head-rinsing to stimulate the nerve-sense system and the catabolic impulses coming from it. In this way, we counteract the overpowering anabolic processes of the large-headed child. We give an additional impulse to the evening phase of anabolism and blood circulation by giving the small-headed child a warm abdominal compress. Thus, we work with the swinging of the rhythm and in this way intensify the action of our so seemingly simple measures.

Alongside the "normal" problems of school-age children, of which a few examples were named above, we meet today with an increasing number of problems in school that border on the domain of curative education. It is a difficult question, and one that must be decided from case to case, to what extent such a borderline case can still be tolerated in the classroom. This decision depends not only on the problem of the child himself, but also to a great extent on the class situation and the teacher's possibilities.

As an example of such problems, let us take kleptomania,[19] which occurs in all degrees of severity from a manageable covetousness to an irresistible drive. What is behind this mysterious craving to appropriate something that is usually not used at all, is forgotten, or is given away? Often the children are very canny in getting possession of the desired object. Yet, when asked about it later, they seem hardly to have been conscious of what happened. An apparently conscious action took place, which in reality was far removed from the control of consciousness. With this discovery we are on the trail of the solution to this riddle, which Rudolf Steiner gave in the Curative Education course.[20] Between the conscious and the unconscious, between the upper and the lower organizations of the human being, something is out of place. The upper organization, man's conceptual and imaginative organization that supports itself on the brain, must develop a sense for assimilating everything, taking in from all sides, gathering information. In contrast, our lower organization, the will organization, must learn to keep to itself, not to reach out and grasp; it must

develop a sense of "mine" and "yours." The essence of kleptomania is in this, that what is right for the upper organization
slides down into the will organization and appears as the
material tendency to appropriate things.

Rudolf Steiner draws our attention to a physiognomic symptom of kleptomania: a narrowing of the temporal region,
which he calls "narrow-headedness," caused by atrophy of the
temporal lobes. This symptom is often so striking that one can
already make a tentative diagnosis on this basis alone. Despite
this, no mention of it is found in the literature, although this is
purely a matter of physically perceptible fact. It escapes notice
because the attention of the present-day investigator is directed
primarily at psychological connections. Yet there exist neuro-
anatomical data pointing to the significance of the temporal
lobes for kleptomania. "One of the most striking behavioral disturbances appearing after bilateral removal of certain parts of
the temporal lobes of apes is the drive . . . to grasp everything
the animals see, and to take it into the oral sphere."[21] To be
sure, this behavior is immediately interpreted, quite arbitrarily,
as a "loss of the capacity for visual recognition," though the
bare phenomenon says nothing except that an experimental
impairment of the temporal lobes leads to the drive to take
everything to oneself.

The treatment of kleptomania is derived from its essential
nature: what has sunken must be raised; what has fallen out of
consciousness must be brought back to it; the weakened upper
organization must be strengthened. One of the most effective
curative pedagogical measures is the telling of so-called "moral
tales." For instance, one might tell about how a certain person
was quite crafty in setting about to steal something, and how in
the end he came to grief after all. In this way, the kleptomaniac
is presented with a picture of his own behavior, which is raised
to consciousness from the subconscious realm where it had
sunk.

Everything that helps to restore to consciousness contents
that have dropped from it works against the tendency to kleptomania. Thus, it is good, for example, to remind children of

things from their earlier life. Young kleptomaniacs may be advised to keep a diary.

The twelve-year old kleptomaniac boy discussed in the Curative Education lectures was given injections with Lobus temporalis D10, alternating with injections of a mixture of Hypophysis D10 with Mel D10. The reason for ordering Lobus temporalis is obvious from what was said about atrophy of the temporal lobes. The hypophysis activates the relationship between man's upper and lower organizations. Honey stimulates the sensory-imaginative activity in the head. The bee flies out and brings back the result of its flight into the hive, where it is processed further into honey. This is nature's picture for the perceiving and imagining activity of the soul in the sense organs and in the head. The sensory-imaginative activity in the upper organization of man is strengthened by the therapeutic administration of honey.

Curative eurythmy is modified for treatment of kleptomania so that the movement of the limbs, which proceeds practically without consciousness in the kleptomaniac, comes under increased influence of the consciousness. This can be achieved by applying a ligature to the legs below the knees during the curative eurythmic exercises (A and E with leg jumps). The pressure of the ligature provides an additional perception, which directs the consciousness to the limb region.

From all that has been said about the activity of the school doctor, it can be seen that the medical, pedagogical, curative pedagogical, and curative eurythmic measures described are not directed only at immediate visible success, but primarily toward a distant goal, that is, to steer the development of the growing person in such a way that he will have all his powers about him later. Then he will be able to engage fully in life as an adult.

Chapter VI
Developmental Disorders in Childhood:
Aspects of Curative Education

Over the past two decades there has been a fundamental change in attitude toward the "handicapped child." While formerly the problem was excluded from public attention, today there is a wide interest in and willingness to help the handicapped. In medical practice as well, disorders in the mental and emotional development of children play an increasing role. In pediatric clinics, the differential diagnosis of these phenomena has been increasingly successful, especially since a large number of somatic bases and causes have been uncovered, and preventive measures have been found for some of them.

With the growth of child psychiatry into a separate discipline and the extension of psychology, there has been a corresponding growth of interest in the soul development of children. More attention is also devoted to the seriously handicapped; unlike formerly, their right to the best possible treatment and help is now acknowledged even for those whose possibilities are extremely limited. Where complete recovery is out of the question, modest improvement is considered worthwhile. With these developments, curative education has gained in scope and importance. It still lacks the close cooperation of doctors, however, although this is continually urged. The source of the inadequacy of this cooperation lies in our present-day medicine, and it must remain unsatisfactory so long as we do not gain a deeper insight into the developmental connection between bodily functions and faculties of the soul. With the one-sidedly natural scientific orientation of our times, it is quite difficult to accomplish this, so that for this reason the joining of pedagogical and medical viewpoints must remain an unsolved issue.

This gap can be closed by means of a conception of human development extended by spiritual science. It is from this point of view that we will begin our considerations of developmental disorders. In this regard, Rudolf Steiner provided the important insight that, correctly understood, pedagogy has a healing character, and this is true for the healthy child as well. Our concept of pedagogy must be wide enough to include the mother's attitude toward the infant, the human environment of the child, which serves as a model, provision for the development of motor abilities, and the psychological interaction with the environment. Only by way of education will the child be able to achieve true human development; he needs the help and the model of other human beings to become a full human being himself. Biological processes alone do not yield human development; quite the contrary, in regard to soul development they contain pathogenic factors that must be balanced in education. The soul faculties are not in a direct line of development from the bodily functions; rather, they must acutally reverse the purely biological, vital tendency of these functions.

We owe to Rudolf Steiner the fundamental discovery that man's conscious soul life is based on processes of catabolism, dissimilation, and elimination. The active balancing of anabolism and catabolism makes it possible for the gradually incarnating individuality to interact freely and immediately with the environment, without being determined by the physical body with which it is associated. Just as the materials of which a musical instrument is constructed must recede in their individual tendencies, just giving the tone a certain timbre, so the organism must become a transparent medium for the soul-spiritual. Here, however, the comparison with the musical instrument ends. It is the soul-spiritual entity that first builds the organism for itself out of its own forces. In the course of development it must gradually give the organism a form appropriate to itself, repeatedly "melting it down" and remolding it. Here the help of the other human being as an educator is needed.

In developmental disorders these basic processes are made more difficult, but they remain the same in principle, even when the goal of free unfolding of the individuality is no longer attainable. The bodily nature, the physical-etheric, is often so unbalanced that it can be harmonized only with special therapeutic measures, pedagogical as well as medical. In many cases only an improvement, not a cure, is possible with the present state of knowledge. In contrast to other diseases where the individual soul life keeps the upper hand, the incarnation is permanently impaired here, so that the developmental disorders can be called incarnation disorders. We can approach an understanding of such a fate by taking into account the fact of repeated earth lives, or reincarnation.

This approach is of tremendous significance in treating such children and furthering their development. With the defect approach, which sees only the irreparable damage and not the spiritual individuality struggling with it, all that can be done is to try out the remaining pedagogical techniques and add to them medical corrections for restlessness, irritability, torpidity, etc. This cannot bring about a true cooperation of pedagogy and medicine, since basic patterns of development, applying to both healthy and handicapped children, are not taken into consideration. This developmental orientation, on which Waldorf education is based, is also missing in ordinary school pedagogy.

Developmental disorders appear in an enormous variety of forms. In a large number of them we find damage in the central nervous system, and there is a tendency to see this as the sole basis for the soul-spiritual symptoms. This approach is restricted to finding correspondences between pathological manifestations and particular organic alterations in the central nervous system. In other disorders, such as those of a psychotic nature, all evidence of an organic disorder is lacking. Without further insight into functional relationships, we are forced to limit ourselves to describing, ordering, and classifying symptoms. With the help of the spiritual sciences we can come to a better understanding of the underlying processes and approach the essence of the various symptoms, which will give us a basis for treatment. Rudolf Steiner described several facts that are fundamental for this in the course on Curative Education.[1] With an understanding of the members of man's being, we can see that the human organism with all its organs and limbs is a differentiated instrument for the life of the soul, and that the soul life exists primarily and creates for itself the bodily nature for each incarnation. The soul's manifestations, which we observe, are really the secondary results of this activity. They are dependent on the correct functioning of the nervous system in that they are brought to consciousness by it; the proper functioning of the whole organism, however, is also a prerequisite for them. In order for it to serve as an instrument for translating the soul-spiritual into earthly action, this organism is built in a polar way; that is, the upper part, with the nerve-sense system, centered in the head, is opposed in principle of action to the lower part, containing the metabolic-limb system. Anything happening at one pole is accompanied by a corresponding and opposite occurrence at the other. All processes are based on a resonance effect; every positive has its negative on the other side. This polar phenomenon arises through the arrangement of the members of man's being at the two opposite poles.

The head, as the consciousness pole, contains the ego organization in the center, surrounded by the astral, etheric, and physical bodies. In contrast, in the metabolic-limb region—the will pole—the ego organization acts from the periphery inward, enclosing the astral body, the etheric body, and the physical body. We can picture this to ourselves by taking the bones as representing the physical body. In the head the bone formation is on the outside, the member of the higher being residing progressively further inside; in the hollow bones of the limbs, it is located centrally, surrounded by the members of the higher being with the ego organization outermost.

Between the two poles the rhythmic system arises as something completely new, as a quality of its own. It is not so much involved in earthly activity, as the head system is through substance, or the limb system is through forces; rather, its activity depends on the healthy functioning of both poles.

With every disturbance of one pole, the functioning of the other is also impaired, but the disease picture is primarily determined by the side where the main weight of the disorder lies. If we can make these conceptions our own and learn to see developmentally disturbed children in terms of the polar phenomenon, then we will have a new access to the pathological symptoms; we will not grasp them statically as determined findings, but more dynamically as processes. In order to recognize directly the relation of various disorders to the supersensible members of the human being, however, the supersensible faculties of a spiritual researcher are needed. We must bear in mind that circumstances in this realm are a great deal more complicated than on the sensible plane; for this, we must have recourse to the spiritual teacher. Nevertheless, we can learn to recognize the higher members of man's being by their manifestations.

In his course on Curative Education, Rudolf Steiner described several pairs of opposite diseases in detail: juvenile epilepsy and hysteria; overabundance or deficiency of sulfur in the protein in its effect on conceptual life; feeble-mindedness and mania in children. These, and discussions of mental illnesses given in his courses for doctors and in other connections, enable us to observe several great classes of developmental disorders according to the viewpoint described above.

Primary Disorders of the Human Form

Let us first look at those disorders that are associated with obvious deformities. When a handicapped child is presented to us, the first question to arise is: Is there anything striking about his physical appearance so that it would be obvious from a photograph that the child is not "normal"? In many, the forms and proportions are not especially striking, while in others the deviations are seen at first glance. When not pronounced, they may appear only as dysplasia of the facial area. Although developmental disorders overlap at many points, those with primary deformities have their own character, which is connected with definite soul-spiritual manifestations.

In terms of the polar organization of the organism, the human form is a product of the head forces. Of the members of man's being, it is the astral body that actually gives the forms their characteristic shape. The most defined formation is the head, primarily in the structure of the face, where the ego is most clearly manifested in its shaping of the outer form. We recognize a person by the face, and most especially by the eyes. We can also designate the head pole as the form pole. Since imagination and thought are associated with the nerve-sense system, deformities are especially noticeable in this area. An undersized, defined form makes for clever and sharp thinking, as with a dwarf or Rumpelstiltskin; an oversized, undifferentiated form will be stupid, like a giant in fairy tales. If the proportions are disturbed to the point of pathology, then the large-headed child will have trouble in condensing his thoughts, while the small-headed child will be too caught up in sensory impressions.

In most cases of developmental disorders, there are insufficiently defined or deviant forms in which the physical body is not sufficiently grasped by the higher members of being. So-called "feeble-mindedness" or "imbecility" is usually encountered in connection with deformities. The "village idiot," for example, is characteristic of this. The catalog of syndromes is copious: the pointed head, the tower head or moderate hydrocephalus, the low forehead, deformed ears and nose, enlarged chin and mouth or receding chin, chaotic placement of teeth, short neck, etc. Trunk and limbs are also affected: flat-chestedness, pigeon breast, kyphosis, lordosis, scoliosis, stubby limbs, club or flat feet, syndactyly or extra fingers or toes, abnormal hair growth, etc.

Such patients are "feeble-minded" in the actual sense of the word; their perceptions are dull and are practically limited to their own bodily sensations. The power of comprehension is primarily impaired in them, while the deviations in emotional life are to be seen as secondary. Their capacity for contact is not impaired, but in their pronounced orientation toward the human environment they lack a sense of distance, while they are hardly affected by the material surroundings. Usually, they display willingness to meet demands and pride in doing something right. The most important fact about these human beings is that they are not mysteries to us. We can put ourselves in their places quite well and understand their ways of reacting. Their feeble-mindedness fits with their outer look. Their simple feelings, their fearfulness and joy, even their greed in eating, are all understandable and suit them well, whether they belong to the "type" of the ever-suffering or the uncritically happy, the importunate braggart or the colorless and timid, the blatantly aggressive or the eternally insulted. Their appearance, their lack of intellectual capacity, their dullness when stimulation is lacking, and their affective reactions are all well-integrated, forming a unity. The "flow" of the soul may be impaired, retarded, or distorted in these deformities, but it is never interrupted or corrupted, as we shall see in different cases we shall examine.

In Down's syndrome ("mongolism") we have a clear connection of a certain kind of deformity with corresponding physical symptoms. This relatively common, well-defined syndrome was described by F. Husemann and W. Pache, whose contributions are also reflected in the present discussion. We can see that Down's syndrome is a circumscribed developmental disorder that that does not belong—unlike others—to the overlapping groups of disorders, because it is connected with a definite chromosomal anomaly (like several less common disorders, such as Klinefelter's and Turner's syndromes) and thus appears uniformly in the basic design of every cell. This affects the whole organization with a uniform syndrome of its own, whose origin is to be sought not in, but above, the chromosomal signs; these are to be regarded only as the physical recipients and mediators of superordinate forces. In this connection the reader is referred to Karl König's monograph, *Mongolism.*[2] This disorder presents the picture of immaturity, of a development of the entire organization only up to a certain stage, so that the undifferentiated forms and the psychic conditions both reflect this; they are from a single mold. As to the polar construction of the organism, in this disorder the polarization is insufficient. The head system and the metabolic-limb system are caught up in one another and not differentiated enough. The head does not rise out far enough and the limbs do not reach into earthly conditions. In the "giant embryo" of hydrocephalus, the head will not come down into the conditions of earth; the whole organism remains "head" and the limb pole atrophies. Here, the question is not of staying in the cosmic world, but of being fitted into an unformed, overly soft body.

J. Bort[3] characterizes the fate of these individuals with this image thus: "They have fallen from heaven and are not received by the earth," which is in accordance with the frequent premature birth of these children. Their organism is not a suitable instrument for individualization by the ego. Individual traits only go as far as the soul, and are at best only faintly apparent in the physiognomy.

We will dispense here with a detailed outer description of the child with Down's syndrome. Deficient forming and lack of vertical growth are the common denominator of all the physical symptoms; this, as well as the muscular hypotonia, indicates a failure of the astral forces. In the extreme weakness of the ligaments and connective tissue (which also accounts for the protruding tongue and the tendency to sit with both legs folded under the body) and in the weak warmth economy we see the insufficient activity of the ego organization. The whole picture is that of a weak etheric body left on its own; this can also be seen in the tendency toward obesity. This "unripeness" for conditions on earth is also shown in certain specific weaknesses and defects. Blood circulation is always insufficient (tendency to livid coloration), and the warmth organism has great difficulty in asserting itself against the environment (susceptibility to diseases of the upper respiratory tract). The endocrine glands function adequately. Skin and mucous membranes are thin (just as their "skin is thin" emotionally) and are prone to infections. Congenital heart defects, duodenal stenosis, cryptorchidism, etc., are common. The deficient "earth-ripeness" becomes most apparent at puberty. There is practically no ability to reproduce, and the first signs of aging (cataracts, arteriosclerosis) appear. Though the child with Down's syndrome may at first be able to withstand the heaviness of the earth, after puberty there is the danger that heaviness and torpidity will take over his soul life, especially if good education or training is lacking.

When we look at the soul life of the Down's syndrome child, we find a special appearance. Because of the weakness of both

the head and metabolic poles and their lack of clear separation, the rhythmic system is dominant and functions quite independently. A close relation to everything rhythmic is typical
of these children. Since they are hardly touched by the head
forces and the life of ideas that leads to the past, and since they
are unable to perform willful, goal-oriented movements pointing toward the future, they take refuge in the rich, happy soul
life offered by the rhythmic system, which is connected only
with the present and marks time, as it were. Their soul life requires stimulation from the human environment, however,
and is based on imitation; like the whole phenomenon of
Down's syndrome, it is connected with a sort of caricatured
persistence of the first seven-year period. This is what makes
these children so charming in their theatrical conduct. Their
otherwise awkward movements take on a comic expressive-
ness. Feeling is all—genuine, warm feeling without the shadow
of a thought or an ulterior motive. They are a help in any class
for this reason, but there is the danger that they will be valued
only for this aspect. They will be spoiled as the happy clown in
the family and their educational advancement neglected simply
because they like to "make believe" and would rather "play"
school than actually learn. But if they have not learned to
maintain a reasonable attitude and to exert themselves for
work and duties, the result later on, when their charm has succumbed to the increasing heaviness, can be sad indeed.

Another side of this life of simple feeling is fear. From a lack
of comprehension through their intellectual weakness, they
easily fall into panic if something seems unfamiliar or not
right. Sympathy is a fundamental part of their being; if something does not meet with their sympathy, complete negation
seems the only alternative. There are no gradations of lesser
acceptance or mild refusal. This stubbornness should never be
attacked directly or "broken"; it yields easily to diversion.

The spiritual incapacity is in accordance with their deficient
physical differentiation. The head simply cannot act as an
organ for thought; we might wonder if it were different, given
their appearance. These children live exclusively in the concrete and cannot think abstractly; this they have in common

with all forms of simple imbecility. The ability to concentrate, that is, the voluntary capacity to stay with something, is quite weak, but training can bring progress in this. Their good memory for concrete details and situations is associated with an inability to rise, through forgetting, to the general and conceptual. The intellectual content of their language is on a corresponding level, while their speech is often unclear and broken due to a clumsy articulation, and the voice is often rough and unmelodious.

There is much variation in the degree of retardation among these children. In light and moderate cases, learning is quite possible, and the children can live well in the family if professional counseling is available and a curative kindergarten and school are not too far away. In severe cases they remain in need of special care. They learn to walk quite late, if at all, cannot be toilet-trained, and never speak. Nevertheless, their soul responsiveness may be quite alive. In some patients there are signs of cerebral damage going beyond that of simple Down's syndrome; that is, extreme strabismus and nystagmus, motor disturbances with a paralytic character, impulsive restlessness, and lack of human contact. The most obvious explanation is that the susceptible nervous system is open to damage from further noxious stimuli.

We have discussed Down's syndrome at some length because of its frequent occurrence (1 in every 600 to 700 births), and because of the uniform picture it presents. In the context of this work, we classify it under the heading of disorders of the human form.

Two other deformities are characteristic of the different possibilities of the two poles of the human being: hydrocephaly and microcephaly. In their polarity, they show how the formative forces act from the head into the limbs. They are not simply exaggerations of large- and small-headedness, but pathological syndromes going far beyond these.

In hydrocephaly there is a persistence of the embryonic proportions. The rest of the body remains small, with pronounced acromicria. In our own work we experienced this strongly in a pair of hydrocephalic twins, one of whom had small but well-formed hands and feet, while his brother had only fin-like appendages, which could not function as hands or feet.

In contrast, the microcephalic child has been pushed too deeply into the rest of his body; the limbs, and especially the extremities, are englarged to the point of acromegaly. The posture of the microcephalic child is somewhat bent forward, and he often shows a certain propulsion in his walk; the hydrocephalic, in contrast, tends to hold his head tilted back. When they rock with their head and upper body, a common habit, the hydrocephalic will rock slowly in a frontal plane, sometimes humming at the same time, while the microcephalic prefers the sagittal plane, and the movement is more of a flinging or throwing. We easily come to picture the hycrocephalic as one who has not quite come down to earth; his head, despite its weight, puts no burden on him. The microcephalic, in contrast, is completely taken over by the weight of the earth.

Their soul manifestations match this picture well. A child with hydrocephaly is completely oriented toward contemplation and is not so eager to do something himself. Generally, he loves music and is quite musical, a further sign of his cosmic connection. His whole being seems bright. His emotional life is quite active and full of trust; his human contact is good, though his mental faculties may be impaired to varying degrees. His friendly attitude attracts those around him. He is not often teased by the other children since he offers no provocation. There is a story of a village boy with a head so large he could barely carry it. In good weather he would be put in a specially made swing under a tree; this became the meeting place of all the villagers, because everyone liked him.

One can usually make good contact with the microcephalic child also. He tends, however, to be somewhat obtrusive and to irritate those around him, not from any intention but just from his manner. He is not inclined toward observation; he always wants to do something immediately before he has even heard what he is to do. His activity is "headless"; he will grasp eagerly at an object, only to knock over half a dozen others in his clumsiness. His manner is good-natured and ungainly but can turn into anger and aggression. These children have less affinity for music; often they are thoroughly unmusical.

In these two pictures, we see headless will and will-less head contrasted. We can imagine the action of the formative force from the head into the limbs as in a balloon man: if the air stays in the head, none comes into the limbs; if the head is compressed, the limbs are blown up.

We have now examined several developmental disorders associated with deformities and have determined these common features: in simple forms of feeble-mindedness, intellectual comprehension is impaired more than emotional life; human contact is not impeded; we can put ourselves in the place of these children and empathize with them. They need not be riddles to us; they are more oriented toward their fellow humans than to things.

Regarding the polar organization of the human being, we can determine the following: the flow of the soul resulting from the interaction of the poles may be distorted and sluggish, but it is never interrupted; the resonance is muted but not extinguished. The soul faculties of willing, feeling, and thinking are severly impaired, but their connection to one another is not broken, and no one part has made itself independent. Feeling has its correct relations but the light of thinking and the directive force of the will are lacking, so that further development is obstructed.

Psychic Disorders with Diffuse Cerebral Damage

When a deformity or handicap is obvious from the outer appearance, the observer is prepared for inadequacy of the soul-spiritual faculties. When, however, a child is well-formed bodily, the disorder is experienced as a discrepancy. This problem will occupy us increasingly in the following disease syndromes. First, we will look at a group of disorders sharing a common basis, which we will call the "shattered structure."

Looking at these apparently well-formed children we are quick to notice their peculiar gaze; it will not meet our own, but looks straight through us or wanders without focusing. This miming reflects no inner involvement.

Direct eye contact seems impossible at first. Our efforts to arouse their interest in something meet with no response. If they are able to answer questions, such as their name or age, they do so without inner participation, in an unmodulated voice that shows no trace of feeling. Certain impressions of the environment can take them over completely with a compulsive attraction. They have to run to the door, to open and shut it, turn the key, play with the light switch or the water faucet. Their attention will fixate on some object or mechanical gadget. In severe disorders, the object is just touched, shaken, or smelled. There is no separation between them and the impressions; they cannot turn their attention to these by choice but are completely taken hold of by them. Their disturbance can be observed especially well in their motor activity, which is quite striking. They hop about, go on tiptoe, and make stereotyped movements with their hands that are often complicated and dextrous. In their motor disinhibition they perform astonishing feats. They can balance (though not when asked to do it as an exercise), ride scooters, etc. Everything proceeds with great instinctive sureness and without consideration. They often show a particular capacity for setting things spinning, such as building blocks, dishes, and even chairs. These children do not appear stupid at all, and they develop an amazing facility with objects, which fascinate them. Thus, such a child can put together electric trains and set them going, use the record player or the radio, and many similar things. When we want something of them, however, we come up against the greatest difficulties. Only the daily, repeated tasks of eating, washing, and going to bed are executed well, even with a certain fastidiousness. With close contact, it is possible to build up quite a good connection with these children, and they develop an attachment and even tenderness in their indirect way. Academic progress is difficult to achieve since they cannot concentrate and display no inner connection with the material presented. They seem to learn much in an incidental way, however; if they once are engaged and link up with a task, their efforts are touching. Unfortunately, these efforts often become compulsive and stereotyped.

Parents find upsetting the apparent contradiction that, though the children have isolated abilities and clear possibilities of learning something, no corresponding progress can be achieved. They have the impression that all that is needed is the right therapeutic trick and everything will be all right; so they often wander with their problem from one specialist to the next.

In contrast to children with other syndromes, these children have nothing dark or demonic about them; they do not seem "possessed" or plagued by inner fears and images, although there are overlapping points with other classes of disorders, as we shall see. With the multiplicity of forms in which these disorders occur, it is quite difficult to draw a well-defined picture and still take into account the large scale from the mildest to the most severe forms. Much attention is given today to the "formes frustes," in which the children pass for "normal," attend regular schools, but stand out for their restlessness, poor cencentration, and disturbed affective relations. Here we will deal only with the severe cases as we most commonly see them.

When we look at the child's history for possible causes, there are usually indications of brain damage through difficult premature birth, asphyxia, encephalitis, etc. Even when there are no definite indications, it is possible to recognize "the organic" as opposed to the psychotic. There are also physical signs related to this, such as attenuated finger tips, bayonette fingers, weakness of the ligaments, asymmetry of the skull, endocrine anomalies, etc. These, however, are not necessarily present and may be regarded as secondary. In contrast to the deformations discussed above, here we are dealing with over-formations, or externally caused alterations or aftereffects of the primary diencephalic-hypothalamic disorder. This symptom complex is normally described under the categories of cerebral damage, encephalopathies, and postencephalitic symptoms. Exact delimitation of these syndromes is extremely difficult, as the literature continually stresses. It is known today that the particular cause (inflammation, oxygen deficiency, intoxication) is of less importance than the timing, localization, and extent of the damage. Such syndromes are found with damage to the fine structure of the nervous system, mainly in between the brain and the central centers. Gross lesions cannot be detected; everything seems still to be functioning and yet profound developmental derangement is found on such a broad front.

One can picture this kind of damage as countless fine cracks permeating the nervous system. A mirror with fine cracks will still reflect light but the image will be distorted. It is appropriate to compare the nervous system with a mirror. It is not a system of electrical switches; rather, on a sound physical basis it forms an etheric mirror for our conceptual and imaginative life. In the deformities we have discussed previously, this reflection is distorted as in an untrue mirror; here, however, it is continually interrupted.

So far, we have only looked at one side of the phenomenon; now we must pursue it from the point of view of polarity. In the lectures on Curative Education, Rudolf Steiner described the head-pole together with the nervous system as the synthetic system. The head is the greater synthesizer, while in the rest of the organism everything is separated analytically. All processes carried out in the bodily organs, such as the liver, kidneys, heart, and lungs, correspond to an activity in the brain; here, however, they are synthesized. The individual organs have tasks not only for the physical, but also for the soul life. A healthy soul life can only exist when harmonious integration takes place in the head with the ego at its center. With such diffuse damage, however, this is impossible. The etheric body cannot overcome the cracks in the physical structure. This is why we classify the whole phenomenon as a "shattered structure."

The consequence, however, is not a disorder predominantly of thinking and conceptual ability, but of the will and emotional life. Because the ego is not properly centered in the head —which is shown in the peripheral gaze and deficient fixation as well as in the whole behavior of these children—and the head provides no counterbalance to the rest of the organism, the latter is as if cut off; it cannot undertake any purposeful, ego-directed relation to the world, especially not to the human environment. Therefore, the astral body moves into the foreground, promoting the instinctive faculties (balancing, spinning). Sensory impressions are not digested but lead to immediate reactions.

With this we have characterized the pathological process, but this does not absolutely cover the field. Depending on the severity of the disorder, the individuality asserts itself and struggles with the obstacles.

Here we end the discussion of this type of cerebral damage. We have described in their more common forms the significant psychic disorders that present a definite contrast to the first group considered.

Flooding of the Soul Life with Organic Forces

Apart from the head system, up to this point we have considered the significance of the organs for the life of the soul only in a general way. In fact, it is quite differentiated. The indications given by Rudolf Steiner[4] enable us to pursue the relation of physical and soul processes in detail, and thus to come to a correct understanding of it. In healthy people, this is well illustrated in the four temperaments; in psychopathology it provides us with an insight into otherwise mysterious phenomena, for example the endogenous psychoses. (A thorough discussion of this will be found in the chapter on psychiatry in Vol. III.) For our considerations, it is important to remember that disorders of the soul are connected with the etheric rather than the physical organs; hence, the organ in question need not show pathological alterations or functional impairment.

Numerous children with severe developmental disorders show no sign of even the slightest physical defect or injury. Often there is no hint of psychological causes to which the child might have reacted, such as traumas or a damaging environment. Such children present quite different pictures—even more so than those discussed above—but we can pick out several typical characteristics. What is striking is their great inner involvement. They appear to be occupied, driven by forces that are inaccessible and at times genuinely uncanny to us. As with the previous group, we can attain no eye contact, but here the gaze is unsteady; it looks at us forlornly for a moment, and then looks away, apparently directed inward. The facial features are often quite beautiful, especially when the children are still small; later, the face is sometimes distorted in peculiar grimaces, quite different from the contortions seen in the other disorders. Phases of excitement with a bizarre, pressured character may alternate with stupor and catatonia. Movements will be unsteady, clumsy, and exaggerated, and then completely normal again. There is quite a varied catalog of automatisms. These children, too, are attracted by particular objects with which they play in a stereotyped way and develop a singular dexterity. Sometimes it is balls, soap bubbles, and round things that fascinate them; sometimes it is certain noises they try to produce; sometimes it is water that attracts them. Whatever occupies them, it is their driven, sometimes almost possessed manner that characterizes them. On occasion we will find children playing with imaginary objects, and to take them away produces a violent reaction. Indications of hallucination are not uncommon. They may stare into a corner and by the expressions on their faces it is obvious that they are not just staring.

Their capacity for learning is often astonishing and comprehension does not seem to be restricted, but they do not connect with anything. They may learn some quite complicated procedures in one area, while they hardly get past beginning in others. There will be specialists in arithmetic and other narrow areas; there are also abilities that we cannot explain, such as naming the correct day of the week for any given date. Speech and the ability to express themselves vary greatly, but the quality of modulation is always lacking. Refusal to speak (mutism) also occurs. No real contact is possible; something always seems to stand in the way.

The list of symptoms could be extended *ad infinitum*, since these patients are anything but boring, although the endless drama is hard to bear. In the most severe cases, not even the everyday functions are mastered; speech does not develop and the mental level remains exceedingly low.

What we have described are psychotic manifestations; they

can vary widely in extent and degree of severity. Only the most pronounced syndromes can be called childhood schizophrenia. This and the difference between the Central European and Anglo-American concept of childhood schizophrenia do not concern us here. What is important for us is to see the indications in this direction.

The basis for the symptoms described is to be sought in the lower organs. In the psychotic process, these press out their etheric substance. In this way, the soul life is inundated with forces that really ought to be contained in these organs and that should show through only as nuances of temperament. In these cases, however, the whole soul life is occupied and thrown into extremes of excitement and stupor, depression and euphoria, compulsion and illusion, bottomless anxiety and frenzy, depending on the organ in question. In children, we must remember that the organs are not yet isolated, independent, or differentiated; they hold together closely, so that the entire organism is confounded.

The pathological flood of feelings swamps the imaginative life. It is clear that this process flows from below to above. The mirror of the brain can no longer receive outer impressions freely and purely and digest them objectively in thought. Everything is colored from the inside, or even displaced by inner images. These images always have something dark and demonic about them, which emerges in the drawings of these children (and adults).

This concludes our description of a third group of developmental disorders, which we can call "flooding of the soul life with organic forces."

As is known, psychotic symptoms are also not uncommon in patients with organic brain damage, but usually they are not so pronounced. The psychotic patient's mental capacities may also be lost, resulting in a syndrome like that found in organic brain damage.

This crossing of symptom complexes can be understood better in terms of the functional polarity of the human organism. If the head pole is damaged and cannot fulfill its synthesizing function, the lower organization, lacking the counterweight it needs, becomes unstable. This instability can (though it need not) extend to the etheric structure of the organs, producing psychotic symptoms. Since the organs do not "press out" forces, however, these symptoms lack the severe character of primary psychoses. Conversely, in the primary psychoses, the head pole lacks the counterweight of the lower organs, which is the analytic function. These are normally supposed to restrain their own tendencies in favor of the soul life, complementing the reflecting function of the head with the foundation of being, which we experience in our will power. This firm anchoring in the metabolic-limb system is loosened when the organs become too independent and do not contain their forces. These released organic forces roam around in the imaginative life and bring what can be called a false vitalization or "inflammation" of the soul into the physical-etheric nervous system. The more rigidly ordered nervous system cannot manage this stress; in time it loses its etheric structure and we see symptoms like those in cerebral damage.

The original causes for primary psychotic disorders are hard to fathom. This is why they are designated as "endogenous," for they cannot be understood within the context of one life on earth. Due to their mysterious character, they have been called the "Delphic Oracle" of diseases. Through the concepts of reincarnation and destiny, insight is gained into the greater picture, for which Rudolf Steiner provided the fundamentals and concrete examples.

We have not yet mentioned the possibility of reactive causes. It is known that early childhood frustration, damaging environment, and psychological traumas lead to the most severe disorders. Earlier, we indicated the importance of education in the development of the child and his gradually changing dependence on environmental factors for his growth as a human being. We have also pointed to the significance of the organism's functional polarity for the soul life. From all of these factors we can see that there is no sharp distinction between endogenous, organic, and functional disorders, and that quite different causes can evoke similar symptoms. To be sure, reactive disorders are usually associated with their own particular symptoms; these are examined in the chapter on neuropathy and child neuroses. At certain points and at a certain degree of severity, however, the pictures overlap. It is known that reactive sensitivity and neurotic tendencies often accompany minimal brain damage. An example of the relationship between organic and reactive disorders is the injury suffered by sensitive children from the modern urban environment, that is, over-stimulation, constant distraction, passive stimulation by radio and television, the necessity of reacting in traffic, insufficient contemplativeness, and the loss of one's own activity because it is continuously determined by stimuli. These factors can lead to syndromes resembling minimal brain damage, with restlessness, poor contact, awkward and inexpressive motor activity, and a capacity only for instinctive reaction, such as occurs on a bicycle in traffic. The nervous system is damaged in a similar way; it is only because the damage has occurred gradually and at a later point in development that there are differences in the general appearance of the child from the minimally brain damaged child—mainly in the greater capacities he has already acquired.

A rare disorder will be added to this list—one that has been at the center of professional attention in recent times—that is, childhood autism.[5] The symptoms were first described as a separate syndrome in 1943 by Kanner in the United States (infantile autism), and independently by Asperger in Austria (*autistische Psychopathen*).[5] Since then, many child psychiatrists have occupied themselves with its research and interpretation. Attempting to surround and describe the disorder from all sides is like trying to catch a fish that slips away just when you have it in your hand. The essence of this disorder, however, which becomes evident on meeting these children, is familiar to experts as an unmistakable experience that has an imponderable element, since it lies in the child's ability to recognize the personalities of others. Of the first two descriptions of autism, we relate better to that of Asperger, since it considers the whole scale, from slight variations from the norm to the most severe disorders, whereas Kanner tries to present it as a circumscribed syndrome. In the meantime, many works have been produced on this theme.

Let us try to sketch a typical picture of moderate severity. In their outward appearance these children demonstrate nothing abnormal, except perhaps that they are especially beautiful. Many could aptly be described as enchanted princes or princesses. As a rule, there are no indications of organic damage. The disorder begins in early childhood, even if it is not recognized in the first phase of life, and it exists in principle from birth on. Mothers usually report early difficulty in contact with the child.

Once again the gaze is striking, making an empty impression; it is not fixed but has an intelligent expression. This is why we experience it as such a discrepancy that it provides no contact. We have the upsetting sensation in meeting these children that everything could really be quite normal, so what is the matter? The whole outer impression bespeaks a pronounced personality, yet this is not found when they are confronted, while the sovereign manner in which they assert their "will," that is, their pathologically one-sided tendencies, shows personality character. When dealing with them, we do not have the feeling of helping a "poor creature"; rather, we are commanded by them. This also happens with other handicapped children, but the aristocratic poise with which these children get their way is incomparable. Their expression has an unchildlike, precocious quality; it is neither suffering nor happy, but simply indifferent. Their intelligent appearance does correspond to their potential. They can easily grasp cognitive connections if it suits them, but they cannot enter into our world of values, or into our utilitarian and causal relation to things. Our world is foreign to them. They seek a mode of life that would keep everything the same; everything must go in the same routine; everything must stay in the same place. For this, and for their physical necessities, they foster their relation to their mother in a sort of symbiosis and react strongly to any separation.

Characteristic of their speech are lack of emotional coloration, monotony, too-high pitch, etc.; there is one specific trait, however, that is indicative of the essence of the disorder: they have great difficulty with the use of the word "I." Either they speak in the third person—indicating a discrepancy with their general power of expression—or, if they have learned the correct use of this concept with their intelligence, they still remain unsure of it. All signs indicate that they lack the conscious experience of "I" and therefore a centering of their personality. They experience themselves not as distinct from the world around them, but as a part of it, not as an integrated, harmonizing part, but as a helpless boat on high seas. Even the recourse to instinctive certainties is not given to these children.

We must seek the essence of autism in a disorder of the ego function. Lutz[6] describes it as an intrapsychic disorder of the relation of the ego to the soul faculties of willing, feeling, and thinking. It lies in the innermost realm of the soul.

According to spiritual scientific understanding of the body and soul, such a central psychic disorder as this must also have its physical-etheric basis. A concrete insight requires a direct spiritual investigation. The many indications given by Rudolf Steiner on abnormalities of soul-spiritual development, especially his statement that the origin of mental diseases must be sought in physical disorders in the lower part of the human organization, makes it possible for us to propose an interpretation. In all probability, autism, like the psychoses, is due to a dysfunction of the lower organs. A relationship between childhood schizophrenia and autism is continually suggested. In both of them, contact and ego functioning are disturbed. They also share an elementary and mysterious quality. While the psychotic process is based on the pressing out of etheric substance from the organs, however, the autistic process differs in that the etheric participation of the organs is too meager for the soul life. Not even a temperamental coloration flows up from these organs because the ego does not engage in the lower organization sufficiently. Here the ego is supposed to work inward from the periphery, the three members of being being arranged in the opposite order from in the head, where they surround the ego. The centering of the ego in the consciousness pole, however, is dependent on the correct peripheral activity of the lower ego organization. Thus, no point of condensation comes into being in the ego consciousness. Willing, feeling, and thinking cannot be brought together.

When the healthy equilibrium of the etheric forces in the lower organization is disturbed, this lability may result in an oscillation between psychotic and autistic symptoms. It is possible for similar disorders to arise from organic damage in the central nervous system, that is, the same process in reverse. Recent literature does indicate organic findings in a certain number of autistic children.

With this we conclude our discussion of developmental disorders, emphasizing that we have discussed only select and important forms of soul-spiritual impairment that play a great role in practice.

In summary, it has been our intention to describe certain select developmental disorders in the light of the understanding of man and of psychopathological phenomena as Rudolf Steiner described them in the course on Curative Education. The basic principle of the polar construction of the physical organization, in its significance for the soul life, has been central in this discussion; every deviation at one pole results in a disorder of the functions of the other pole, and it is possible to recognize from which side the symptoms are determined. In the deformities, as a primary disorder of the formative forces of the head, we found that the flow and resonance needed for a real life of the feelings were still preserved in the rhythmic system, but that comprehension was impaired by sensory and imaginative weakness and deficient connection with the will. In the case of fine-structural cerebral damage, which we characterized as shattered structure, the emotional life is drawn into the disorder, since the poles become dissociated and the rhythmic system lacks support on both sides. The head provides no rest, the limbs become independent, and we see isolated instinctive manifestations, since the astral body makes its own tendencies felt. In some cases, the dissociated state of the lower organs influences the condition, bringing forth psychotic symptoms. In primary psychoses, in contrast, the center of the disorder is in the lower organs, which press out their own etheric forces and discolor the emotional and imaginative life, thereby flooding the soul life with organic forces. The child is occupied from within and cannot experience the world clearly. Experiences are determined from the inside and human contact is seriously impaired. It is no longer possible to put oneself in the child's psychological position. The rare childhood autism also seems to be connected with the lower organs, but in this case the etheric forces, far from being pressed out, are too meager for the soul life. With the lability of these organs, autistic syptoms can also alternate with psychotic symptoms.

In view of the delicate cooperation of the entire organization required for the soul life, it will be understood that the developmental disorders need not have the character of sharply defined disease syndromes, such as measles or scarlet fever, but are classes of forms that can overlap.

Curative Educational Guidance and Treatment

Above all other measures, curative education is of the greatest significance in childhood developmental disorders. We must restrict our observations to a few fundamental features of this work.

Such an essential knowledge of the pathological symptoms as we have tried to gain should suggest the treatment directly. This understanding includes the therapeutic approach and connects pathology and therapy. When we have an idea of this, curative education is not just a collection of recipes but is based on a curative invention of measures to serve our goal. This is the domain of the curative educator, not of the doctor. Cooperation consists, not in blurring the boundaries between their spheres of duty, but in mutual advising from both the medical and pedagogical perspectives. The doctor's insight, penetrating into the physical processes of disease, helps in transcending mere psychologizing.

Curative education aims not "against" the pathological process but at the healthy forces of development, which operate despite all handicaps, and it seeks to overcome the disorder in alliance with these. In reality, curative education addresses the spiritual personality that cannot incarnate properly. The con-

stant and steadfast appeal to the individuality is the basis of
the pedagogical effort.[7]

We may differentiate between curative pedagogical guidance
and treatment. The guidance is directed toward the patterns of
development that are part of the healthy child as well. In this
respect, the general principles of education and curriculum,
but not the content and goals of achievement, are applicable.
They must be altered to suit the degree of the children's handicap, but this will not involve a reduction of the level or a primitive variant; it must be a transformation to the archetypal form,
a translation into practical life situations. This endeavor is
nurtured in the social context of an entire class or group. Curative pedagogical treatment is directed at the difficulties in the
specific case. It need not always take place on a one-to-one
basis, because a good curative educator builds the treatment
into instruction and group activities. It is not widely recognized
today that pedagogical measures not only are helpful in a
general way, but also can be directed at specific disorders
affecting physical conditions. Curative pedagogy is generally
viewed as a nonspecific basis therapy, while psychotherapy is
recommended for more specific treatment. The curative educator should be a psychotherapist at the same time, however;
he should not work only toward achievement, which in general
is assumed too narrowly to be the function of education.

Rudolf Steiner presented the foundations for genuine curative educational measures with numerous practical examples
in his course on Curative Education. In his activity as a private
tutor, he himself took on a hydrocephalic child. At ten years of
age, the child was severely retarded in development. Steiner
was able, by treating the child solely with pedagogical means,
to bring about a complete normalization of the disorder so that
this boy was later able to pass the school certificate examination and study at a university. The proportion of the head to
the rest of the body also improved considerably in the process.

Curative education approaches the children by way of the
senses and through movement. Attention to and nurture of the
senses, in their twelvefold aspect, and guidance of the children
through movement, are two chief provinces of curative educa-

tion. Above both of them stands the artistic element and the religious attitude, not in the confessional sense, but as a basic mood. The capacity for artistic experience and for reverence enables the handicapped child to experience himself within humanity. Introducing him into the practical activities of life brings him satisfaction and places him within the social community. In the handicapped, we can see how education is possible even when the intellectual capacity remains weak.

The curative educator works not only through the medium of his efforts, but also directly through his personality. He is the therapist and the therapy at the same time. As was described in Rudolf Steiner's course on Curative Education, he works with each of the members of his being on the next deeper member of being of the child. His efforts receive great support from curative eurythmy, hydrotherapy, appropriate diet, and medications.

Medicinal Treatment

Medicinal treatment according to spiritual scientific principles is most helpful in many cases and often contributes decisively to the development of the children. Nevertheless, we must beware of overvaluing these possibilities compared to others. Success is much harder to evaluate than in other diseases because this is a constitutional therapy—a lengthy, intimate process in which many factors interact. In a favorable course of development, it appears to others as though it would have come about by itself anyway. Judgment of the effects is only possible with the help of the intimate observation of those who take care of the child. Therefore, the doctor depends on their ability to observe and on their observations. Experienced curative educators understand this quite well and value the help of remedies highly.

Fast and impressive effects are achieved today with psychotropic drugs (neuroleptic drugs, tranquilizers, etc.). This presents a great temptation to therapists; we must keep in mind that they are not a real help to development. These drugs are capable of pacifying, retarding, perhaps loosening or uninhibiting, but not of helping the patient, if we are looking toward the development of the human capacities and not mere manage-ability. In any case, these drugs make contact with the child's personality even more difficult. In severe situations such emer-gency measures are unavoidable, and we are grateful that they exist. Good educators, however, would often rather go through the greatest difficulties than see their access to the child slip away because of such effects.

In contrast, with medications derived from spiritual science, we try to alter the disturbed resonance by a sort of stimulation and relief, so that the organism will be able to come by itself to a capacity for healthy regulation.

First, we will mention some medications with a broad action that are called for in many disorders. A common finding, not only in movement disorders, is hypotonia of the muscle and softness of the ligaments with hyperextension of the joints. The deficient tone, the laxness in the whole movement system, is an expression of insufficient astral involvement. Hyperactive children also show this hypotonus, though the astral body is otherwise quite assertive. What is missing here is an important stimulating factor for the circulatory dynamics, especially for the flow of blood to the heart and on to the brain. We also find indications that the entire circulation is not in order; there is a tendency to cold hands and feet, livid coloration of the skin and lips, and occasionally pulse irregularities. For this reason, a sustained treatment of the circulation, but not with short-term analeptics, is a great help. Cardiodoron is such a remedy. It can be given in liberal dosage (3 × 20 drops) over a long period of time.

Another remedy is Calcon, a typical constitutional medica-tion for the child's development. It has a calming effect in affec-tive lability.

More specific therapy is achieved by the use of the metals. They present us with the classical keyboard for treatment in accordance with the insights of anthroposophy and science. As "minerals," they appeal to the ego organization, which is important in developmental disorders. For a description of their action, we refer the reader to the comprehensive chapter in Vol. II. Lead, and most especially tin, play the leading role in the treatment of hydrocephaly, while silver is the remedy for microcephaly. Lead promotes the incarnation process; some caution is advisable with it because it can push too deeply into the physical organization. Lead also brings the necessary separation between the child and the world around him; this is needed when a child's liking for all sorts of dirt and foul smells is too great. Tin is effective in certain forms of restlessness in which we get the impression that the organism is too dry. It regulates between the solid and fluid elements. When a restless child seems like a fish out of water, one should think of tin.

There are many indications for iron. As a developmental remedy for children, it assists proper coupling of the ego and the organism. To mention just some important points, iron promotes engagement of the astral body in muscular and psychological hypotonia. All states of weakness, especially when connected with anxiety, are indications for iron (meteoric iron). As a stimulator of the astral body, it influences the speech faculty and supports the organs of speech, especially in the iron-sulfur compound pyrite. Gold, in accordance with its central position among metals, is the chief medication in developmental disorders as well. In deformities connected with general laxness of the organization, it is effective in medium potencies (D10–15) and as an ointment rubbed in a clockwise direction over the heart region. In diffuse cerebral damage, especially of the diencephalon and midbrain, it is indicated together with Apis D30; in psychoses it embraces both the manic (low potencies) and depressive (high potencies) phases. Karl König and others developed a special remedy for children with contact disorders, using gold with myrrh and olibanum (frankincense); it is produced as Myrrha comp. It has a wide range of action and is also combined with corpora quadrigemina and belladonna.[8] We have given only a few examples of the possible applications of gold. As with all metal therapy, the physician will apply it only on the basis of an intimate knowledge of the processes involved.

Copper plays an important role in the treatment of epilepsy, and is also effective in releasing all other forms of crampedness that manifest themselves in body or soul. It promotes contact.

While iron provides the courage for contact and gold the open-
ness to the other person, copper removes the obstacles that
stand in the way. Mercury appears to have only limited use in
developmental disorders. Silver, however, has great therapeutic possibilities. We have already mentioned microcephaly in
this connection. Silver is connected with all anabolism, since it
mediates the physical form in the earthly incarnation. It is the
decisive medication in the numerous forms of underdevelop-
ment in which we have the immediate sense that the bodily
meagerness prevents any full development of the soul life.
Silver is the basic remedy in all degenerative diseases of the
nervous system, and its applications described for physical
and psychological shock also play a large role in curative education. In psychotic processes, it is capable of reuniting the
etheric body with the organs. It is indicated for children especially in its vegetative form of Argentum per Bryophyllum.

Since all processes in the human organism are planetary and
hence also metallic processes, which permeate the organism
throughout from the head to the limbs, it makes no sense to
speak of the metals only in connection with individual disorders. Now we shall turn again to the general forms discussed,
though we shall mention only the most important by way of an
introductory survey.

For the deformities, the chief medication is Hypophysis
cerebri. It promotes the process of formation operating from
the head on the rest of the organism and brings the two poles
into a better interaction. Nicotiana tabacum provides formative force without the specific direction from above to below.
The higher members of being, which have a difficult time taking hold of and shaping the unwieldy physical body, are aided
with metal therapy (silver, gold, iron, possibly tin and lead).
The astral body can also be supported by the effects of arsenic,
for example in the form of Levico baths. The permeation of the
organism with light can be improved with Carbo vegetalis.

In Down's syndrome, Hypophysis is once again the main
remedy, combined with Thyreoidea and perhaps Pancreas and
Gland. suprarenales. Here, one can also use silver in connec-

tion with quartz to strengthen the skin-forming forces. In heart treatment with various drugs, Cor bovis has proven suitable for guiding the medicinal effects to the heart. Assimilable vitamins deserve consideration. The administration of "trace elements" by means of Terracoron, as described by Haubold, is also recommended by König. The neurotropic preparation Fragador can also be used toward the same end.

Cerebral lesions of all kinds—not only those discussed here, but also cerebral palsy, for example—require Arnica. Arnica "makes" nervous system, according to Rudolf Steiner. It can be applied internally and externally. Of the metals, silver has a basic relation to the brain; also, we have spoken of treatment with gold in conjunction with Apis. Gold is directed more at the midbrain and diencephalon, while silver embraces the entire process of brain formation. Silver, gold, and perhaps iron are the most important metals. Myrrha cps. also has a special range of action here. If the metabolic forces penetrate into the head region too strongly, Cephalodoron is indicated. Also of importance are the guiding medications derived from the animal kingdom, in the form of Cerebrum preparations. Belladonna offers special possibilities; it can also be applied in other forms of developmental disorders and always produces impressive effects. We can understand the great breadth of action of belladonna in the light of our depiction of the polar structure of the organism; Rudolf Steiner indicated that it, like hyoscyamus, strengthens the correspondence between the upper and lower systems by building a "framework" at one pole, which produces a corresponding, opposite configuration at the other pole.

The best proven remedy in psychotic disorders is hyoscyamus, which is closely related to belladonna. While belladonna is given in high and low potencies, depending on whether we wish to stimulate the central nervous system or the metabolism, hyoscyamus is used chiefly in low potencies or unpotentized. In acute conditions, injections of 0.1 per cent, 1 per cent, even 5 per cent are of great help. Treatment with phosphorus, which appeals to the ego, is another important measure. Rudolf

Steiner advised the use of phosphorus extremely frequently in pathological manifestations of the soul life.

With this we have introduced a selection of medications just suited to the disorders discussed. A thorough knowledge of these remedies is a prerequisite for their use. This presentation is limited to a rough sketch, a suggestion.

Chapter VII

Inflammation and Sclerosis as Basic Tendencies of the Ascending and Descending Halves of Life

Inflammation

Although inflammation is recognizable to the impartial observer as a typical manifestation of disease, and although it counts among the oldest concepts relating to disease, it is still the object of vehement dispute in our times. The way in which this phenomenon is conceived always bears the stamp of the age in which an author lives. Thus, this is a good example of how the innumerable facts discovered by research do not bear their meaning within themselves but gain it from the underlying image of man.

Hippocrates saw in inflammation a process by which disease material was "cooked" by heating, and then subjected to pepsis, that is, digestion. In this process, either the foreign material was overcome and assimilated (this corresponds to breaking down and resorption in the digestive tract), or else there was a "crisis" and discharge to the outside (corresponding to excretion). Sufficient material has been provided by modern research to understand the profundity of this remarkable statement.

The classic description of the inflammatory process derives from Celsus (1st century A.D.). He characterized the main symptoms of inflammation as *rubor, calor, tumor,* and *dolor.* In accordance with the "holistic" approach of the ancients, the subjective experience of pain, a reaction of the life-sense, is mentioned without further ado alongside the objectively observable symptoms. Similarly, Galen (2nd century A.D.) added a fifth symptom, *functio laesa,* to these.

To Greek physicians, these signs and symptoms were the expression of a displacement in the equilibrium of forces, and in the light of the viewpoint represented in this book, we can now

come to understand in a new way that it is just these four striking signs and symptoms that always appear in an inflammation. As mentioned before, fever or a local increase in warmth
enables the ego to penetrate more deeply into the metabolism,
bringing form and structure to the organism or the inflamed
area.

The second characteristic, *dolor* or pain, is an enhanced
awareness process. The patient is too aware of the part that
hurts. This awareness process, however, arises through the
astral body. Characteristically, there is an increased concentration of hydrogen ions in the inflamed tissue. An acid character is always an indication of astral activity. The so-called
pain reactor substances arising in the tissue are also acid. Also
histamine, serotonin, and other biogenic amines released during inflammation are an expression of the activity of the astral
body (see p. 272 f.).

Tumor denotes the swelling of the tissue. The water organism,
and hence the etheric body, is intensely active at this place, but
without sufficient penetration by the ego and astral body. The
pain and fever indicate the attempt by the astral body and the
ego respectively to permeate the area properly once again.

The *rubor* or reddening, finally, is a sign of hyperemia,
which brings the "material" for the increased warmth as well
as the swelling.

Calor:	Fever, local hyperthermia	Ego
Dolor:	Sensation, pain	Astral body
Tumor:	Swelling, edema	Etheric body
Rubor:	Hyperemia, flow of material	Physical body

These symptoms show that the inflamed area has fallen out
of the equilibrium and harmony of the whole. The healthy pink
of the skin represents a balance between redness and pallor,
that is, between blood and nerve processes. The same applies
to body temperature.

The basic conception of the essential nature of inflammation
is of the greatest importance for pathology and therapy. One
essential factor in inflammation is warmth or fever. Though
the processes involved in this have been investigated in great

detail, their significance for the whole of the human being is not yet understood in so far as it transcends the pathological and clinical findings. For this reason, a thorough examination of the interpretations and findings is necessary.

In retrospect it seems tragic that researchers such as Gustav Ricker, and also Aschoff and Andral, who contributed so much to our knowledge of inflammation, believed it necessary to give up the concept of inflammation altogether. This was certainly not because they knew less than Celsus and Galen, but because the microscope showed them such a plethora of details that also occurred elsewhere that they lost sight of the essential character and unity of the inflammatory process in its significance for the totality of the organism. The use of the microscope all too easily causes the researcher to lose his eye for the whole. Büchner, a student of Aschoff, recognized this danger and strongly emphasized the biological significance of inflammation, which Virchow said was a protective process.

The fundamental works of Gustav Ricker in this field are actually extremely informative, even if he lacked concepts adequate for interpreting his findings. Ricker's conception is based on the functional unity of the terminal blood stream (arteriole, capillary, network, venule). He speaks of the "innervated blood stream" and sees inflammation as the reaction to irritation of the nerves in the terminal areas of circulation. This results first in increased circulation (hyperemia), then in decreased circulation (ischemia), after which a third stage follows with continued increase of the inflammatory stimulus: a stronger blood flow due to paralysis of the smooth muscles of the arterioles.

In this way Ricker moves the critical factor to the stimulation of the nerves of the terminal circulatory vessels. In accordance with the accepted view of circulation, he regards blood as a completely passive element, the movement and distribution of which is determined by the vessels, and these in turn by the nerves. Ricker even denies the active arterial hyperemia with accelerated blood flow in the inflamed area. True, this is not always present, and passive hyperemia with retardation of blood flow to the point of stasis is felt by pathologists to be the real disorder.

For a full understanding of these phenomena, we must credit blood with a more active role. Particularly in the capillary area it is not at all a passively moved substance but possesses an active "primary flow" as an expression of etheric life (see chapter on the heart, Vol. III). Vascular regulation, however, is an expression of the astral body, which acts through the nervous system. A disturbed interaction of blood and nerves provides the opportunity for inflammation to develop.

As we have mentioned many times, the astral impulses travelling by way of the nervous system have a contracting, forming, and catabolic character, while from the metabolism—and from the blood, its main representative here—comes a centrifugal, anabolic, enlivening function. Mediating between the two poles is the primordial picture of health, the rhythmic system.

Ricker repeatedly referred to this rhythmic process in the terminal blood vessels in the tissue. Its interruption is the first sign of disease at the beginning of the inflammation; instead of a rhythmically alternating flow, there is now only opening of the arterioles and therefore hyperemia. The healthy rhythm of the arterioles is by no means mediated by direct neural influences, as denervation has demonstrated. The rhythm is an immanent activity of the organism and conforms to laws of its own.

Gustav Ricker's contribution is twofold. First, he showed the interaction of blood and nerves in the process of inflammation, and at the same time he recognized the importance of the rhythm between these polar processes and of its cessation in the pathological process. The fact that he came to a completely one-sided interpretation of his findings can be attributed, as we have said, to the prevalent erroneous conception of blood and its motion.

We see that the three stages of inflammation described also show a rhythm; blood and nerve processes predominate alternately. In contrast to the innate rhythm of healthy blood flow, here there is an involvement of the dynamic of the entire organism, namely, blood and nerve, the former ultimately predominating.

The involvement of the nerve processes must be understood dynamically, not in terms of neural tracts alone. The ultimate dominance of the blood pole is quite logical; sometimes it represents a counterattack against the "cooling" of an organ or of the organism through outer or inner influences (see below).

> The course of inflammatory processes is *not* influenced by denervation of tissue; however, cutting the sympathetic fibers, or clinically performed periarterial sympathectomy, unleashes the blood supply, improving circulation and speeding recovery.[1]

So we find two opposite phases in inflammation: decreased and increased blood flow. These can also be discovered in the state of metabolism: a catabolic phase, setting in quickly after the inflammatory stimulus, is immediately followed by anabolic processes. This succession of anabolism and catabolism is the functional foundation of an animate organism and is characteristic of its oxidative metabolism. It is clear that the catabolic phase, the breakdown of proteins, expresses an activity of the astral body; the amoeboid motion of the leukocytes, phagocytosis, and parenteral digestion also testify to this. The succeeding anabolic phase shows the increased action of the etheric body in the building up, cell division, granulation, and formation of new tissue. It is important to see between these two phases not only a mediating rhythmic process (see above), but also the element of warmth. This is the connective link between the two phases; it does not arise passively but is an expression of the activity of the ego, which directs the catabolism through the astral body and structures the anabolism after its own design through the etheric body.

This sequence—catabolism, warmth, anabolism—occurs in physiological growth as well. The old must always perish before the new can be fashioned. This implies a purposeful catabolism, which makes an anabolism possible. Growth and regeneration are thus connected with the possibility of inflammation. Only with a proper valuation of this condition is it possible to understand the character of human growth and its connection with the inflammatory reaction.

In the picture of inflammation, the catabolic, aggressive character is the more imposing side, so that the following anabolic formation of new tissue is less noticeable, especially as this is more dominant in chronic processes. It is an essential characteristic of the higher organisms that any new formation can proceed only on the basis of a preceding catabolism.

In acute inflammation we observe varying degrees of extravasation of plasma (serous inflammation) and blood components (purulent inflammation) through the capillary walls. At first the polymorphonuclear leukocytes separate out of the blood and are deposited on the vascular walls. Then they crawl actively, like amoebas, through the walls (diapedesis) and move toward the damaged area (emigration). The same is true of the eosinophils, which can even predominate when animal parasites are present. The monocytes begin their emigration later, and last come the lymphocytes. The latter, however, do not go so directly to the focus of the disease as do the polymorphonuclear leukocytes. Erythrocytes can also be carried along (hemorrhagic inflammation), so that there is a conglomeration of all blood elements outside the blood stream, forming an exudate.

Thus the inflammatory process begins with a separation of the blood elements (emigration of the leukocytes), which normally form a unity (through the dominance of the ego organization). When the leukocytes migrate through the vessel walls, they emerge from the domain of the ego organization and begin immediately to develop a stronger life process of their own (amoeboid movement, phagocytosis). They thus regain the measure of vitality that they lose by entry into the ego organization.

The connective tissue, into which the exudate penetrates, also reacts with stronger vitalization; the wandering cells (histiocytes) resting in the tissue begin to enlarge, divide, and separate from it. Metschnikoff recognized in this a transitory biogenetic regression, and compared the function of the leukocytes and histiocytes with the enteral digestion of invertebrates. Robert Rössle saw inflammation as a parenteral digestive process in the tissue, and thus took up Hippocrates' conception in a modern form. His determination that the "mucous membrane" of the intestinal tract is an organ in a state of physiological inflammation maintained by bacterial flora clearly shows the connection of the metabolic system, represented by the intestines, with growth and inflammation. Again we have the succession of catabolism and anabolism, so typical of inflammation.

At the end of the inflammatory process there is a mass destruction of leukocytes and erythrocytes, which releases additional etheric forces, making them available for the healing process. This finds a practical application in injecting the patient with his own blood, either irradiated or not. In many cases of chronic fatigue, or when the organism is no longer capable of mounting a proper inflammatory process, such injection of one's own blood can help.

Inflammation can also end with the expulsion of pus. This can be seen as a component of the blood which, having absorbed pathogenic agents or toxins, has become an inner foreign body and must be expelled for the maintenance of the organism.

By limiting and, to some extent, isolating the focus of inflammation, the organism creates the necessary polarity between healthy and diseased tissue that is the prerequisite for healing processes. The healing process is heralded in the blood by the "lymphocytic-eosinophilic healing phase." The stage in which the antitoxins are formed is characterized by the appearance in the tissue of plasma cells belonging to the lymphocyte group and appearing wherever vital processes are particularly intense (digestion, pregnancy, etc.). The appearance of the lymphocytes is the sign that the etheric body has reunited the organism into a whole.

Inflammation is thus based on a partial and transitory regressive metamorphosis of the blood. It gives up the unity provided by the ego organization, so that its now independent, and thus more vital, elements can eliminate the injurious intruder more easily; only then can the part that was affected by inflammation be rejoined to the whole.

If we look at inflammation as a reaction to a stimulus, we can agree with Letterer's description: "Inflammation is the price paid by the metazoan organism, which has grown continually more differentiated, for the ability of its living substance to be *irritable*." Accordingly, inflammation is essentially linked to man and animal, since only in these has there been an internalization of a soul life, which is the precondition for such responsiveness to stimuli. In the final analysis, inflammation is in this way brought about by the astral body and its specific interaction with the etheric body.

Undoubtedly, the stimulus comes mainly from without. Intruding foreign substances (bacteria, viruses, foreign bodies) are confined locally by the inflammation, broken down by humoral (antibodies) and/or cellular means, that is, "digested" in the sense of Hippocrates or Rössle, and thus "denatured." After this digestion, they are ready for resorption. If this is not possible, then elimination takes place by means of "melting down" of tissue (suppuration) in which the organism sacrifices parts to preserve the whole.

There are also inner factors that can set off, control, or maintain an inflammation. Among these is not only the occurrence of fever or inflammatory reactions without recognizable cause, but also the type of reaction in the specific inflammation, which for its part is also not caused by the specific agent alone.

Fever

A special role is played in the inflammatory process by fever, that is, the general increase in temperature. As we have shown, warmth is a specific vehicle of the ego; accordingly, in a fever the ego engages more intensely in the organism, or more precisely, in the metabolic system. This means that it is no longer so free, which is why consciousness is dimmed according to the intensity of the fever. Here we have the key to understanding febrile reactions: if the need or readiness of the ego to penetrate into the metabolism is strong, then there will be a high fever; the opposite is also true. Since this is the natural state of affairs in the child, he tends to get fevers easily. These questions are treated in detail in the section "Childhood Diseases" (p. 40 ff.).

In all febrile reactions, we must see not only the organic alterations, but also the ego as effective agent and goal of the reactions because the physical manifestations are oriented toward it. Not only the body, but also the soul-spiritual being of man undergoes a metamorphosis through fever. It is especially important to keep this in mind with therapeutic measures.

In recent years investigations have been published that show that fever plays a significantly positive role in the state of the organism's defense system. Because of their far-reaching implications, we shall present these findings.

The customary views still take their form primarily from the study of bacterial infections. The humoral formation of antibodies is as well known as cellular defense. Less attention is given to fever and local increase of temperature in local inflammation. These play a critical role, however, particularly in viral diseases. Lwoff[2] demonstrated that the defense against various viruses depends much more on the temperature of the organism than on humoral or cellular reactions. It has been found that in viral infections, the replication of viruses generally stops *before* the antibodies appear, or when the number of antibodies is still too small to be effective. But there is often an increase in number of viruses despite antibodies. In viral infections, other factors of the inflammatory reaction seem to be more important. According to Lwoff, these are temperature, pH, and interferon; it is thus nonspecific factors that play the decisive role in viral infections. Interferon is formed by the leukocytes; the lower the pH and the higher the temperature, the more of it is produced. Accordingly, anti-inflammatory steroid hormones such as cortisol decrease interferon production.

The most decisive factor in this process is temperature, as can be seen by the fact that the infection can also be overcome without interferon production. There simply exists a certain antagonism between high temperature and the well-being of viruses.

Since 1921[3] it has been known that the growth of the tobacco mosaic virus is temperature-dependent. When the plants are kept between 20° and 30°, the typical pathological symptoms appear; above 30° the plants are considerably less sensitive; at 36° the lesions that appeared at 20° disappear again. Therapeutic use has been made of this fact in the plant world.[4]

More recently, many animal tests[5] have been conducted that repeatedly indicate the same thing. If the test animals (rabbits, mice) are infected with viruses (myxomatosis, coxsackie-virus, or other different strains of viruses) and kept at low temperature, the mortality is high, up to 100 per cent. If they are kept in identical conditions but with a room temperature of up to 38°, then all or many survive. Intermediate temperatures give intermediate results. In this, it is significant that the rectal temperature changes by only one degree during extreme variation of the environmental temperature. Stated abstractly, a decrease in body temperature of only 1/10° causes an increase of viruses by a factor of 2. A change of body temperature of 2° in the mouse causes a fiftyfold change in the viral LD_{50}.

In other words, the virulence of viruses is not dependent only on the viral strain, but also on the body temperature of the host; the lower the temperature, the more virulent the viruses.

This polarity of viruses and warmth is understandable in the light of the exposition in the chapter on infectious diseases (Vol. III). There it is explained that viruses belong to the "cold" nervous system, while the bacteria show a relation to the metabolic system. This is why fever, as the expression of the inflammatory metabolic reaction, is able to curtail this polar effect, undermining the viruses' existence.

Accordingly, the course of a disease is also different if the temperature is lowered with an antipyretic. Tests of Kirn et al.[6] show that amidopyrine favors viral proliferation by lowering the temperature; specifically, the titer of viruses in rabbits given amidopyrine (pyramidon) was 100 times higher than in the control animals that had fever. As a result, the lesions were much larger and the mortality 2.7 times higher in the test animals.

It has also been known for a long time that the influenza virus multiplies well at 35°, badly at 37°, and not at all at 40°. Corresponding findings apply to the polio virus.[7]

Lwoff summarized these findings and the meaning of fever as follows: "Pyrogens call forth fever, and the fever helps the organism to fight the infection."

Although these relations have been extensively confirmed experimentally, and the "therapeutic" action of antipyretics has been shown negatively in animal experiments, these findings have still received no consideration generally in the medical treatment of viral diseases, which remain so problematic.

Fever is not only of critical importance for the defense against viruses. If we see in viruses their affinity to the nerve-sense system, then we can see fever as a reaction overcoming an excessive nerve-sense tendency of the organism. Since the ego lives in warmth, its involving itself or holding itself back ultimately determines the intensity and duration of the inflammatory reaction. The problem of hyperergy and anergy is also related to this. In general, hyperergy is equated with allergy; in this sense, allergy is a typical expression of inflammation. These matters are discussed more fully in a later chapter (see p. 282).

In this way, the inflammatory process represents the archetypal phenomenon of self-healing, or at least an attempt at this. Because of the liberation of etheric forces from the blood—the organism's inexhaustible reservoir of life—a properly overcome inflammation means a sort of rejuvenation for many people. From this point of view, and according to experimental findings, it is not advisable to disturb this process routinely with powerful measures, such as antipyretics, as is the custom today. Rather, the doctor should try to support and guide the natural course of the inflammatory process as much as possible.

Naturally, an acute inflammation with high fever can also be too strong, so that the organism cannot manage the transformation and dissolution involved. This danger, however, is overestimated today. Since we shy away from the dramatic course of a highly febrile illness, and since we now possess the means to prevent it, a positive view of the importance of acute febrile illnesses is being increasingly lost, especially as final judgments are generally made on the basis of observations in too short periods of time. Another danger arises from this situation: the exclusion of inflammation will lead to a preponderance of sclerotic processes; this danger is generally not yet recognized.

Chronic Inflammation

Special mention should be made of the unique characteristics of chronic inflammation. In the great majority of cases the striking symptom of fever is absent, or the temperature stays within subfebrile limits. Even in local processes, any limited

temperature increase is inconspicuous. In addition, pain is usually absent in chronic inflammation. When it does occur, it has
a rather dull, indefinite character, touching more on the sense
of life, the sensation of living, than the shooting, piercing pain
of acute inflammations that forces itself on the consciousness.

But what is the meaning of the absence or insufficient development of these two striking symptoms, which ordinarily lend
such drama to the inflammatory process? According to our ex-
positions above, we can say that both the ego (fever) and the
astral body (pain) are but weakly involved in the process; these
higher members of being withdraw from the whole process.
Therefore, the etheric and physical bodies no longer receive
the impulses needed to cause a healing process. Real healing
involves restoration of the form or function of an organ or the
organism, so that the ego can develop fully in its spirituality on
the basis of this physicality. This is the reason why the ego involves itself so strongly in the first period of life, in order to
transform the organism in such a way that it will be in accordance with the ego (see the chapter, "The First Epoch of Life").

In any case, the etheric and physical bodies do carry out the
process of healing and transforming the organism, but they
lack the "architect" of the ego that is needed to structure and
direct this process and thus bring healing. When the involvement of the ego is missing in an inflammation, the reactions of
the etheric and physical bodies proceed without direction,
sense, or aim.

Since the anabolic processes are the domain of the etheric
body, we will not be surprised to find that chronic inflammation has an intensely productive or proliferative character; excessive granulation tissue is formed. As an expression of
regeneration and healing, this anabolic growth process is indispensable to the organism. When the leadership of the ego is
missing, however, this reaction overshoots the mark and we
have keloid formation, excessive granulations, etc.

If the tendencies of the physical body take too active a part in
the process, the reactions will tend toward hardening and
"physicalization." Thus, in the course of a chronic inflamma-

tion, an organ may be penetrated with scar and connective tissue, as in cirrhosis of the liver.

Now it can be asked why the ego holds back in a chronic inflammation. In many cases after an acute phase, it will be found that the underlying disorder (for example, a foreign body) cannot be overcome despite the efforts of the organism. The ego tires and withdraws, since it is unable to bring about healing and is more "interested" in the whole organism than in a part.

In other cases, however, there is a primary lack of affinity of the ego to the metabolic system; it does not engage in the metabolic system so deeply in the first place and no acute febrile inflammation can arise. In this way, the organism ultimately comes under the sway of the processes at the opposite pole from inflammation: sclerosis, deposition, and induration. This is the case not only in primary chronic rheumatoid arthritis, for example, but also in carcinoma formation in which there is little tendency to febrile reactions (see below).

So we can also understand Rudolf Steiner's indication that in chronic processes, the ego is not sufficiently "interested." The approach we have described also makes clear why chronic diseases can often be healed only after the process has been activated or the entire metabolism has been transformed by an intercurrent febrile disease. It is the art of the physician to reawaken the interest of the organism or ego in the chronic process (for example, with phosphorus, heat therapy, etc.) and restore the disturbed balance between inflammatory and sclerotic tendencies in the organism.

The inflammatory process, as a capacity, accompanies man through his entire life; its appearance, however, is more frequent and pronounced in youth. After the middle of life, it decreases in importance, though it remains to some degree until death.

The Balance of Middle Life

For an understanding of human health and disease, it is quite important to recognize the processes of sclerosis and inflammation not only in the area of pathology but also in normal development. That is, the pathological processes of inflammation and sclerosis are not something foreign, appearing out of nowhere, but are the result of physiological processes pushed to the extreme. To understand this clearly, it is necessary to recognize the two extremes as a polarity.

Just as inflammation is a tendency of the metabolism (especially the blood), sclerosis is a tendency of the nervous system. Inflammation and sclerosis are the dynamics of blood and nerve exaggerated to the point of pathology. Accordingly, health consists in the equilibrium between these two polar forces, not in the absence of one or the other. Both tendencies, therefore, are needed for health. Whether or not they take on a pathological nature is dependent on place (or organ) and time (age).

Let us consider the sclerotic tendency. When we realize that the human organism has come from a predominantly watery element in embryonic life, then we must call the state of the newborn relatively "hardened." Rudolf Steiner saw in this hardening tendency, so necessary for normal development and formation of the organism, essentially the same process as appears after the middle of life as a sclerotic tendency. In youth, this process expresses itself in normal forming and structuring of the solid organism (nerve-sense system, skeletal system, teeth). This same process that in youth is a "healthy" one, however, appears in later life as the cause of many diseases. This is because in youth the anabolic process, essentially connected with inflammation, is still dominant. The equilibrium between these two opposed processes, which we call health, is thus labile and dependent on age. Neither tendency as such is pathological, but only when in excess or when one appears in the wrong place or at the wrong time.

We see that the formation of the skeletal and nervous systems is a process of mineralization or devitalization; as such it is linked with the potential for sclerosis. Without our susceptibility to certain sclerotic diseases, we could not have skeletal and nervous systems, nor the higher faculties connected with them.

Here we have the mirror-image of the situation described above for growth, regeneration, and the capacity for inflammation.

As the growth process shows, in youth the anabolic processes are dominant. The physical vehicle of the anabolic process par excellence is the blood, which constantly renews itself throughout life even when all other organs are already in a state of catabolism. As we have shown, an excess of the blood process is manifested in a tendency to inflammation or in dwelling too long in purely anabolic processes; these cannot be given further direction if the sclerotic process does not begin at the right time. Such is the case in rickets.

The sclerotic process is responsible not only for physiological hardening of the predestined organs (bones, teeth) at the right time, but also for the necessary transformation, metamorphosis, of the formative forces, and maturation that are a precondition for the further development of the human being. This is necessary not only in youth but also in later life. Too long a period of apparent youth and physical vitality holds the danger of a hardening and sclerosing of the life of the soul. Thus, extended youth can exist only when there is insufficient transference of active life into the spiritual realm by means of breakdown and metamorphosis of biological life and of anabolic processes. For this reason, healthy involution in later life must entail a certain harmonious atrophy of the organs and the whole organism. It is precisely the unused, untransformed vital forces that can be the foundation for hardening and sclerosis in later years.

The physical lightening of the organism with advancing age indicates this process clearly. Once again, however, the process can go too far, resulting in the familiar demineralization of the bone system, osteoporosis; this is another normal physiological process that becomes pathological when increased to excess.

A premature process of sclerosis leads not only to early physical hardening, but also to a premature development of the soul, just as with retarded development there is a "bypassing" of certain developmental steps that can occur only at a certain time of life. Development is a matter of the right time. (The ancient Greeks still had a concept for this time quality, for which they used the word *kairos*.)

In the period around middle life, anabolic and catabolic processes should be in equilibrium. At this time, at about the thirty-fifth year, the ego has also reached the culmination of its development; the consciousness soul is "born." In the lives of many eminent people, the thirty-fifth year also plays a special role in their destinies. At this time, the human being has the greatest possibilities for outer development. He is at the high point of his life in this respect.

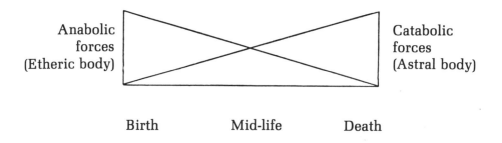

Anabolic forces (Etheric body)		Catabolic forces (Astral body)
Birth	Mid-life	Death

This is also reflected in anatomical data. The absolute weight of the liver, both in well-nourished and malnourished people, is at its maximum in the fourth decade and reaches its minimum in advanced age. It is similar with the pancreas. The liver is the central organ of the anabolic metabolism and the main vehicle of the etheric body. When we see that in the second half of life the liver loses about half its weight without any outer cause, we must regard this as a sort of archetypal phenomenon of aging.

These facts show us that beginning in middle life the etheric body withdraws increasingly from the metabolism; this, in turn, is because the astral body and the ego consume and transform the etheric body increasingly in the course of life.[8] This "consuming" of the etheric body by the higher members of man's being offers him the possibility of spiritual development; it is also the real cause of aging.

From our point of view, it is really quite natural that the development of the pancreas, as the central gland of the catabolic metabolism, runs parallel to that of the liver, especially when we have recognized that the anabolic and catabolic processes in the healthy organism stand in an inner equilibrium with one another. It would make no sense if the pancreas were to break down more food than the liver could manage.

This harmonious interaction of pancreas and liver causes the gradually decreasing appetite of the aging person and his tendency to prefer simpler foods.

The metabolic process becomes weaker after the middle of life. If this fact were to serve more as a guideline for the dietetics of the elderly, many elderly people would suffer less from diseases and troubles that to a large extent stem quite simply from an overloading of the metabolic system.

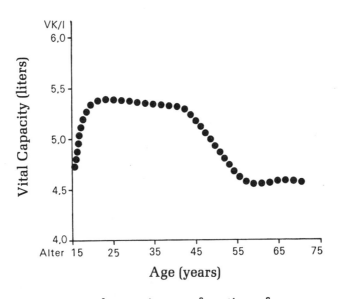

Vital capacity as a function of age

(From: R. Amrein, R. Keller, H. Joos, H. Herzog, "Neue Normalwerte für die Lungenfunktionsprüfung mit Gauzkörperplethysmographie." *Dt. med. Wschr.* Vol. 94, page 1785. 1969.)

The vital capacity of the lungs also shows an increasing and declining development as the above figure shows. The lung, however, is to be regarded as an organ of the astral body, and its rising and falling development is an expression of the incarnation tendency of the astral body, which rises in youth and begins to fall in middle life. Diminished respiratory volume in the aging must be compensated with more frequent breathing, as is known. There is always the danger here of a certain oxygen deficiency. Thus, we see that this (spatial) lack of breathing surface, coming from the diminished vital capacity, is compensated by the increased movement of the lungs (per unit of time); the rhythmic system "heals" itself, since it is the ultimate source of all healing processes.

The decrease in vitality, or in etheric forces, shown in the atrophy of the aging organism is also expressed in a corresponding decrease in the regenerative capacity of the tissues. This is found in the skin, which withers, and also in the blood. With increasing age, the red bone marrow is increasingly replaced with yellow marrow. As a result, relatively few red blood corpuscles are formed, so that in old age the blood is relatively poor in young erythrocytes. The fact that old erythrocytes are less resistant to hypotonic solutions than young ones allowed Bürger and Hendt to base a biological age index on this resistance to hypotonicity.

The decrease in vitality is expressed generally in the spontaneous alterations that all colloids undergo; these are designated as "secondary solidification" or "hysteresis." Naturally, this occurs in the protein colloids of the protoplasm as well. Tissues with poor or absent blood circulation, such as the cornea, lens, eardrum, the lining of the large vessels (especially the aorta), are particularly susceptible. Bürger calls them "bradytrophic tissues," and they succumb quite early to such hysteretic alteration. As Bürger emphasizes, however, this must be seen not as the cause but as a consequence of the aging process, that is, of the abating of the etheric forces. The latter predominate over the physical substances at the beginning of life (growth, propagation, regeneration). The diminishing of these functions indicates the gradual dwindling of the etheric forces;

with this hysteretic alteration of the tissues, the aging process attacks the cell itself. The tissues become dehydrated. Thus, the water content of the body in the embryo is still 85–90 per cent; in the newborn, about 75 per cent; throughout the course of life, 65 per cent; and in old age, 60 per cent. This is natural with the lessening of the etheric forces, and it results in a preponderance of the physical processes and hence in greater susceptibility to disease, especially of a sclerotic nature. The less the physical organism has been dissolved through involution, the greater the susceptibility will be (see above).

That the brain shows the earliest signs of aging can be especially striking. It attains its greatest weight between the fifteenth and twentieth years in men and between the twentieth and twenty-fifth years in women. Hence, the brain is ahead of all other organs by about ten years in regard to aging. This remarkable fact can be understood when we remember that the brain is taken in hand by the astral body immediately after birth and before other organs; the cessation of cell division in the brain is a clear sign of this. The brain and nervous system are already in a physiological "state of age," a state of fixed rest, at birth. We can say that the brain and nervous system are the image of the sclerotic process (meaning the actual nerve substance, not the blood vessels serving it). This enables them to fulfill their physiological functions.

Sclerosis

We have shown that the sclerotic process as such has a physiological function in the human being. Certain organs, the skeletal system, for example, require a physiological sclerosis to fulfill their function. This process becomes pathological only when it appears in the wrong place and at the wrong time; pathological manifestations arise in this way. As such, they appear pathophysiologically or as gross organ pathology, and are investigated as such; quite often, however, the underlying dynamic is no longer seen. Several examples will serve to illustrate this.

Arteriosclerosis is a special case of a predominant sclerotic tendency in the organism. This was formerly seen primarily as calcification, so that it was understood as a sclerotic process. Today, the preliminary stages, or forms, of a pathological reaction have been recognized ("unspecific mesenchymal reaction") and have directed attention back to the whole organism. Also in recent times, through biochemical research, the emphasis has been shifted to lipid metabolism, so that arteriosclerosis is regarded primarily as a disorder of fat metabolism. Such a disorder is undoubtedly present, but its presence still says nothing of the origin of arteriosclerosis. To understand this, we must learn to recognize the dynamic of the higher members of being manifesting itself in the disorder and in the substance. The final state of "calcification" expresses clearly the pathological tendency that can lead to this state by completely different paths.

Deposits of cholesterol are first found in the aorta, especially at the branching of the intercostal, large abdominal arteries, and coronary arteries. Outside of the blood, there are cholesterol concentrations particularly in the bradytrophic tissues (lens, cornea, tympanic membrane, intima of the vessels, cartilage). The content of calcium and total dry substance of these tissues rises proportionately. In contrast, the cholesterol content of the skin falls with increasing age, since skin is not among the bradytrophic tissues. There is now sufficient experimental data showing that a high exogenous intake of cholesterol produces slightly increased deposition. It is quite possible that this plays a role today as one factor in sclerosis, since the customary diet of our civilization is much too rich, not only in fat, but also in animal products (see the section on nutrition, p. 230), so that a dietetic limitation of fat consumption, primarily as prophylaxis against arteriosclerosis, is fully justified.

An endogenous factor undoubtedly plays the greater role in the phenomenon, however; after all, the body produces cholesterol itself, and many animal tests were performed with extremely high doses of cholesterol, doses that were at least unphysiological for the particular animal. This one-sided overestimation of the importance of cholesterol or the fat metabolism in arteriosclerosis is a product of our times. It diverts attention from other equally important factors as well as from prophylactic and therapeutic possibilities. The essence of the disease escapes attention when attention is fixed on only one aspect of the disorder.

When speaking of endogenous factors, we mean not only the body's production of its own cholesterol, but, more important, the general state of the tissue. The predilection of the brady-trophic tissues for cholesterol deposition indicates a diminished metabolic process and a minimal blood process. Here, the balance between the inflammatory blood processes and sclerotic nerve processes is shifted in favor of the latter.

The extent to which cholesterol, a physiological and necessary substance, exercises a pathological function here by appearing in excess and in the wrong place can be understood from a knowledge of the essence of this substance, which is described in detail in the section on steroid metabolism (p. 253 ff.).

As it happens, cholesterol deposition is actually preceded by an increase of the mucopolysaccharides and by intimal edema. It is significant that the actual pathological process is not in the appearance of the lipids within the cells, but in the fat deposits turning into fibrous plaques, resulting in fibrous induration. Here, again, we see the pathological process in a falling out from life: falling out of the cell's metabolism, which is at least potentially capable of dissolving, and into a state of fixity, physicalization.

What we have said of deposition of cholesterol in all brady-trophic tissues applies equally to the progressive increase in the calcium content of these tissues, often accompanied by a simultaneous decrease in serum calcium. "Calcium is also among the precipitated substances that migrate increasingly into the bradytrophic tissues in advanced age" (Bürger).

There is thus the strange fact that calcium is deposited in the vessels while its concentration in the blood, and often in the bones (osteoporosis), decreases. The bone becomes less earthly, while the vascular system becomes more bone-like (transmineralization).

This is typical of something we have often mentioned, that it is not the sclerotic tendency as such but its occurrence in the wrong place that is pathological; here, it is even accompanied by decalcification, again in the wrong place. The bone system is the image of the ego organization, and the human being may withdraw too much from this system in the physiological excarnating process of aging. But the ego also lives in the blood, which carries the anabolic impulse. The displacement expresses a false clinging to life, leading to deposition of the "earth remnant," calcium. Accordingly, the principle of healing will involve removing the sclerotic process and also limiting it to its physiological place. This can be accomplished by the therapeutic use of lead, as detailed below.

Consequently, there is here a pathological displacement of the sclerotic tendency from the bones to the blood system. Now the astral body lives intensely in the latter, especially in the vascular system, but because of the rigidifying of the vessels it cannot "play this instrument" properly. The result is a rigidifying and narrowing of the soul. In fact, "ossification" may appear much more strongly, or earlier, in the soul-spiritual realm than in the physical. Indeed, the physical processes and signs are really expressions of the workings of spirit and soul.

By virtue of the preservation of the life processes, which leads to rigidification from lack of proper transformation, the affected individual can live for many years, even with pronounced arteriosclerosis, without obvious impairment of his vital well-being. He is less aware of his slowing down than are those around him. The psychological alterations, often involving outbreaks of anger and criticism of others, also become understandable in view of the hardening and practical imprisonment of the soul in the body. These manifestations are an expression of the absence of this transformation.

There is no doubt that hypertension will also promote the development of arteriosclerosis. This certainly goes beyond the fact that the most severe arteriosclerotic alterations takes place at those points in the vascular system that bear the greatest stress. The blood pressure is actually a direct expression of the activity of the astral body (see chapter on the heart, Vol. III), specifically of the astral dynamic running through the nerve-sense system and having an awakening, contracting tendency. In this way, the astral body acts not catabolically in the metabolism, but rather in its dynamic form through the nervous system, in which the sclerotic tendency is inherent. This accounts for the considerably higher risk of sclerosis run by hypertensives.

Finally, let us consider the interesting sex difference. As is known, men are generally more inclined to sclerosis than women, so long as the women continue to menstruate. After menopause, however, sclerosis can occur and can even proceed more rapidly than in men. The most obvious explanation is naturally that of hormonal influences; in fact, estrogenic and androgenic hormones do (respectively) lower and raise the cholesterol levels. Still, the question remains why this obvious relationship exists. In earlier chapters it was shown that the man connects himself more strongly with his body and with the earth. He lives qualitatively more from the nerve-sense system, which gives his thinking its characteristically masculine, abstract stamp. In contrast, the woman must remain more cosmic, especially while she is capable of reproduction, in order to be able to receive such cosmic forces during pregnancy. These circumstances mold the feminine essence even in its quality of soul. In fact, we can read these differences even in the hormones, estrogens having a more cosmic character than the androgens, which are more earthly (see p. 263f.).

Another expression of the essential stamp of femininity is found in the higher sulfur content of female tissues. Comprehensive studies, primarily those of Bürger et al.[9], have shown that the sulfur content of female body tissue is generally higher than that of the male body. Tests were done on tissues of the central and peripheral nervous system, cardiac and peripheral muscles, tendons and nails. Bürger speaks of a "genuine, chemical sex dimorphism." These findings are understandable when we see sulfur as a substance whose function is to internalize the imponderable, that is, to bring cosmic forces into organic connection. "The world spirit works through sulfur" (Rudolf Steiner). This sex difference in substance can be understood in light of the essential differences of man and woman described above, and through an understanding of sulfur as a substance.

As a result of these force relationships, man is more inclined, through his organization, to "physicalization," and therefore to sclerosis, than is woman. When she loses the natural cosmic connection in menopause, she is exposed even more than men to the hardening earthly forces, unless she creates this connection in a new and independent way through her own spiritual activity.

Of course, this also applies to the man as well, but now we have touched on the deepest problem of sclerosis and overcoming it. True prophylaxis consists of overcoming the earthbound intellect and of the development of a spiritual activity (in the sense of Rudolf Steiner's *Philosophy of Freedom*). The occurrence of sclerosis is only partially outwardly based (through fat consumption) and is also partially endogenously based (heredity, lasting displacement of the equilibrium of inflammatory and sclerotic tendencies by suppression of the former), but to a considerable extent, it is also dependent on the human being's spiritual conduct of life.

Depending on the localization and intensity of its manifestations, this disease can also be the starting point of diseases of other organs. We will mention only the brain and heart now. Both can put a dramatic end to life by rupture (apoplexy) or occlusion of vessels (embolism, infarction). In one blow, the blood destroys the organ it has built up and provided with nourishment throughout life. To the everyday consciousness this may appear as a terrifying event. But could not the ego, in its higher consciousness, sense such a dramatic solution as a blessing compared to a life of protracted illness, lived on a level of mere biological "functioning"?

If it is so that the pathological process consists in a displacement, then it ought to be possible to free the blood system of the sclerotic tendency by directing this back to its proper place. This is, in fact, possible with the use of lead, which has a specific affinity not only to the bone system, but also to the functioning of the nervous system. By means of a special combination of lead with honey, a connection is established with the ego organization, so that the whole of this process can come under the direction of the ego again. The preparation is called Plumbum mellitum, and is used prophylactically in D12 as Scleron (in more advanced cases, preferably in D20 as injection).

This tendency to rigidification can also be fought with belladonna, since belladonna is connected with insufficient engagement of the astral body.

In nature we find a polarity in the birch tree that can be put to therapeutic use here. The formative tendency in the bark of the tree involves deposition, rigidification, and sclerosis, while the tendency in the leaves is toward dissolving and secreting.

Cancer must also be mentioned at this point. As we will show in the chapter, "Causes and Treatment of Carcinoma" (Vol. III), this is a typical "cold" disease. It will be surprising at first that we count cancer among the sclerotic diseases, but when we see sclerosis and inflammation as a polarity, we gain insight into the problem of cancer. It has been stated in the past that cancer and inflammation have something to do with one another, and almost always the conclusion is that there is a certain antagonism between the two. In view of their fundamental importance for the spiritual scientific conception of disease and for the eminent practical consequences flowing from this understanding, we will describe these circumstances in detail.

At the end of the last century, the pathologist E. von Rindfleisch[10] contrasted inflammation and tumor formation with one another. He arrived at the conclusion that "inflammations do not arise spontaneously, but they heal spontaneously; tumors arise spontaneously, but they do not heal spontaneously." And Rokitansky knew about the antagonistic relationship between tuberculosis and cancer. Lambotte[11] pointed out in 1896 the striking rarity of the otherwise common inflammatory diseases of the fingers in the history of cancer patients. In 1910, R. Schmidt[12] published investigations that showed that infectious diseases, especially those of childhood, were much less common in the anamnesis of cancer patients than of other patients. Of 241 cancer patients, he found 99 who had never had a febrile illness. With a pronounced "diathesis inflammatoria," as he called it, contraction of cancer was a rarity. Schmidt called the number of febrile infectious diseases in a patient's anamnesis the "infection index," and found that this is particularly low in cancer patients. He is clearly recognizing the polarity of carcinoma and inflammation when he says that the disposition to cancer causes an immunity to infectious diseases. His vivid descriptions seem quite modern and pertinent today when he speaks of the special importance of the childhood diseases as the main representatives of the infectious diseases. He says that there is a change in the state of immunity and that the constitution is "loosened up" by infectious diseases in such a way as to lower the disposition to malignancy. "In avoiding the Scylla of the infectious diseases, we would steer toward the Charybdis of malignancy."

In more recent times, a great number of studies have confirmed this. In examinations of case histories Engel[13] found that of 300 cancer patients, 113 had never had an infectious disease, while this was true of only 16 of a control group of patients without carcinoma. The localization was also interesting. A low infection index is related much more to carcinoma of the rectum and colon than to stomach or breast cancer. The strict critical investigations of Sineck[14] led to results pointing in the same direction. Schier[15] also confirmed Schmidt's results. In 1941, Feld[16] reported an "empty anamnesis" in 62 per cent of the cancer patients studied. According to Kürten,[17] there is a partial weakening of the capacity for fever in cancer patients. A synopsis of these problems is given by E. Hass.[18] Later, Feyrter and Kofler[19] indicated the notably decreased disposition in rectal cancer patients to allergic-inflammatory diseases. From the ear-nose-throat field, we note that patients with carcinoma show a markedly low or completely absent tendency to infectious and allergic diseases (in comparison with patients with rhinitis vasomotorica, nasal polyps, and carcinoma nasi).[20] Felix Ungar[21] found, looking at 64,385 case histories, including 4,192 of cancer patients, that "on average, the number of infectious or childhood diseases was more than three times as high in the patients without cancer than in those with it." When these patients are classified according to their

"inflammatory diathesis," it becomes clear "that in cancer patients this diathesis is indeed generally significantly lower than
in the majority of the other patients. In the few patients who
contract cancer despite a relatively strong inflammatory tendency, the course seems usually to be especially malignant."

Since allergy is a typical inflammatory disease, there is also a
corresponding polar relation between allergy and malignancy;
that is, allergies appear seldom or not at all with cancer.[22] Pirquet, the creator of the concept of allergy, must have seen this
connection clearly, as his last work, *Allergie des Lebensalters*
(Allergy and Age) bears the subtitle "Malignant Tumors."

G. von Bergmann[23] writes: "The carcinomatous metabolism
appears in just those places where the body is no longer capable
of an active inflammatory metabolism. In vitro, the metaboliza-
tion of the carcinomatous metabolism, that is, the destruction
of the cancer cell by the inflammatory metabolism, can be
clearly shown. Tests at my clinic[24] show that sections of malignant tumors from rats and from human carcinomatous tissue
are quickly destroyed when placed in inflammatory exudate;
as the exact values for sugar, bicarbonate, oxygen, and acidity
(as measured by pH) show, the specific metabolism of the carcinoma cell can no longer be maintained in this environment.

It has long been known, though its significance is not appreciated, that in the uncommon cases of cancer in which a spontaneous recovery has occurred, this has usually been associated
with a highly febrile illness. In 72 leukemia patients, Huth[25]
found spontaneous remissions, which in more than one-third of
the patients were connected with purulent infections or pneumonia. These are the same diseases that preceded spontaneous
remission in 26 cases of sarcoma and 33 cases of carcinoma.

Many therapeutic attempts have been made to intensify this
inflammatory healing reaction. The first published data on this
were probably the work of Busch[26] in 1866. A compilation of
the results from different clinics, with reports of documented
recoveries from malignant tumors, is found in the work of
Bruns.[27] In 1883, in the Charité in Berlin, Fehleisen[28] transferred erysipelas to cancer patients, especially those with skin
tumors, with quite mixed results, however. Coley[29] made simi-

lar attempts, treating different malignant tumors with killed
streptococci. The cases treated at that time were followed up
and the results published, showing, particularly in sarcoma
and carcinoma, astonishingly long survival and, in some cases,
healing.[30] Attempts have also been made to heal cancer by
means of raised temperature; this has involved both animal
tests[31] and the use of hyperthermia for human tumor therapy.[32]

If this antagonistic relationship between inflammation and
cancer has, in fact, been known for so long, why has it had
scarcely any practical consequences? One reason is that the
concept of polarity needed for a full comprehension of this
situation is missing. Another is that the significance of fever as
an integrating factor in inflammation is not properly appreciated. Modern pathology still includes no realistic conceptu-
alization of inflammation. It cannot, therefore, take the step of
moving from tentative tests of the therapeutic application of
fever in cancer to the much more important consideration and
valuation of inflammation or fever as the organism's own
defense against the tendency to tumor formation. This is of the
greatest prophylactic significance for cancer. It is the warmth
organization that is disturbed in cancer patients. Either they
show subnormal temperature, or else they cannot react to an
adequate stimulus with fever, or with sufficient fever.

On the same lines, we find that patients with Graves' disease
show a considerably lower incidence of carcinoma than average. In Graves' disease, or hyperthyroidism, there is an extraordinarily strong engagement of the astral body in the metabolism, accelerating the metabolism as in inflammation and
simultaneously raising the body temperature. Here we are not
dealing with the dynamic of the astral body when it works by
way of the nervous system, which is associated with the sclerotic tendency, but rather with a continuous metamorphosis, a
breaking down and combustion of living substance. This is the
basis of the antisclerotic action of iodine, which has long been
known, though it is not often used today.

In myxedema, on the other hand, we find a sharp increase in
the serum cholesterol level, and the vessels become highly

arteriosclerotic. This is the classic example of insufficient meta-morphosis of the purely vegetative formative forces that fall prey to sclerosis in this way. The metamorphosis is only made possible by the astral body, as it engages in the metabolism through the thyroid gland (see p. 82).

It may be confusing to find that inflammations are fairly reg-ularly found in the area of a tumor. This could, in fact, lead to the erroneous impression that these inflammations have a pathogenic significance in the arising of the tumor. In reality, however, neither simultaneous occurrence nor regular succes-sion implies anything about a causal connection. This can be recognized only on the basis of an essential relation to the whole phenomenon.

The inflammation found around the tumor is always of a chronic character and arises not primarily, but as an insuffi-cient reactive attempt by the organism to reincorporate the proliferating parts—living foreign bodies—into the whole by disintegrating them with a febrile inflammation. This attempt, however, must fail so long as the fever formation is inadequate, that is, so long as the ego and astral body do not engage in the metabolism and restructure this unorganized life. For this engagement and structuring, however, especially on the part of the ego, warmth is essential. We must repeatedly emphasize the critical significance of warmth for an understanding of cancer and its therapy.

In the light of these descriptions it should not be surprising to find that a predominant sclerotic tendency leads to still other diseases that have not been mentioned, for example, the class of rheumatic diseases, gout, and diabetes. All these dis-eases have in common the tendency to deposition and "physi-calization" of the organism.

It is known that diabetics show sclerotic changes in the vas-cular system as well as hypercholesterolemia. Here we see the same tendency as in all the diseases treated in this section: a substance is not taken up into the living being but is left to the forces of hardening and deposition. The substance typically affected in diabetics, namely, glucose, happens to be so soluble that it does not precipitate in tissue but can be excreted. Nevertheless, we are dealing with fundamentally the same process. The frequent combination of diabetes with obesity and gout also points in the direction of metabolic processes that have not been taken hold of and given direction.

Chapter VIII
Hysteria and Neurasthenia

We will discuss the illnesses of hysteria and neurasthenia even though they are rarely diagnosed as such today. Hysteria, in its full-fledged form, may occur less frequently than in earlier decades. Neurasthenia, however, is the background of a great variety of disorders. These may be seen as different functional illnesses today, but they are not recognized as a unified disease syndrome. In particular, the two disease types, hysteria and neurasthenia, which also may overlap one another, tend to be lost in modern terminology like "vegetative dystonia" or even more vague diagnoses. When we sift through the symptoms of many different common disorders, however, these two archetypal disease dispositions appear behind them. These pictures are thus important for recognizing a patient's constitution, as every human being is inclined in one or the other direction, in the sense we give these disease tendencies. The fact that we often see a mixture of the two tendencies does not contradict the accuracy of the observation. How often do we find distinct pyknic or asthenic constitutions or a pure choleric or phlegmatic temperament? Far more often mixtures of temperament and constitution are observed. Methodologically, it is of prime importance to arrive at the archetypal picture and to recognize its action in the individual symptom.

Hysteria[1]

C.L. Schleich called hysteria a "metaphysical problem," and he is right; there is scarcely another disease that points so clearly to the metaphysical or supersensible side of the human being. The questions, "How does the soul affect the body?" and "How does the body affect the soul" seem to blend into one another before our eyes. We have scarcely noted a sign when we find it transformed or gone altogether. Hysteria has been called a "protean neurosis," which is a good characterization of its outer appearance, though it does not bring us closer to the essence of the disorder.

Rudolf Steiner wished to see the concept of hysteria in the context of the whole human being; more exactly, he saw it as a disturbed equilibrium of forces operating in the upper and lower organisms. The process of digestion can serve to help us understand this. In digestion, all chemical and organic forces in the food taken into the organism ought to be mastered by the "upper organization"—the forces of the nervous and rhythmic systems—"so that they are inactivated and have no effect inside the organism." Now it may happen that

> the upper organization is not equal to the task of taking the lower in hand, in order thoroughly to "cook" its contents—more exactly, I might say, "to etherize" it; in this case there is in the organism a predominant process that is foreign to it, a process such as occurs in the outer world but such as should not occur within the human organism. Because the physical body is not directly affected by it, such a process first makes its appearance on what we might simply call the "functional" level, in the etheric body, the *archaeus*.[2] If we will choose a useful expression, which is taken, one must say, from only certain forms of this irregularity, then we must choose the expression hysteria. We will choose hysteria as an expression for the metabolic processes becoming excessively independent. . . . For if such manifestations are associated with hysteria, this is a situation where extrahuman activity has become too strong in the lower parts of the human organization.[3]

We can trace the manifestations to the situation described in the supersensible members of man's being. Anesthesia is one of the commonest symptoms. Characteristically, it does not hold itself within boundaries defined by the nerves but appears to be defined quite arbitrarily: in the region of a finger, a glove, a cuff, with a circular or irregular outline. We need only to sketch such anesthetized areas on an anatomic drawing or over an anatomic drawing in a textbook, and it will be clear that such a sensory disturbance has nothing to do with nerve pathways.

The anesthesia can affect one half of the body, the left side being more commonly affected. Extensive investigations have shown that the left side of the body is less sensitive than the right in healthy individuals as well. The etheric body is not as clearly bound with the body on the left side as on the right. Consequently, the astral body also cannot connect so strongly with the physical body on the left side; the somewhat decreased sensitivity of the left side expresses this. We do not speak of hysteria until the astral body has withdrawn from the physical body so far that anesthesia and other symptoms appear. Childhood hysteria, according to Rudolf Steiner in his lectures on Curative Education, is of a different nature from that of adults. Since the members of the child's being are not yet consolidated, there can be a "flowing out of the astral body." This determines or affects many forms of behavior in children.

When Janet spoke of a "weakness of psychic synthesis," he was quite right in respect to the psychology of hysteria; he was pointing to the weakness of the ego. Hysteria is not just a psychological problem, however, but a psycho-physiological one, and the concept of the astral body provides for just this double relation.

Hysterical paralysis represents a heightening of the process that leads to anesthesia; the astral body, which governs movement, withdraws not only from the periphery (the skin), but also from the musculature beneath. For this reason, hysterical paralysis is generally also of a flaccid nature; the reflexes are unchanged and there is never a degenerative reaction, even if the paralysis leads to atrophy from inactivity.

A special form of flaccid paralysis is aphonia. In this, the vocal cords are relaxed when the patient intends to speak, although he has no difficulty in coughing or clearing his throat, both of which involve tension of the vocal cords. Here is more evidence that the symptoms do not conform to the course of the nerves, but are the expression of representations (mental pictures).

The same is true of astasia and abasia; the patient cannot

stand or walk, although he can perform all the necessary movements with his limbs while lying in bed. Once again we see the same phenomenon: the hysteric cannot realize, cannot "incarnate," certain representations, although the relevant nerves are completely intact. These last three manifestations have a special place in that standing, walking, and speaking are the most original activities of the ego in the organism. Consequently, disturbances of these functions indicate an extreme weakness of the ego's ability or will to hold inside the organism; we must remember that willing as such is below the level of ordinary consciousness. To this extent, we can call hysteria a disorder of the will.

The symptom of anorexia can be regarded as a further penetration of the anesthesia into the domain of the metabolism, or as a withdrawal of the astral body from this area. The appetite is within the domain of the sense of life; it is the expression of a healthy cooperation of the etheric and astral bodies. If the astral body withdraws from this region, food cannot be digested properly; it would act as a foreign body, bringing the danger of a metabolic disorder or intoxication. A common finding is extreme meteorism. Anorexia is usually connected with vomiting immediately after eating, characteristically without nausea. Given the inner situation described, this makes good sense; the healthy part of the organism is ridding itself of food that it would not be able to digest.

Further symptoms of the astral body's withdrawal from the metabolic region are stubborn obstipation, oliguria often lasting for days, and menstrual disorders with severe pains; here, the metabolic system is not sufficiently astralized or "aired through." Therefore, the astral body must work on the physical organ with the greatest intensity in order to bring about the process of menstruation, and its reactively intensified activity is experienced as pain. We see here the astral body switching from inactivity to a partially excessive activity. The name hysteria—*hystera* is the Greek word for womb—shows that originally there was a sense of the organic nature of the disease. Because of the exclusively psychological approach, the organ relation of this illness is no longer seen, especially since there is no "organic" trouble with the uterus. The trouble is that the forces underlying this organ are uncontrolled and thus come to the fore, giving the personality a one-sided cast. The situation is similar to that in the choleric; gall predominates in him regardless of whether the gall bladder as an organ is sick or not.

Besides the anesthesias, the most varied dysesthesias and paresthesias occur, such as numbness, disorders of heat or cold perception, burning, piercing, pricking, itching, formication, etc. The first of these stem from a failure or loosening of the astral body, but the burning, etc., clearly indicate astral activity. In them we can see contemporary or healing tendencies; the astral body is trying to take hold of the physical body, since it cannot penetrate it in the normal way.

We must generally keep in view that the life of the astral body is always manifested in polarities: inspiration and expiration, contraction and relaxation, sympathy and antipathy, waking and sleeping, etc. Thus in the above symptoms we can see how the astral body "flows out" and also how it may try, in reaction, to take hold of the physical body too strongly in other places. This can also be seen in the hysteric's oversensitivity and abnormal sensations, which can lead to neurologically detectible hyperesthesias of certain regions. The patient experiences this as a "soreness," as Rudolf Steiner called it, which usually affects only individual parts of the body, especially the head. Here the withdrawing astral body retains a loose connection with the physical body and imparts its experiences of the surroundings to it. This loose, "disorderly" connection of the astral and physical bodies produces the abnormal sensations that are like those arising from long, light touching, for example, from tickling a hair. The need arises to scratch, rub, press, etc., which is experienced as pleasant because it produces an increased awareness of this place and thus a stronger engagement of the astral body. These very conditions are found in hyperesthesia.

The physical body is taken hold of one-sidedly when a contracture gradually develops out of a flaccid paralysis. In tremor there is an alternation between relaxation and spasm. In contracture and tremor, more or less conscious representations ("pensioner's spasm") can play a causal role. Here the dynamic of hysteria touches that of neurasthenia.

The hysteric's strongest motor performance is the "grand mal seizure." To the observer this may be the most impressive symptom of the pathological condition, but it can, in fact, be seen as an energetic attempt at self-healing. This extreme tension of the musculature represents the astral body's taking hold of the whole motor apparatus, a complete contrast to the "flowing out of the astral body." The different forms of shock therapy have their natural model in the hysterical and epileptic seizure.

We need not stress the obvious and essential difference between the epileptic and the hysterical seizure. The epileptic collapses unconscious, often injuring himself seriously in the process; associated manifestations are tongue biting, foaming at the mouth, tonic and clonic movements, urinary and fecal incontinence, fixity of the pupils, passage into deep sleep, and the relatively short duration of the attack. The hysteric, in contrast, actually never injures himself; he seems to retain a bit of consciousness, which always gives the attacks a theatrical nuance. None of the epileptic manifestations described are present.

Another important difference is that hysteric seizures and symptoms can often be provoked by suggestion, while the epileptic is utterly inaccessible to suggestion; he is simply subject to the course of his illness.

The hysteric's suggestability shows a certain affinity of hysteria with hypnotic phenomena. Both hysteria and hypnosis are based on the same dynamic. In the latter, the astral and etheric bodies in the head region are released (Steiner also used the phrase, "snapped out") usually only on one side of the head, through the hypnotist's suggestion. Through this process the hypnotized individual loses consciousness, simultaneously coming into direct etheric-astral contact with the hypnotist through the released part of his supersensible members. The hypnotist then functions in place of his ego.

In the hysteric, the free part of his etheric body, the part not demanded in the process of metabolism, acts as a sort of "resonance organ" for all soul activities around him. This is the reason for the extraordinary variety, changeableness, and rapid succession of signs and symptoms. It also explains the hysteric's capacity for fantastic embellishment of his experiences, even for vivid and credible confabulations, and it accounts for his moodiness and unpredictability.

This enhanced faculty of resonance also brings with it a greater susceptibility to psychological traumas (fright, grief, etc.) as well as to the hysteric's own desires and representations. His ego is carried off by the intensified wishes; it is too weak to bear the real world or become part of it, so it finds solace in a world of illusory substitutes.

Hysteria most often breaks out after puberty, that is, when the relation between the astral and etheric bodies is not yet consolidated. Excessive etheric forces may still be present, and the astral body does not yet engage strongly enough; furthermore, the ego does not become free until the twenty-first year. As the ego becomes freer, it struggles more and more against the unrest and disorder coming from the astral body; in one's twenties ít is actually forced by the demands of outer life to do this (occupational independence).

In the cases where recovery begins at about this time, we speak of "developmental hysteria," in contrast to "degenerative hysteria." In the latter, we observe a progressive tendency to form new pathological symptoms and there is a decreasing will to recover.

On the Treatment of Hysteria

In view of the fact that the psychic manifestations of hysteria are only one side of the whole phenomenon—we must also find the associated physical symptoms—it is necessary to proceed differently in each case in accordance with the physical manifestations, despite the uniform genesis of the disorder.

The first thing to investigate is whether, and how, the patient manages the process of digestion. If there is obstipation, it will usually be atonic, stemming from insufficient engagement of the astral body. Besides the appropriate medications (for example, Artemisia comp. dil.) and massage of the abdomen and shins with Ungt. Cupri praep. 0.1 per cent, curative eurythmy is indicated. When there are difficulties in the protein metabolism, or when the ego must be engaged more strongly in the metabolism, injections of Ferrum sidereum D10/Pancreas D10 aa will bring results. In metabolic irregularities (for example, alternation of obstipation and diarrhea, excessive dependence of digestive processes on soul activities and vice versa), Stibium praep. D6 trit. can have a regularizing action.

Bryophyllum (kalanchoe), belonging to the Crassulaceae, was recommended by Rudolf Steiner as a virtual specific for hysteria (inj.: D5, D3; per os: 5 per cent). Bryophyllum has such a strong vitality that a new little plant springs from each notch in a leaf. Subcutaneous injections (preferably in the thigh) draw the astral body to the site in order to overcome the foreign etheric process. This forces a rather intense engagement of the astral body, which the organism cannot bring about of itself. Since bryophyllum also brings about a better connection of the etheric body in the metabolic region, especially in the genital area—the sphere of the influence of silver—bryophyllum or Argentum par Bryophyllum can also be used as soporifics.

Menstrual weakness is an expression of the insufficient astralization. One effective medication for this is Teucrium scorod. D3–D6, which "gives form to the organs of the lower body," according to Rudolf Steiner; others will be mentioned in the chapter on gynecology (Vol. III). Excessive bleeding, however, provided that there is no organic disorder, may indicate a lack of involvement of the ego organization; Marmor-Stibium injections D6 aa or Tormentilla D3-6 are required here. If the formative forces withdraw too much from the uterus and push upward, then the patient senses this upward pressure; this is manifested most strikingly in globus hystericus, but also in other sensations. In these cases, Asa foetida D2-4 is indicated.

In cases of pronounced weakness of the nerve-sense system (dizziness in standing up and walking, great susceptibility to fatigue, hypersensitivity of the sense organs), Quartz D10-15 trit. and Arnica D10 are good choices. If there is a dependence of the symptoms on the phases of the moon, then during the waxing phase, we may give Argentum praep. D6 trit., and during the waning phase, Phospher D10 dil.

Arsenic may also be indicated. Rudolf Steiner described the

action of arsenic thus: "If it is noticed that the organs as such become too vital, that they develop too strong life forces in themselves and become etheric in a way, then the remedy that can have a healing action is the administration of arsenic.[4] Particularly the natural compound of arsenic with iron, scorodite in D6, is indicated.

The purpose of the medicinal therapy outlined here is to affect the bodily disposition to hysterical reactions, that is, to bind the excessive etheric force of the lower organism by setting a strong activity of the astral body and ego organization against it. A purely psychotherapeutic treatment of hysteria may well bring transient success, but there is the danger that the manifestations will simply change into others if the excess of etheric forces is allowed to remain. This danger also exists, however, with the therapy proposed here; trusting too much in the patient's reports of the efficacy of the medication, the doctor may change the therapy too soon. Then it becomes the patient who is really directing the therapy. A certain consistency is required in the application of remedies for these affections, as is the patience to allow the remedies to take effect.

These patients often need strict direction at first. It is important to get their cooperation and to give them various assignments—artistic, mathematical, scientific, or philosophical—anything to widen their sphere of interest and to free them from their egocentric merry-go-round. With young people, we must be sure to determine whether they have found an occupation that is right for them; if they have come to a dead-end here, or are "running idle," this can be a source of their trouble. Therefore it is often necessary to give conscientious occupational counseling to set these young people on the right path, for the hysteric has not yet found the direction of his ego.

Neurasthenia[5]

This is another "total" disorder, one diametrically opposed to hysteria. What was said above of hysteria is true also of neurasthenia: it is disappearing as a working diagnosis from medical diagnostics because its manifestations are no longer recognized as forming a whole. Rudolf Steiner sees its essence in the fact that the "upper process," that is, the action of the ego and astral body from the nerve-sense system,

> proceeds in such a way that it makes too great demands on the upper organization. . . . It comes to an end, as it were, before it is mediated through the heart to the lower organization. It is thus too spiritual, too—if I may use the expression—organic-intellectual. So the other pole of these irregularities appears: neurasthenia. . . . We have in neurasthenia a functioning in the upper organization that taxes the upper organs too much, so that what really should take place—mediated through the heart —in the lower organization, occurs in the upper organization and runs its course there. Hence, the activity cannot penetrate downward, mediated through the damming in the heart, into the lower current.[6]

Rudolf Steiner considered it much more important to attend to this "outer physiogonomy of the disease picture" than to study the pathological change of the organs at autopsy, because these are really only the physical result of pathological processes. If we strive to focus on this "physiognomy" of the disease, we find that all diseases incline either toward the hysterical or the neurasthenic. Of course, the use of these concepts will have to be extended in such an approach. As we have said, Rudolf Steiner saw neurasthenia as the polar opposite of hysteria; the ego and astral body engage too strongly and become stuck in the nerve-sense system. This clinging of the astral body is expressed in the sleep disturbances so common in neurasthenia, as seen in difficulty in falling asleep, insufficient depth of sleep, and awakening too early. Difficulty in falling asleep can also occur in a healthy person if he works late into the night, for example, or drinks coffee to stay awake. Then the peculiar condition arises of a cramping of the astral body in the head, often accompanied by headache or a feeling of hotness of the head with sweating, usually only of the head and chest. In present-day terminology this is called sympathicotonia; this provides no explanation, however, for the localization of the symptoms.

If such nightly over-exertion of the head becomes a habit,

then the astral body will not withdraw sufficiently even when sleep finally comes. The patient's sleep never becomes deep enough, and the next day he feels "beat," not even as fresh as the night before. This is related to the fact that falling asleep is impeded by sudden, convulsive starts: the astral body is beginning to withdraw, but thoughts and feelings pull it back into day consciousness, that is, into connection with the nerve-sense system. In these cases, soul and spiritual conflicts, as well as organic diseases and all the intermediate problems between them, can actually play a role.

In the daytime as well, this too-strong connection of the astral body to the nerve-sense system persists and the sense organs become oversensitive. Particularly in the area of the eyes, muscular cramps and pains can occur when focusing on close objects. Patients may also complain of "awful" pains, reminiscent of trigeminal neuralgia, rheumatism, or even tabes. This heightened susceptibility to pain is an expression of the excessive astral activity through the nerve-sense system, which can lead to cramping and to the familiar vicious circle of pain—cramp—pain, etc. This also explains the heightened reflexes as well as the frequent tremor of the fingers and tongue. Often the back is given as the center of the pains (spinal troubles, cramping, poor posture, etc.); this is natural when we know the spinal cord to be the carrier of the astral currents flowing from the head.

The same situation arises on another plane when the cramping tendency of the astral body penetrates to the vascular system. Understandably, the blood pressure is usually elevated. This tendency can also affect the heart so strongly that the patient experiences precordial pain and pseudangina pectoris (cor nervosum) or strong palpitations of the heart. At this stage, these are "only functional" conditions, but they may rightly be regarded as precursors of true angina pectoris or overloading of the heart, since this initially transitory cramping and taxing of the cardiac vessels is complicated by the generally sclerotic tendency of neurasthenia (see below).

If the cramping reaches into the region of the metabolic system, then there will be episodes of sweating, nervous stomach, hyperacidity (the relation of the astral body to acid formation has been mentioned), and colitis in various forms, especially ulcerative colitis. There will also be manifestations in the renal system, specifically, a predominance of the catabolic tendencies and an insufficient transformation into the anabolic function (see chapter on the kidney, Vol. III). This can lead to spastic urination and production of urine with a low specific gravity.

Finally, if the astral body becomes so cramped in the physical body that it cannot fulfill its function of connecting the organism with the outer world, the patient becomes completely dependent on his physicality, and in this physical bondage he loses his spiritual freedom. It is characteristic of this state that the patient has a sense of heaviness ("like a weight on my head" or "my legs sink into the earth"), or he complains of dizziness, by which he means not real vertigo, but the insecure feeling of being unable to fit his body into space. This state of physical bondage also provides ground for the development of the various phobias. There is no question but that the contemporary scientific picture of the world favors the development of phobias, compulsive thoughts, and states of anxiety, because it sees man only as part of a meaningless nature governed by mechanical and chemical laws. It is also no wonder that a person who has become so strongly bound to his body tires more easily than a healthy person ("nervous exhaustion"), that he cannot make a decision when necessary, and that he cannot carry through with a decision he has made because he lacks the energy. He suffers from weakness of the will, really a paralysis of the will, since he has largely lost all healthy relations to the outer world and to his own metabolic system, the carrier of the will.

From a psychological point of view, the neurasthenic tends toward introversion, the hysteric to extraversion. In developmental terms, hysteria is based on unduly prolonged youth and neurasthenia on premature aging. This points to the predominant disease tendency in each: in the hysteric it is more to the inflammatory diseases, while in the neurasthenic, it is to sclerotic processes (see preceding chapter). Finally, it should also be mentioned that the female organism is more likely to display a hysterical constitution, while the male is more prone to neurasthenic traits, as well as to an asthenic constitution. This should not be taken as a rigid schema, however, though its essential accuracy becomes obvious to anyone who has studied the matter in detail.

From what has been described we can see that the various manifestations of neurasthenia stem from the fixation of the astral body in the head system, that is, sleep differences, various pains, heart trouble, tendency to compulsive thoughts, and weakness of will. Both the common terminology (cor nervosum, nervous stomach, nervous exhaustion) and the known connections (neuropathic genesis of ulcerative colitis) point to the nervous system; a further step, however, is required for recognizing its essence and arriving at a genuine therapy. It may be said that the name "neurasthenia" is perfectly suited if we think of it not only as weakness of the nervous system, but as weakness because of the nervous system. This also explains why we can see neurasthenic symptoms as functional forerunners of organic nervous diseases.

The life of the neurasthenic is centered one-sidedly in his nervous system. It dominates the rhythmic and metabolic systems, drowning them with its own tendencies. The layman sums up the situation quite rightly with the expression, "nervousness." It is clear how our present civilization with its early and constant overstimulation of the senses, and its overloading of the head through emphasis on memory and intellectual thinking, displaces the human constitution broadly in the neurasthenic direction. This influence is further enhanced by the parallel neglect of the metabolic and rhythmic systems, that is, the lack of training of the will and emotional life. So we see that neurasthenia is a typical result of modern civilization. Rudolf Steiner referred to this danger at an early date. He warned that if humanity continues to acknowledge only the physical and material and does not find the connection to the spiritual world, then there would result a voluminous rise in cases of nervousness, neurasthenia, and abnormal fear of diseases. These phenomena are all to be observed today, though the deeper causal connections are not seen.

Modern life, with its overevaluation of intellectual thinking and its neglect of feeling and willing—especially in education—forms man's physical constitution in a pathologically one-sided way. This raises once again the deep connection of education and healing described in the chapter on the school physician. All education should be healing, just as all healing must ultimately be educational.

As for the individual neurasthenic patient, we now understand his preoccupation with his condition; he interprets his symptoms in a hypochondriacal manner and attributes too much significance to them. As one or another symptom predominates, he is afraid he has now this disease, now another. We can see why he is more inclined than other patients to change doctors.

On the Treatment of Neurasthenia

In view of the situation described, the physician's main task will be to convince the patient that he is not suffering from serious organic illnesses but that his troubles are of a "functional" nature. He must be careful, however, not to belittle them or tell the patient that he is "really healthy" and "just nervous." With this scientifically "correct" diagnosis, the patient rightly feels misunderstood, becomes even more introverted—in reality, more ill—and is ultimately made into a psychopath.

Nowadays, it is common practice to cover up the manifestations of neurasthenia with suppressive measures, primarily tranquilizers. There is a danger in this simple and effective treatment! The patient is no longer aware of the pressure, tensions, troubles, etc., and feels relieved. Only later does he notice that the effect is purely symptomatic, that his troubles set in again with all the greater intensity after he discontinues the medication. In this way, he becomes drug dependent. The pathological dynamic, the too-intense and uncontrolled action of the astral body, however, remains present and ultimately leads to further imbalance of soul, bringing even more difficult problems for the personality. The constantly growing number of people who are seriously ill but without any pathological clinical findings belongs largely to the neurasthenic group. This fact, as well as the great consumption of tranquilizers, is evidence for our description and speaks of the need for a causal therapy.

It must be made clear to the neurasthenic that he should try to avoid too much strain and exertion, should bring more variety into his activity, and must change the structure of his life. Any kind of artistic activity is an especially good compensation for the one-sidedness we have described. Curative eurythmy can be put to rewarding use here; the vowels are of especial therapeutic value. Physical activity also forms a good counterbalance, so long as it is not too strenuous or frantic, as sports often are today.

In addition, we must try to strengthen the head system, which has been weakened etherically either from overexertion or because of the constitution. In milder cases, this can be accomplished with Prunus spinosa D4 or D5 dil. or as injection; for a deeper effect we can use Argentum nitricum D12–D4 dil., 2–3 × daily 5 drops, or D20 as injection twice weekly. Injections of the patient's own blood (2 ml) stimulate and strengthen the astral body, especially in conjunction with Argentum praep. D6–D10.

We can approach the disease from a different angle by following the inward penetration of the astral body to the kidney system. As will be described in the chapter on the kidney (Vol. III), the renal system has the function of transforming the astral impulses coming through the nervous system, which have a catabolic action, and giving them an anabolic direction. In the neurasthenic constitution the catabolic impulses are dominant, as the tendency to cramps shows. We can attack this situation with copper, which is associated with the kidneys (Cuprum sulfuricum D6 dil.; copper sulfate baths; later, Cuprum praep., perhaps olivenite, the natural basic copper arsenate). Carbo (D8–D20) stimulates the renal system in its anabolic aspect in which the impaired functioning may be expressed in deficient "airing through" of the organism (hypoxia and resultant conditions). This treatment is directed especially at the circulatory symptoms (Carbo betulae D20 inj.). As in other organs, the disorders of the renal system mentioned here are, apart from frequent spastic urination, without organic findings. With functional involvement of the heart and circulation in the disease process, Cardiodoron (perhaps Cardiodoron/ Plumbum inj., especially for sleep disturbance) is indicated.

Since in many cases we are dealing with a dominance of the astral body in relation to the ego, the latter must be strengthened by the use of phosphorus and its salts. Kalium phosphoricum D6 dil. has an empirically determined (homeopathically) healing relation to neurasthenic troubles. We can understand this reaction when we remember that the domain of potassium is the watery-etheric element. The ego takes the phosphorus of Kalium phosphoricum, and the potassium then strengthens the watery-etheric element. In this way, both of them help, through the ego and etheric body, to release the neurasthenic's severely cramped astral body. An extension of this medication is Kalium phosphoricum comp., in which the Kalium phosphoricum effect is complemented with Kephalodoron, which addresses the threefold arrangement of the human being and brings about a vitalization of the nervous system. Aurum helps these patients to find their center. This combination has repeatedly proved itself in treating mental overexertion, for example, from academic examinations. Acidum phosphoricum D3 dil. acts as a general tonic in states of exhaustion; likewise, Levico baths (see p. 85).

Independently of this basic treatment, special problems or organs can naturally be treated directly (for spine, heart/circulation, and sleep disturbances see relevant chapters). Nevertheless, the basic therapy outlined here, which treats the disease at its cause, is more promising and more significant in the long run.

Chapter IX
Fundamentals of a Biochemistry and a Pathophysiology

Substance and Function

If we take the action of the soul and spirit in the body as a reality, then we must also recognize that there are organs and substances that have specific capacities for receiving these impulses. This is, in fact, just what is expressed in the original meaning of the word "substance"; it "stands under" (*substare*) a supersensible influence; it is a vessel for what was called an "imponderable." The transformations of substances therefore give recognizable indications of the higher members of the human being. Patho-anatomical findings alone show only what has already become, that is, more or less final states. Physiological and biochemical investigations come closer to life, but with them we are always dealing with various interacting and overlapping processes. Nevertheless, it is in this dynamic of the most varied processes and functions that the human being lives. "The essence of the organism lies in activity, not in its substances. The organization is not an association of substances, but an activity. The material bears the impulse to activity in itself."[1]

In the metabolism, opposite processes continuously confront one another (for example, deposition—dissolution, contraction—expansion, anabolism—catabolism, inflammation—sclerosis, absorption—secretion, oxidation—reduction, etc.), so that in the physiological domain none of them occurs in pure form. Rather, there is a continual variation around an equilibrium that must be actively maintained by the ego. In this way, a rhythm develops that forms the foundation for a healthy organic activity. To be sure, one side can predominate for a time, but then there must be a compensation by means of the opposite process.

The perpetual, rhythmic beating of the heart is the primordial picture of the alternating interaction of polar processes. The tireless activity of the heart is possible only through the enduring, measured alternation of systole and diastole, contraction and dilation, work and rest. The predominance of one side leads to functional disturbance and disease.

The equilibrium of metabolic processes can be altered by both inner and outer causes. An inner cause may be a disturbance in the members of man's being. An outer cause may be a physical influence, such as cold, heat, wetness, etc.

Nutrition

> *One who understands nutrition correctly understands the beginning of healing.*
>
> Rudolf Steiner

Apart from air, food is the terrestrial substance with which the human being has the closest contact and which he must confront on the most intimate terms. He is also in a position to alter it more than any other substance. For these reasons, man's relation to food is instructive in regard to his relation to the earth in general.

With his heterotrophic mode of existence, the human being must nourish himself on the bodily substance of living creatures. Only the plant is capable of consuming exclusively inorganic materials in an autotrophic mode of existence. It can take in light and combine it with terrestrial materials in such a way that living substance arises. This substance contains the etheric formative forces that originate in the life processes and that are the mark of all real foodstuffs.

If we do not realize this, and if we see the essence of food in its material components, then we are giving the vessel more importance than the content and are missing what is most essential. Calorie consumption tells of the "caloric value" of a food, but not of its formative forces. In evaluating the calorie content of a food, we must remember that this speaks only of quantity and not of quality. This becomes quite obvious when we consider that coal or benzene has a high calorie content but cannot be used as food precisely because of its qualitative nature. The quality of a food rests on its content of formative forces. Since these come from living organisms, for example, the plants, they form a whole. These have specific forms dictated by the species, that is, the etheric bodies of the different plant species.

When a human being eats a food, he reverses the formation of these substances. In a differentiated process of catabolism, the proteins, fats, and carbohydrates are broken down in their outer and inner structures. This begins with the mechanical disintegration in the mouth and continues with the action of the digestive enzymes. This is illustrated in detail in the following sections.

Since each plant is constructed according to its own etheric body, etheric effects of a specific kind are connected with plant food. These cannot be transferred directly into the human etheric body since the latter does not correspond to that of the plant. The food, therefore, must first be divested of the residual foreign etheric processes. This occurs through the catabolic processes in digestion. In this way, the formative forces, which initially formed the food from inorganic substance, are released from it, becoming free again (see section on light metabolism). Only when they are not in bound form can they have a stimulating effect on the human etheric body.

In animal foods there are also astral processes. This foreign astrality must likewise be overcome by the human organism in the catabolic processes of digestion.

In sum, we can say that the purpose of this breakdown of food is not only the facilitation of absorption; the latter, after all, is not at all disturbed when protein breakdown is insufficient, which is what permits allergic reactions. Rather, the whole food must be broken down, because otherwise its own astral and etheric qualities would be absorbed with it, preventing the formation of specifically human, quite individual, bodily substances.

It is most important to understand that the essential element of a foodstuff is its formative forces and that these must never come into combination with the bodily substance but must be released. Only such freed etheric forces can stimulate the human etheric body to new formation and anabolism. This requirement of catabolism as a precondition for anabolism is an essential characteristic of the heterotrophic mode of existence of man and animal.

The breakdown of food in the gastrointestinal canal is species specific, and beyond this it shows great individual differences. The same food will be altered quite differently in the organisms of a pig or dog, or in a human being. Accordingly, not only the excreted products but also the substances that ultimately become absorbed are species-specific and individually varied.

Moreover, the human being can alter food much more extensively than an animal. A much greater amount of the foreign quality inherent in natural substances passes into the animal's body than could be tolerated in the human organism. A striking sign of this is found in the fact that the flesh and fat of animals fed on a particular food, for example, on fish, take on the odor, consistency, and chemical properties of that food. In the human metabolism this does not occur nearly to the same extent as in the animal.

Since digestion is a process of catabolism, primarily the astral body must be active in this region, for catabolic processes are characteristic of a type of metabolism that is proper only to animate (ensouled) beings. The astral body brings about this breakdown of food with the help of certain enzymes that conform to the particular food in each case. The food is subjected to the laws of the organism into which it comes and is removed from outer laws.

This becomes clear when we contrast the transformations a food undergoes in the external environment with those it undergoes in the gastrointestinal tract. In the first case, microorganisms cause putrefaction of the protein, a sugar solution begins to ferment, and fats become rancid. These alterations in protein, carbohydrates, and fats do not appear in healthy digestion. The higher members of the human organism must

work continuously to prevent the inherent tendency of substances to decompose in this way.

In contrast to these types of catabolism, the healthy catabolism
of the gastrointestinal tract consists of the fermentative hydrol-
ysis of proteins, the breaking down of carbohydrates into di-
and monosaccharides, and the breaking down of fats into fatty
acids and glycerins. Thus in the metamorphosis of food there
is a limitation of foreign life, so that it cannot penetrate into
the organism, and the type of catabolism inside the human
body is of a fundamentally different nature from that outside
it. While chemical and physical processes in nature can be
grasped through laws of chemistry and physics, all transformations within the organism proceed in the organism's own
appropriate way. Rudolf Steiner spoke of an "anti-chemistry"
and an "anti-physics" that appear within the organism and
must continuously control the chemical and physical processes
during life.[2] The guidance of these transformations in the
organism is accomplished by enzymes that are formed in the
glands and that originate in the activity of the higher members
of man's being. The enzymes are the vehicle of these members
in the metabolism.

In the mouth, a coarse, mechanical breaking down of the
food takes place and this in itself is already an indication of the
way that man deals with food. Inadequate activity here is
enough to lay the foundation for a great variety of gastrointestinal disorders, especially in old age.

The strong acid formation in the stomach points to the
engagement of the astral body there. The alkaline reaction, the
sterility, and the maximal absorption in the small intestine correspond to a strong activity of the etheric body. The last step in
the path of digestion occurs when food remnants are dis-
charged from the metabolism and enter an almost lifeless, mineral realm. This is in the large intestine, where chiefly the ego
organization is active; nevertheless, the processes of the outer
world increasingly gain the upper hand here. Of course, the individual areas cannot be exactly separated; there are smooth
transitions.

The infant's digestive system is not yet so differentiated. It is

well known how sensitively he reacts to food; he still does not
have the strength to deal with earthly substances, so nature
provides a nutrient substance, milk, which demands no forces
of its own from the infant and thus makes the incarnation process possible.[3] Only gradually does the infant learn to overcome
the foreign nature of other foods and to develop his own
forces. Full development is not reached until puberty, when
the astral body is freed from its activity of forming the organs
and when these have reached the point of complete functioning.

When the formation of the organs is completed, the human
being is in a position to face the earth fully. The human being's
position in relation to the earth is also expressed in his relation
to food, the terrestrial substance with which he has the most
intimate contact. The more strongly he is incarnated, the more
intensively he will overcome the forces in food and put them to
use for himself; man's way of dealing with food is really just a
partial expression of his relation to the earth in general. In infants and old people, therefore, the ability to digest is not yet,
or is no longer, so strong as in youth, in accordance with the
degree of incarnation at these times of life.

The Gastrointestinal Tract

There is a growing recognition today that the quality of digestion can be an indication of underlying diseases. Bacteriologi-
cal research has provided abundant experimental evidence of
the great importance of the natural intestinal flora as a good
index of the state of the digestive system. We must not, however, be led to the idea that these bring about health. In fact, a
particular species of bacteria is able to take its place in the
functional context only when the intestinal medium is suited
to it, and this will be true only when food is correctly managed
by the organism. This will result in an optimal nutrient medium
for an adequate intestinal flora (E. coli or Lactobacillus bifidus).
If the human being cannot master food properly, the catabolic
process will in part take other, inadequate, hence pathological,
paths. Their metabolic products then form the basis for unphy-

siological microbes, and a condition of abnormal bacterial flora develops.

If, through a weakness of the higher members of man's being, one cannot sustain the physiological type of catabolism, the food reaches the lower intestine in an insufficiently transformed state and succumbs to its own tendencies. It then forms a favorable medium for certain bacteria so that an infection can come about. For their part, these bacteria are foreign bodies within the organism and cause toxic damage partially through their own metabolic products and partially through the way in which they alter the intestinal products. Both are foreign processes. In this case, we thus see that elements of the outer world remain insufficiently overcome in the lower intestine. Inasmuch as every foreign body lodged anywhere in the organism under unsterile conditions will evoke an inflammation, the organism reacts to the food remnants (and bacteria), which have remained foreign due to faulty catabolism, with an inflammation of the intestinal mucosa. We are presented with the picture of enteritis, or gastrointestinal catarrh, in its various forms. Under healthy circumstances, food is broken down and denatured in the small intestine to such an extent that the intestinal contents are almost sterile. Foreign (outer world) contents are normally found only as far as the stomach and then again in the colon.

We can distinguish the different effects of this weakness in utilization according to the kind of nutrient that is affected. If the breakdown of protein is insufficiently controlled, a putrefactive dyspepsia develops; if the disorder lies in the insufficient breakdown of carbohydrates, we see a fermentive dyspepsia; defective fat utilization will result in steatorrhea. In the adult, these disorders cannot always be separated from one another. It is also known, for example, that fermentive dyspepsia can change into a putrefactive dyspepsia. In any case, the underlying factor is a weakness in the breakdown of food; its true cause is endogenous and it expresses itself more in the carbohydrate metabolism in one instance, and in the protein or fat metabolism in another. Let it be said in advance that it is the etheric body that continuously fights against putrefaction, the astral body that prevents the decomposition of fats leading to rancidness or steatorrhea, and the ego organization that suppresses fermentation of the carbohydrates, leading to fermentive dyspepsia.

Fermentation and putrefaction in the gut lead to bloating. There is, however, no direct correlation. The cause of this disorder is to be sought in the air organism, which is controlled by the astral body. The engagement and dynamic of the astral body, however, varies greatly in different locations. In the gastrointestinal tract it brings about the breakdown of food by acting through particular glands on the chemistry of the metabolism. In contrast, it is freer in the upper organism. The faulty "airing through" of the organism is manifested most clearly in the respiratory system. Thus, bloating represents a displaced dynamic of the air organism. The activity of the astral body, which is healthy in the upper organism, has a pathological effect in the lower organism and vice versa. In this way the lower organism suffers from a partial lack of catabolic forces, so that the food does not undergo the necessary alteration. Instead, there is a tendency to gas formation and the conditions are favorable for proliferation of gas-forming bacteria. Since the "switching" of the mode of astral activity appropriate to the upper organism into that appropriate to the lower is a function of the renal system, the symptom of flatulence indicates a disturbed kidney radiation (see chapter on the kidney, Vol. III). Medicinally, the air organism is reached through the kidney system by means of Carbo, which is indicated here.

In a certain way we have the opposite of dyspepsia in chronic obstipation. Naturally, this is influenced by diet, bodily movement, etc.; the basic cause, however, is that the intestinal content is too strongly formed, or overstructured. The spastic component of obstipation clearly shows an excessive involvement of the astral body, which is working too strongly in the contracting dynamic acting from above. Chronic obstipation is a clear expression on the part of the astral body, which acts more in the nervous system, of the total constitution of the higher members of man's being. This leads to a rather introverted attitude and to a certain anxiety and shyness. As always, the animal kingdom offers us examples of these qualities in their most extreme, pronounced form. In certain animals, such as the rabbit, deer, goat, etc., we find this overformation of the intestinal content pushed to the extreme. They have a physiological obstipation. These animals are all very marked nerve-sense animals, and they show corresponding traits of psyche, such as excitability, fearfulness, etc. In contrast, the typical metabolic animals, such as cattle, show a physiological diarrhea, which is just as much an expression of their whole nature as is their sensory obtuseness.

Parasitic infection can also be understood in this light. It is known that children are particularly susceptible to parasites. The concept of infection, however, is not sufficient to explain this fact; after all, no human being can really escape the possibility of infection. Certain individuals are simply more susceptible than others. In the healthy organism, the astral body is so strong that no foreign astrality can survive within its domain. This is most obvious in pinworm infestation; these worms are much more sensitive than ascaria. Tape worms, on the other hand, are so resistant that almost everyone is susceptible to infestation by them; this is not true of pinworms. Thus pinworm infestation gives us an indication that the affected individual is insufficiently incarnated. In children this is normal; the astral body is still active in organ formation and not so intensely active in catabolism, so that children easily succumb to infestations of the intestinal canal.

Besides the effects of insufficient processing of food, a too-intensive processing can also lead to a great variety of illnesses. We can mention the excessive utilization of food in the various forms of obesity. In adiposity, the readiness to assimilate food is more important than the amount of food taken in. This is especially true in the human being. For instance, it is relatively easy to fatten animals, though this also depends on the species; in the human being, however, who is not often constitutionally inclined toward it, a large weight gain is difficult or impossible to force. The connections between psychological disposition and appetite have been known since ancient times. The expression "to lose one's appetite" (after a soul experience) illustrates this. The syndrome of anorexia mentalis also shows the critical importance of man's relation to food as an earth and life substance. We see from this that "the human organism unfolds, through all its parts, activities that have their impulses in it alone."[4] Outer influences, in this case food, do not have such a compulsive, determining influence on man as on the animal. For this reason, limitation of food intake for obesity, or a fattening diet for cachectic patients, will only deal with one side of the problem. Of much greater importance is the human being's way of dealing with food.

A typical disease process of the gastrointestinal tract is ulcer formation. To be sure, ulcers can appear almost anywhere, but this "endogenous" occurrence is so typical of the stomach that we speak of peptic ulcer disease. We cannot go into the various theories about ulcers at this point, but it is obvious that peptic, inflammatory, central nervous, vasospastic, and psychic components all play a role. We may well ask what stands behind these separate components and why it is the stomach that is most often affected by ulcer formation.

In both phylogeny and ontogeny there is a typical formative gesture expressing an internalization: gastrulation. In the lower animals, this corresponds to the primitive cavitation in the coelenterates. This formation of inner space provides the basis for internalization of a soul element. Cavity formation, invagination, is a typical astral gesture.

So we see that the stomach is a receiving organ not only for food, but also for the astral body and its action. We have referred many times to acidification as a typical expression of the astral body, and also to the catabolic action of the astral body in the stomach.

This physiological process can, however, become too strong. As a result of an agitation of the soul, which is not overcome, the astral body can engage so intensively and excessively in catabolic processes that the gastric and intestinal walls can be affected. This excessive activity suppresses the sustaining activity of the etheric body, which protects the stomach from auto-digestion; the result is over-acidification, vasospasm, and resultant conditions.

Furthermore, ulcer disease can be seen as a textbook example of how a soul experience or problem that is not possessed and mastered by the ego moves one step lower into the organism, and how the individual must now deal with it on this level. The organ affected is that one which has the same function in the physical body as the one that is disturbed on the soul level. The solution and mastery of a conflict with the outer world is, in fact, a process of digestion.

Therapy can approach the process from different sides. The forming force of stibium has an internally structuring effect on protein, that is, on the etheric body. In this case, it helps to prevent the "sliding down" of soul processes to the organic level. We are thinking primarily of Stibum praep. D6, Antimonite D3–D6, and Kalium aceticum cum Stibio. Copper takes in and transforms astral impulses, giving them an anabolic direction. For an inner effect, the carbonate compounds are indicated, in this case, malachite, natural copper carbonate. The combination chamomilla/malachite comp. is especially well-proven. Finally, we must guide the patient, so that he learns to gain control of the situation of conflict with his own ego.

In conclusion, let us give therapeutic indications for the disease processes discussed above. The astral body can be stimulated to a stronger catabolic action in the gastrointestinal tract by means of arsenic. It induces the astral body to engage itself in the metabolism. "Arsenicization" was equated with "astralization" by Rudolf Steiner. Low potencies are indicated since we are aiming at metabolic effects.

If we are dealing more with a weakness of the ego organization, as is expressed in a fermentative dyspepsia or in a weakness of protein metabolism, then iron is used. Iron gives the initially destructive, catabolic impulse that precedes anabolism; this succession is characteristic of the whole digestive process. Specifically, we make use of siderite (natural iron carbonate) or meteoric iron (cosmic iron), which has a broader effect. Since these cases usually involve the pancreas, in which the ego organization manifests by the production of corresponding enzymes, we can guide the action of meteoric iron to this gland by the use of pancreas (10 per cent to D6); a well-proven combination is ferrum sidereum D10/pancreas D6 aa as injection. This administration of organ preparations does not represent a substitution therapy, which would be impossible with the small amounts with which we are dealing, but an appeal to the etheric body in this region, an attempt to "interest" it in the particular organ.

The stimulating effect of bitter herbs on the digestion, and the contrasting effect of the intensely bitter taste, strengthen the organism's interest in the food. Bitters contract and internalize; they deepen the engagement of the higher members of man's being in the body; one expression of this is the stimulation of secretions.

When we consider the plants that have long been used for digestive disorders, we find that roots are almost always used because they contain the substances and processes needed (gentian, chicory, ipecac, avens, etc.). Recognition of the three-fold constitution of man and plant provides us with an actual rationale for understanding the application and mode of action of these plants; the root corresponds to the nervous system and is used when we wish to have an effect there (see p. 319f.). Since the formative forces coming from the nervous system are insufficient in digestive weakness, these can be specifically strengthened by the use of roots, especially bitter ones. Their use thus represents a "causal" therapy. If, on the other hand, there are sulfuric, dissolving, and enlivening processes or substances in the roots, the corresponding effect will not be formative but stimulating, tending to promote and enliven metabolism. This may even lead to a weak suppression of consciousness. In contrast, bitter substances occurring in the foliage (wormwood, abrotanum, teucrium, for example) are effective primarily beyond the intestinal wall. For this reason, wormwood and abrotanum will influence the finer, intermediate metabolism in the liver region, while teucrium releases its action only in the pulmonary area.

Dietary Considerations

The effects and consequences of unbalanced or faulty nutrition are usually not evident for hours or weeks; therefore, it is easy to underestimate them. Precisely because the influence of food on the organism is not instantaneous or superficial, however, the positive and negative effects that are eventually observed can be of profound importance. We have seen above that the value of a foodstuff depends on its content of etheric formative forces, which stimulate the human etheric body. Since the etheric body is the vehicle of all growth processes but is also the time body, influences from food also have a structuring effect on it in the course of time. These influences are strongest during the age of growth. Years of unbalanced or inferior nourishment, though it may appear quite complete in terms of calories or the individual vitamins, may have delayed effects that are seen only decades later, or even in following generations. This has been confirmed by experimental findings, and in the light of our discussions it is easy to grasp.

The increase of degenerative and hardening diseases is largely due to faulty nutrition; this notion has been expressed repeatedly and from many sides. It is also plainly evident if we see in food not just the material building blocks to be incorporated in a body but, above all, the formative forces in their real workings (see above).

On the basis of this realization, the formative forces of foodstuffs must be spared as much as possible during preparation. The essential being of a plant, an animal, or a human being incarnates during the process of growth. If this process is interrupted, the living substance gradually succumbs to the death forces of the physical world and rotting or fermentation sets in. This dwindling of life will naturally be most dramatic in those parts of the plant where the metabolism is most lively, namely the leaves. It is not possible to arrest the process of life as such, to stabilize or conserve it; nature, however, teaches us how to deal with the formative forces.

In the roots, the metabolic processes are much more subdued than in the leaves. Although the root corresponds to the nervous system of the human being, it is nevertheless quite vital, in accordance with the essential nature of plants. These life processes are not manifest in the roots; rather, they are present here in a highly structured, "compressed" form. This is why it is possible to store this part of the plant for months without preservative treatment.

In fruits and seeds we have an even greater concentration of formative forces. The being of the plant withdraws, leaving only a tiny physical vehicle, the kernel. Here the dormant etheric life qualities are stored, which are set free and become manifest only upon germination. This stable state makes it possible to keep fruits, and especially seeds, through the winter or longer. Their ability to germinate shows that the life in them is not extinguished. Hence, the formative forces are "naturally preserved" in the seed, because enzyme and substrate are locally separated in it. A precondition for this is dryness (*corpora non agunt, nisi fluida*). Furthermore, both seeds and fruits are always enclosed in a practically sterile casing so that no putrefactive breakdown by microorganisms can occur.

Change begins as soon as this natural arrangement is altered. Injury of the outer husk admits microorganisms, and rotting begins; with water and warmth, growth begins and the formative forces are manifested. Finally, milling will break the separation of enzyme and substrate and will also initiate the aging process.

Put in practical terms, this means that all foodstuffs that are derived from a living process of growth must be consumed as fresh as possible. This applies, for example, to leafy vegetables, fast-growing plants, sprouts, shoots, young vegetables, milk, eggs, etc. These items all suffer the greatest loss of their etheric formative forces from storage and the various methods of preservation.

The closer a life substance stands to the immediate warmth action of life, the less it needs to be changed in digestion, and the less processing it requires to be consumed as a foodstuff. It is by its nature easily digestible. This is true particularly of milk, but also of honey and the ripe fruits of the Rosaceae, which are high in fruit sugar. Moreover, fruit quite generally has a strong affinity to warmth and the blood.

For this reason, the more warmth ether a foodstuff contains, the more important it is to avoid prolonged heating. This applies especially to this group of foodstuffs, that is, milk, sprouts, honey, ripe fruits, etc. In these cases, heating will destroy the formative forces already active in the food and therefore also its food value; this can be seen in the loss of vitamin C during heating. The vitamin content, however, is but one indication of the formative forces; they go far beyond it and are not bound to a definite chemical structure in their action. In addition, there is experimental evidence that heated milk, and particularly condensed milk, have a harmful effect on the growing organism. In animal tests on cats, extending over a period of ten years,[5] the biological action of raw food was compared with that of food treated in various ways. The cats fed on raw milk remained healthy and had normal births from generation to generation. The animals nourished on prepared milk showed, in the space of just a few generations, abortions, shortened life span, various — mostly degenerative — diseases, and skeletal deformities; these symptoms grew in severity according to the sequence: pasteurized milk, dry milk, condensed milk. Repetition of the tests with white rats led to the same result.

By means of the Pfeiffer crystallization method (see p. 379ff.),[6] which directly shows the action of the formative forces, it is possible to recognize the preservation or destruction of the formative forces through different means of processing.

It has already been mentioned that seed formation represents a natural extreme in regard to the appearance of the formative forces. This is the realm of the life ether. Using seeds (grain), one must realize that each kernel represents an organism in itself. Life will only become fully manifest in it again when warmth and water are present. Then the seed begins to germinate and brings the dormant life to expression. Foodstuffs must also be "opened up," in a process similar to germination, so that the unlocking of the formative forces can begin. This will involve bringing in warmth and water. The use of warmth in combination with water for cooking and baking is no doubt the oldest way of preparing food for consumption.

In the preparation of grain, the totality of the kernel must be destroyed by grinding. After this, no real "perservation" is possible. After any interference with it, the timeless kernel of grain begins to "age." For this reason, grain should not be rough-ground or milled until shortly before use, if possible. Storage of flour entails a loss in etheric forces. It also follows that we should not try to separate certain parts out of the organic context of the kernel; milling at a low rate of extraction, producing "higher" grades of flour, does just this. It is not without reason that the starch in the kernel is joined in the husk by vitamin B_1, which has the greatest influence on carbohydrate metabolism.

From this we can see that the question of a diet of raw vs. cooked foods cannot be answered so simply; rather, it depends on the type of food and the condition of the consumer's digestion. Raw vegetables are a stimulus to the organism. It must exert itself to loosen up the fixed state of the unprocessed food and replace the cooking process with its own activity. The Greek word for digestion, *pepsis*, really means "cooking," and indicates a direct knowledge of these facts. Paracelsus said that the "ripening of fruits is natural cooking." This is "what summer does with the fruits." Thus, ripening is a mild form of "cooking" or pre-digestion. This is why cooking can make unripe fruits edible and more digestible.

The stimulus of raw foods is an appeal to the organism's own forces; it is a healing process that can have a positive outcome. Such a diet is indicated for suppuration, or, according to Rudolf Steiner, to strengthen a therapeutically indicated quartz effect.

A permanent fare of raw vegetables, however, would be an excessive load. The forces used by the organism to digest it would be missed in other places. The ultimate effect would be to lower the human—that is, spiritual—capacities, since these would be one-sidedly bound in an organic connection.

Another consideration about raw vegetable foods is that

their effect will be more intense the more seeds and roots they contain. The roots completely lack the warmth and light that are most active in the fruits and that make them "naturally cooked."

The use of roots stimulates the forming and structuring forces. They contain the salt process that corresponds to the nerve-sense system in man; the root therefore stimulates this system. Correspondingly, the blossom and fruits have a sulfuric action that enlivens the metabolism. Finally, in the leaves we find a mercuric action and a correspondence in the rhythmic system.

This should not be seen as a fixed schema, since these are interweaving processes. In addition, the effects described apply to the use of plants not only as food but also as remedies (see p. 317 ff.).

If the relationships of forces described for a typical plant are displaced, then the resulting plant will have great dietetic and medicinal importance; a few examples will illustrate this.

Color is naturally a blossom impulse. If it appears in the root, then we have a sulfuric blossom impulse in the domain of the roots. This is the case with the carrot and beet; hence, their value for the head region and the corresponding functions.

Horseradish also shows a pronounced sulfur process in the root. This is expressed in mustard oils and other highly aromatic substances. In these, sulfur sometimes actually occurs as a substance. This produces a highly stimulating effect, not only for the metabolism as such, but also for the nerve-sense system and the region of the head; this can be directly experienced with horseradish, mustard, and onion. Here we find the sulfur process in the sal domain, that is, the blossom impulse is acting in the root. The root of the horseradish sends the sulfur process from the sal domain up into the nerve-sense system. Hence, its action is not primary and formative but enlivening and stimulating. Some roots, like the horseradish, may possess extremely strong structuring forces despite their sulfuric substances. Horseradish, moreover, is a genuine root, while the bulbs of bulbous plants are only stem parts living in the root area. The latter therefore have a more protective character against the highly forming and hardening tendencies of the nervous system, which they counteract. This, for example, is the basis of the antisclerotic action of garlic.

These heavily sulfuric plants are in a certain way opposed to those that develop the contracting sal process substantially in the form of bitter substances—for example, the Gentiana and others discussed above. Such a property of displacing a typical process (sal or sulfur) to another region is the reason a particular plant will tend to have a medicinal rather than a nutritive application.

At this point, we will briefly discuss the use of the potato as a foodstuff. Plant starch arises through the influence of sunlight, which it contains in a stored form. It makes a great difference if this starch remains in the realm of light, which is the case in grains and rice, or if it is stored underneath the earth as in the potato. The storing organs of the potato, the tubers, may be located in the root area, but they are not roots. The starch in the tubers is, therefore, more subject to the earth forces than that in the root of rape, for example. The latter is a true root, a fully structured part of the plant, while the tuber is rather an enlargement, more or less comparable to a benign tumor or a hyperplastic organ. Accordingly, the effects of potato and rape starch must be different, particularly in the corresponding area, the nervous system, quite apart from their behavior in the gastrointestinal tract and the liver.

Since tubers are particularly heavily pervaded by the earth forces, the action of light in the carbohydrates, when it is released, will not be able to unfold so freely as in a sun-permeated substance such as grain starch, honey, or a sulfurous root like the carrot; it will rather be held in a fixed, physical form. The formative forces also furnish the foundation for our thinking; thus we must pursue the effects of nutrition into this area. This explains Rudolf Steiner's indication that a diet of potatoes promotes thought one-sidedly in an abstract, intellectual direction. Eating potatoes makes it easy to grasp intellectual and materialistic thoughts but not spiritual concepts; for this, thought must be comprehensive and living, lucid (light filled). Of course, this does not mean that potatoes should be altogether done away with as a foodstuff, but in the light of an essential understanding of a foodstuff, we must decide if we wish to favor it or attempt to exclude a harmful effect. When potatoes are eaten, their earthbound quality can be compensated to a certain extent by the use of sulfurous horseradish, for example.

This example makes clear the profound effects foods have on the human body, reaching even into his thoughts, but this is still not seen at all today. We can trace how the spiritual (light) engages in matter and, after its release, once again causes spiritual activities to appear and develop.

Recently, much attention has been devoted to sugar as a "pathogenic factor."[7] Ever since the basic works of Katase[8] it has been known that the addition of cane sugar to food causes acidosis, resulting in varying degrees of bone pathology (osteoporosis, elongation of the hollow bones, deformities, etc.). Later, Sandler[9] found that polio infection occurs only in the hypoglycemic phase after sugar consumption. Finally, connections have been made between sugar consumption and coronary diseases (Yudkin) and acceleration (Ziegler[10]). There are connections between sugar consumption and diabetes, caries, duodenal and gastric ulcers, coronary insufficiency, and varicosities.[11] Since the investigations of Warburg and Jung it has been known that alterations of the intermediate carbohydrate metabolism also play a part in carcinoma.

Evaluation of the effect of sugar consumption on man is particularly difficult, because sugar is used not only for food, but also for enjoyment; this colors our judgment of it, consciously or unconsciously.

Sugar consumption runs parallel to civilization. With his transition into civilization, the human being leaves his bondage to nature and arrives at a great independence, a pronounced ego development. Sugar can be of help in this process. As we illustrate in our discussion of carbohydrate metabolism (see p. 232ff.), sugar is the vehicle of the ego organization. It is an instructive fact, however, that sugar rarely occurs in nature compared to starch and other carbohydrates. The typical food among the carbohydrates is starch, and this is first broken down to glucose. We can take a "shortcut" by the use of sugar. Now, however, we are dealing with the mineral form of a living substance, with all the advantages and disadvantages this brings. Sugar can be immediately absorbed. This results in a heightened sense of self, a heightened ego feeling. This, however, must not be confused with a "strengthening of the ego" in the sense of a heightening of the value of the individuality. Rather, sugar produces a stronger connection of the ego with the physical body, especially with the metabolic system, because the ego is given a greater foundation in the body through the action of sugar, the carrier of the ego organization. The ego is now able to act more strongly in an individual sense, but this need not at all be in the sense of the ego organization; that is, the ideal human structure.

Furthermore, what is true of any isolated substance is true of sugar; the "purer" it is, the more mineral it is, and hence the further it is from its connection with life. The vital sap of a plant, like the blood and lymph of man and animal, always contains a delicate balance of a great variety of substances and never an isolated material. If a substance is isolated, it loses the natural context in which it also occurs in the human and animal metabolism; sugar, for example, in its natural context, always appears in conjunction with vitamin B and potassium. Ingestion of large amounts of sugar will result in inundation of the organism (hyperglycemia), with corresponding counter-reactions and subsequent hypoglycemia. This sudden onslaught is a great strain on the organism in that it disturbs the regulation and control of the carbohydrate metabolism. By consuming sugar instead of starch, the human being avoids having to catabolize the latter; in time, this weakens his ability to deal with these substances.

In sum, we see that while sugar consumption favors or intensifies the experience of the ego in the body, there is a danger that life will develop more in the sense of an arbitrary egoism— the "lower ego"—than is appropriate for the human being. This stronger presence of the ego that sugar has made possible represents an important step in the history of mankind's development. In the development of civilization, sugar played a critical role for ego consciousness, which in turn made this development possible. With the extremely high use of sugar in civilized countries, however, this necessary step is in danger of turning into a problem. There is no doubt that human beings in our day are mainly too strongly bound to their bodies and to the earth; this imbalance is not equalized, and it provides the constitutional foundation chiefly for certain illnesses of the sclerotic-cancerous group. The customary overly high sugar consumption today can further this development.

We must make special mention of animal foods. Because the animal has already overcome the plant substance in its digestive process to a certain extent, the activation of the etheric body from eating animal food is not so strong as from plant food. On the other hand, animal food still contains some of the animal's astrality, which can stimulate the human astral body, provided that this foreign astrality is overcome in digestion.

We must differentiate, however, between different animal foods, and this is by no means only a question of protein. The flesh of an animal is very much the expression of the animal's essential quality. When a human being takes in the flesh of an animal, he comes into a confrontation with its astral body. In contrast, milk is tinged much less with the astrality of the animal. Hence, milk protein is more neutral. When milk is further processed by souring and cheese formation, this is a mild denaturing, representing a certain catabolism and thus a predigestion; at the same time, however, this means a further removal of the astral element. This is why curd is not only the most neutral protein but also the one that is most easily tolerated and most universally usable.

In the light of our earlier discussions, it is clear that the question of whether a vegetarian or meat diet is preferable cannot be answered in a general way. If the etheric body is in need of stimulation, a vegetarian diet will be preferable; if, on the other hand, the astral body is insufficiently incarnated, then increased meat consumption may be required. This will result in greater awakeness, liveliness, increased interest in the surrounding world, etc. After all, animal substance also contains no small amount of phosphorus. This alone will produce a certain stimulation, but the effect goes far beyond this (see the section on protein metabolism). Since, in the humanity of today, the connection of the astral body with the physical body tends to be too strong, it is obvious that high meat consumption cannot be healthy.

In children, food high in protein such as meat leads to a pre-mature astralization and acceleration of development (see p. 101) with all its consequences. If we correlate the time of the doubling of birth weight—that is to say, the growth rate—of various animals and of man with the composition of their milk, we find that there is an inverse relation in regard to the protein content. The protein, and also mineral salt, component is quite low in human milk, and rises with the rate of growth of the various animals. The obvious conclusion is that any increase in protein consumption during the developmental phase of childhood also accelerates growth. (These connections are dis-cussed in detail in the chapter on pediatrics, Vol. III). This effect is more accentuated when the source of protein is flesh instead of milk. In the later part of life, high consumption of meat, when not indicated, may dispose one to chronic inflam-mation or suppuration, and may also lay the foundation for an excessive sclerosis.

The role played by fat has been recognized more exactly in recent years. In general, it can be said that fat consumption is too high today. The qualitative aspect of fat, however, is even more significant than the quantitative. It has been recognized as a pathogenic factor in sclerosis, a connection that Rudolf Steiner made earlier (see section on fat metabolism, p. 246ff.).

Among the fats, those with a high melting point (saturated or long-chain fatty acids) behave differently from those with low melting points (unsaturated, short-chain fatty acids). It is no coincidence that liver fat shows the highest content of unsatu-rated fatty acids. This is an expression of the required activity of the metabolism there. In contrast, the most rigidified fatty acids (C_{24}) are found in the nervous system, which by its nature must be fixed and rigid. From it come the catabolic, sclerotic impulses. What is physiological at this site would have pathological effects elsewhere. Thus, saturated fats are intolerable to the liver as the main organ of metabolism. This does not mean that they cannot be digested here; rather, they cannot be transformed into warmth, which fats must be (see section on fat metabolism). To the extent that the organism lacks the strength, coming from the ego organization, to transform these fats, they remain in the organism as foreign bodies. The relationship here is similar to that between uric acid and gout, or sugar and diabetes: a normally physiological substance cannot be managed and transformed. Particularly the older organism is often incapable of taking nonliving materials into the ego organization and permeating them with warmth. Thus saturated fatty acids enter into the metabolism with difficulty, and in arteriosclerotic patients we find their level increased in the blood, in contrast to the polyunsaturated fatty acids, the level of which will be relatively low. This can be the foundation for atherosclerosis or a fatty liver. The mutually antagonistic behavior of saturated and polyunsaturated fatty acids, those with a high and those with a low melting point, is known. To a certain extent it is possible to balance the negative effect of one by means of the other. In dietary terms, this means that oils with polyunsaturated fatty acids, with their inner relations to warmth and essential affinity to the metabolism, are indicated for corresponding disorders of the fat metabolism. In contrast, congealed fats have a pathogenic action; by their nature they are already "sclerosed" through congealing. Of course, no organism contains completely saturated fats, but only mixtures of various fatty acid components.

Milk fat (butterfat) shows a universal behavior in all its properties. In it there are fatty acids of all chain lengths, both saturated and unsaturated. To be sure, these values alone are not adequate for a qualitative evaluation of a fat. In any case, a natural association of fats must be judged differently than an artificial mixture, for example, one in which unsaturated fatty acids are added to hardened fats, which is customary in the production of margarine. In any case, organisms do not arise from such synthetic mixtures but from a unit.

In dietary recommendations we must distinguish between a healthy and a sick organism. Butter, as an animal fat, and olive oil, as a plant oil, assume middle positions in their respective domains, and each represents the ideal food of its kind. In contrast to them, the polyunsaturated fats actually have a therapeutic character. Unfortunately, tolerability does not necessarily run parallel to biological worth. The saturated (hydrogenated) fats can be excellently tolerated, which, along with their good properties for baking and frying, appears to justify their wide use. What is critical, however, is not their initial digestibility but their later metabolism, and, in this case, they cannot be taken into the warmth organism so that they support the tendency toward sclerosis. In contrast, the polyunsaturated oils are most sensitive to oxidation and heating, which makes their use more difficult.

The cholesterol content of the fats clearly does play a role. Whether or not it will have a negative effect, however, depends less on its quantity than on the organism's capacity to deal with the substance. After all, man and animal form cholesterol themselves. These questions are discussed in greater detail on p. 182 and p. 253 ff.

Carbohydrate Metabolism

The metabolism of carbohydrates, proteins, and fats actually corresponds to the workings of the higher members of man's being, each of which is characteristically unique.

Carbohydrates form the body substance of plants and thus express the pure activity of the etheric body. The force relationships in the plant can be clearly seen in the form of the carbohydrates. In the plant, a consolidation process takes place that leads to the formation of cellulose. Cellulose has fallen out of the metabolism and cannot be dissolved again by the plant. Starch, in contrast, can be mobilized again at any moment; down to its microscopic structure, and in all other respects, it shows the essential quality of the plant, as in potato starch, rice starch, etc. The mono- and disaccharides represent the most active forms of the carbohydrates. Nevertheless, they show properties that do not seem appropriate to a substance that is a carrier of life, since practically all mono- and disaccharides can be crystallized more or less easily. This property is otherwise connected with salts, that is, the mineral structure; it is not present in starch, much less in cellulose. Lignification does not take place according to patterns typical of crystalline substances but according to formative principles determined exclusively by the essential quality of the plant.

The mono- and disaccharides, the sugars, present us with the peculiar phenomenon of a living substance appearing in mineral structure. The "crystals," of which we speak even in proteins, are by no means so pronounced in their crystalline structure as those of sugar, such as rock sugar candy.

The occurrence of an originally living, organic substance in mineral, crystalline structure is a singular phenomenon of sugar. The mineral state is an expression of the earth forces connected with the substance and, in general, excludes the internalization of imponderable, cosmic forces, and also life forces. Other representatives of this state are the salts. In a morphological sense, sugar is a "salt."

This peculiarity of sugar goes far beyond its properties as a carbohydrate; it is practically bound up with the simultaneous occurrence of the sweet taste. To be sure, there are monosaccharides and disaccharides that do not taste sweet—some even taste bitter—but quantitatively and qualitatively these play hardly any role in nature.

The relation of sugar to the ego organization provides a key to understanding this strange phenomenon. "Wherever sugar is, there is the ego organization."[12] It is an essential characteristic of man that he breaks down both food and bodily substance further than the animal does. Naturally, the end products of carbohydrate metabolism are water and carbon dioxide in both cases; still, it is important how these end products are reached. Sugar plays quite a significant role as an intermediate product. It originates in life but is subjected to mineralizing forces that are the embodiment of the death process. This is the way that life is led into death, and this possibility belongs to the essential nature of man. Hence, all substances that really enter the mineral state—the skeletal system, for example—are a manifestation of the typically human "institution" of the ego organization, which distinguishes him from the animal. "Whatever comes within the domain of the ego organization, dies."[13] This dying, or transition into the mineral state, involves releasing life, or the "imponderabilia." The result will be, for example, a salt, what the alchemists called the sal state. This is the case with every crystallization. Yet, there is one exception. Only the sugars are capable of keeping in themselves the life from which they originated and of assuming a mineral-crystalline form while still being organic substances.

The physiological importance of sugar is connected with this property; as a dispenser of calories it has nutritive value, which it owes to its living origin. This value, however, is qualitatively altered by the mineral form into which it has been forced. Mineral structure is essentially foreign to life. For this reason, the calories of sugar are no longer an expression of life, and sugar is not a real food. This is not just a matter of the vitamins, minerals, etc., contained in a product.

In order to experience himself as an ego, the human being requires a transition from living substance into the dead, mineral state. For this reason, only a substance that transfers life into the mineral form can serve as the foundation for the activity of the specifically human ego organization. Only sugar meets this requirement; hence, it is the substantial vehicle of the ego organization.

There is an obvious objection to our discussion, namely, that the animal, just like man, possesses a blood sugar level with corresponding regulation, and like the human being it forms a skeletal system and dies. The bone system, however, has a different function and significance for the animal than for man. The animal can also "die," but it cannot experience death. Hence, it is more appropriate to speak of an animal's "perishing." Similarly, though the animal possesses many substances and processes similar or identical to those in man, either it does not use them, or they have a different significance than in man, in accordance with the essential quality of the particular animal species and of man. In this connection one should mention that glucose is found within the erythrocytes only in man and in the anthropoid apes.

Of the monosaccharides, only three play a significant role:

glucose, fructose, and galactose. In nature, each of these is re-combined with one molecule of glucose to form a typical disac-charide.

The three monosaccharides have quite characteristic proper-ties that express their relationship to the human being. Fructose is extremely active in all physical, chemical, and biological reactions. Of the three monosaccharides mentioned, it tends least toward crystallization and serves most easily for the for-mation of glycogen. From all of these properties we can see that among the sugars, fructose corresponds to the metabolic system. It has a rather sulfuric character.

Galactose shows the opposite behavior. It is "sluggish" in all its reactions; although it is absorbed the most quickly, it still has no real connection with the metabolic system. Because it enters into metabolism with such difficulty, galactose is used in testing the functioning of the liver. In the chapter on the heart (Vol. III), it is shown that the speed of processes in the nerve-sense system relates as 1:4 to that in the metabolic system; thus the lively character of fructose points to the metabolic system, and the sluggishness of galactose to the ner-vous system. Galactose is found only in milk—as lactose—and as a physiological building block of the cerebrosides in the brain. Since galactose is contained in milk sugar (lactose), and since this is the single sugar of mother's milk—thus specifically intended for the infant—this shows us even on the level of chemistry how the formative impulses of the infant are totally directed toward the nervous system (see the chapter on the first epoch of life). This connection between milk and the brain was expressly indicated by Rudolf Steiner, who described the brain as really being congealed chyle in the human being.[14]

Glucose in many respects assumes a middle position between fructose and galactose; it is just this position that enables it to take on its function as blood sugar. Here is the physical foun-dation enabling man—by means of sugar as the vehicle of the ego organization—not to connect himself one-sidedly with the nervous or metabolic systems, but to stand in the middle, em-bracing and balancing these two poles. The significance of this for the physiological functions as the basis of human development is described in detail elsewhere.[15] From what has been said here, however, we can understand that fructose, through its relation to the metabolic system, can be assimilated more easily than glucose and is, therefore, still useful for the diabetic. It contains the blossom warmth process and is therefore sufficiently "opened up" inside to be easily dealt with. The physico-chemical data show this as well. Through its inner warmth, fructose meets the organism halfway, so to speak. Not so much effort is needed to deal with it as with glucose or galactose.

	Monosaccharide	Disaccharide formed by combination with glucose
Nervous system	Galactose	Lactose
Heart	Glucose	Maltose
Metabolism	Fructose	Sucrose

For utilization, all carbohydrates must be broken down into monosaccharides in the gastrointestinal tract. Cellulose, however, cannot be broken down by the human being and is therefore not usable, although it "consists" of glucose. This glucose, however, is bound so fast that the human organism cannot bring it into metabolism; it has become physical and rigid. It is sugar turned to "stone." The human being cannot and should not be permeated with such "rigidified" (but not mineralized) life forces.

Further breakdown of carbohydrates in the intestine, that is, beyond the monosaccharide phase, is pathological and is never performed by the body's own enzymes; rather it is performed by bacteria as we saw with the syndrome of fermentive dyspepsia. This fermentation is prevented in healthy individuals by correct breakdown and timely absorption.

The monosaccharides are at this point absorbed by the intestine. This is an instructive phenomenon: the glucose is phosphorylated in absorption, that is, phosphorus combines with the sugar. This is what first makes possible selective absorption, which is an active process. Thus in phosphorylation the ego combines with sugar by means of phosphorus as the ego vehicle. The further utilization of sugar, the breakdown of glucose in the intermediate metabolism, also proceeds only by way of combination with phosphorus.

Without going into the details here, we can already see that the ego plays a guiding role in the entire carbohydrate metabolism by means of phosphorus, thus structuring the process in accordance with the spirit.

Diabetes Mellitus

The breakdown of carbohydrates into monosaccharides is not disturbed in the diabetic. Since this type of catabolism is brought about primarily by the astral body (by means of ptyalin, the effect of acids in inversion, etc.), the responsibility must be placed not on the astral body but on the ego organization, which takes part in the further breakdown. "In diabetes mellitus, the ego organization is so weakened by its submergence into the astral and etheric domain that it can no longer carry out its action on sugar."[16] The sugar, which cannot be managed, is excreted as a foreign substance (glycosuria). Since the sugar, which is consumed for the most part, remains foreign and does not enter the domain of the ego organization, it cannot be stored as glycogen; in fact, the glycogen-storing liver and muscle are exhausted, because, despite its presence, there is a deficiency of sugar. The diabetic lacks the inner process of meeting the substance halfway; therefore, any consumption of sugar is for his organism an inundation by a foreign substance, which must intensify the disease situation. He cannot defend himself against this, as the characteristic loading curve of the diabetic shows.

We see that despite the large amounts of glucose flowing in his blood, the diabetic suffers from a lack of sugar, since he cannot utilize it. Because of the relative sugar deficiency, the glycogen depots become empty; this, together with the insufficient glucose utilization, leads to hyperglycemia. The excessive supply makes the "pressure" greater; this, in turn, makes utilization somewhat easier, since the utilization of sugar is dependent on the height of the blood sugar level. It was deter-

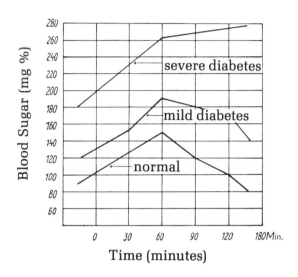

Grape-sugar load (100 g glucose in 300 ccm water.
Blood sugar measured every 30 minutes for 3 hours.)

(From: H. Franke, *Klinische Laboratoriumsmethoden*, Berlin 1952.)

mined in animal experiments that under extreme conditions
(with a blood sugar of 700 mg per cent, compared to a normal
of 80–120 mg per cent) insulin is completely dispensable; sugar
utilization is as great as in a normal animal. This shows that
such a way of utilizing sugar is possible, though it cannot be
taken by a healthy organism. The latter must deal actively with
sugar and take it into the metabolic processes. This occurs by
means of phosphorylation.

In this way the ego organization gains access to sugar, which
is thus able to fulfill its function as carrier of the ego organization. In the diabetic, however, the ego organization is disturbed
or diseased and it cannot do the work necessary to handle and
absorb the sugar, which thus remains a foreign substance. Insulin is required for this transition. Insulin, however, expresses
the activity of the higher members of man within the organism, in their confrontation with food. As is known, insulin is
the secretion of the β-cells of the pancreas and is more or less

missing in the diabetic (or he cannot make use of it). We must, however, look beyond the substance and the organ and come to recognize the forces that bring about the production and secretion of the secreted or excreted substances, for the glands (and their products) are only the "organs," that is, the sites and instruments of these forces. We have already seen that the ego organization in diabetics is too weak to deal with sugar. This process is achieved by way of insulin production in the pancreas, and this hormone is a result of the activity of the ego organization, which uses it to engage in the metabolism.

Insulin thus evokes a rise in sugar utilization and makes possible the transition from glucose to a form that is "proper to the body" and capable of reaction, as has been shown in many experiments. The liver is an organ that is completely determined by the "laws" of the etheric body, so it is through the liver that sugar is taken into the individual's own etheric organism. This, however, can occur only when the sugar has already been dealt with by the ego organization (insulin, phosphorylation). In fact, it is quite probable that the body can utilize only carbohydrates that have gone through the liver-glycogen stage (Meythaler). In any case, liver glycogen always produces glucose, wherever its source.

As a result of the inability to deal with sugar, the necessary steps of healthy catabolism under the action of the ego organization, namely, pyruvic acid and oxaloacetic acid, are also missing.

Many experimental findings point to the diabetic's insufficient ability to manage and transform glucose. For example, it has been found that in healthy individuals, administration of glucose results in a rise in pyruvic acid, the normal intermediate product, in the blood. In diabetes, this rise is reduced, retarded, or altogether absent. This disorder, like other diabetic metabolic disorders, can be eliminated with insulin.

Because of the disturbed catabolism, the acetoacetic acid stemming from the fat metabolism also cannot be utilized. Its prescribed way of catabolism, according to the plan of the organism, would be through oxidation with the participation of oxaloacetic acid. Since this is absent, the organism cannot take hold of the acetoacetic acid, which must be altered in other ways. It is transformed by reduction to β-oxybutyric acid or by decarboxylation to acetone. These breakdown forms, however, are no longer subject to the ego organization, since this takes part in the total digestion by way of the carbohydrate metabolism (through phosphorus). The fat metabolism thus ends in other paths of catabolism. The substances arising in this way can no longer be the vehicle of man's spiritual activity; therefore, they have a toxic effect and in large quantities will lead to diabetic coma.

A further consequence of this disorder in catabolism is the inability to anabolize. Man's life is possible only in a continuous alteration of catabolism and anabolism; every building up is preceded by a breaking down. Both pyruvic and lactic acid—the latter arises in muscular activity—can be built up again to glycogen (carbohydrate cycle). This resynthesis is not possible for the pathological metabolic products named. The significance of pyruvic and lactic acid is that, although as acids they have an astral character, after catabolism they pass into the etheric body and can therefore be built up again, which is not true of acetoacetic acid and β-oxybutyric acid. The same is true of alcohol, which can be broken down further but cannot be built up again. It is a product of fermentation, a process that the organism must continually fight. Alcohol is "hostile to life" by its nature; this, after all, is why it can have a preserving and disinfecting action.[17]

In contrast, unimpeded anabolic processes make themselves known through a high glycogen concentration in the liver, which is, in fact, a practical prerequisite to undisturbed functioning of the liver (see section on the liver, Vol. III). It is also characteristic that an extreme concentration of glycogen (glycogen storage disease, G-6-P-D deficiency) manifests in childhood, a time when the etheric body is still dominant. Glycogen deficiency, on the other hand, is a typical sign of age and of anabolic weakness, not only in diabetes.

Another result of the weakening of the ego organization is its insufficient penetration of the metabolism. Unprocessed etheric forces are left, which no longer fit into the context of the whole. This provides a suitable medium for bacteria, which leads to the formation of furuncles.

Interestingly, the efficacy of the fasting diet for diabetes that is now common in the insulin era is based on the fact that such a diet reduces the metabolism, making it easier for the ego organization to descend into the etheric and astral bodies. This predominance of the etheric body also explains the finding that 70 per cent of all diabetics have pyknic constitutions.

The insufficient penetration of the etheric body also finds expression in the various experiments that have shown the great importance of the hypophysis for diabetes (Houssay, Young, etc.). The hypophysis is a central organ of the etheric body. Animal experiments, for example, show that injection of large amounts of anterior pituitary extract will produce diabetes; that is, when a test produces such a massive stimulation of the etheric body, it can no longer be penetrated sufficiently and the result is a "symptomatic diabetes." This stimulation of the etheric body, however, is "one-sided" and pathological. Just as in diabetes, the excessive and uncontrolled etheric forces (for example, boil formation) go along with a too-weak activity of the etheric body in some places, particularly the liver. The low level of glycogen in the liver of the diabetic indicates this. The nervous system as well is affected by this one-sided weakness of the diabetic, so that degenerative processes may appear (diabetic neuropathy, retinopathy).

At this point it would be worthwhile to comment on the question of animal experiments and the extent to which it is justifiable to apply their results to the human being. The diabetes evoked in the animal experiment had to be called "symptomatic," because the animal has no ego organization as does man. Diabetes, however, is based on a weakness of the ego organization, and consequently an animal can never contract diabetes spontaneously. We have already discussed the objection that the animals have a blood sugar level, etc. The fact is that in the animal these are not subordinated to an ego but to the group soul of the particular species. It is true that the animal, depending on its level, does have parts of the ego organization to a greater or lesser extent; the single animal, however, is unable to make use of them individually.

The difference between animal and human diabetes consists in the fact that the animal is firmly established in its group soul, whose dwelling place is in the cosmos rather than in the animal organism. Through this close connection, the animal is in a state of lasting harmony with nature and with the environment. So long as this connection remains intact, the animal cannot fall ill. Illness is only possible when it is removed from the natural harmony through domestication, tethering, etc., or when the physical basis for engagement of the group soul is damaged, for example, by destruction of the β-cells in alloxan diabetes.

The human being, however, is separated from the cosmic context; this is how he has become an "I" in the first place. For this reason, the framework for the incorporation of the spiritual, namely, the ego organization, has a real meaning only for man as a spiritual being. These facts must be taken into consideration if animal experiments are to be interpreted correctly.

It is also possible to influence the various regulatory mechanisms in the animal and to make inferences about the way in which diabetes manifests itself. It will be impossible to arrive at the causes by the experimental method, however, since they do not lie in the material realm. Only by means of spiritual concepts can we understand the essence of diabetes as a failure of the ego organization.

It is well-known that mostly people in exposed and responsible positions contract diabetes. Largely persons with intellectual occupations are affected. Frequently, the disease becomes manifest after a psychic trauma. This process has become well-known from animal experiments, for example, "captivity diabetes" in cats.

Ultimately, "everything that pulls the ego organization out of its engagement with the body promotes diabetes: excitement occurring not once but repeatedly, intellectual overexertion, congenital defects that prevent a normal engagement of the ego organization in the whole organism."[18] In all of these different possible forms of damage, there is always a displacement of ego activity out of the metabolism into the nerve-sense system.

This approach to the disease explains a number of experienced facts. In earlier times, for example, the only known treatment for diabetes was heavy physical work almost to the point of exhaustion. Unfortunately, the beneficial effects of work therapy for this disease are too much ignored today in the insulin era. Muscular activity helps to guide the ego from the head region into the metabolism. This relieves it of intellectual "head thinking."

A fact pointing in the same direction is that the diseases with which diabetes is combined, or which alternate with it in the line of inheritance, are metabolic diseases such as obesity, gout. Both of them fundamentally involve deposition, one of fat, the other of uric acid. Their common feature is that the substances are not dealt with sufficiently in the metabolism by the higher members of man's being and are therefore deposited, precipitated, or excreted.

On the same lines, we observe that diabetes and sclerosis favor one another. There are similarities in the sugar metabolism of the aging person and the diabetic since the sugar load-curve becomes more similar to that of the diabetic with increasing age.[19] We see that diabetes is thus a premature aging and belongs to the typically sclerotic diseases (see p. 191). Accordingly, the prognosis is best for senile diabetes and worst for juvenile diabetes. The disorders of the fat metabolism in the diabetic, which are discussed in detail at another place (p. 230 f. and p. 251), are also to be seen and understood in the light of this approach.

It is understandable that rich food, even of high quality, is harmful to one with the disease, since the diabetic cannot manage the metabolic load. It is just because of this weakness of the metabolic system that the diabetic tolerates fructose the best, since it is the sugar best suited for the metabolic system. It may be mentioned at this point that diabetes takes a milder course during times of hardship and famine.

In sum, it can be seen from these observations that the situation in our times actually works to foster diabetes. The human being as such, that is, the ego organization, not the ego as personality, is injured. This is worthy of consideration in therapy.

In view of the substitution of insulin and the possibilities of controlling symptoms with oral hypoglycemic agents, a genuine therapy for diabetes is largely neglected today. Therapy will aim primarily at supporting the ego organization and bringing the ego into the metabolism. This is naturally impossible so long as the pathogenic situation remains. This situation, as we have shown, lies in the excessive activity of the ego in the nerve-sense region, which is why "head-workers" are chiefly affected. In them we see one-sided intellectual activity, which by its nature is abstract, cold, and dead. Penetration of the ego into the metabolism is weakened by the continual over-concentration in the head region. For this reason, inter-current febrile illnesses represent a greater strain for the diabetic than for a person with healthy metabolic activity, since the diabetic cannot control these processes. In contrast, a high fever can cause a temporary recovery because the higher members of man's being are incarnated better in the metabolism; this is also the principle behind the therapeutic effect of physical work. More often, however, infections can make a latent diabetes manifest or even produce a coma. This depends on the fever and on the patient's general condition.

The essential treatment for the diabetic is to bring him out of the one-sidedness we have described. The life of a healthy person flows in "light and warmth"; the abstract activities described in the diabetic constantly fight against these. Hence, "light and warmth" are indicated for the diabetic, but not in an unchanged outer form; they must be already assimilated and transformed in a substance. This is the case, for example, in the rosemary plant (see p. 329f.). Rosemary, in the form of a bath admixture for relief of the nerve-sense system, was especially indicated by Rudolf Steiner for diabetes. The use of etheric rosemary oil as a bath oil has proven beneficial. Rosemary is also applied as a dilution and injection.

Copper not only stimulates the warmth organism, but also affects the metabolism in such a way that it can receive the astral body and ego organization better. Copper is especially indicated in combination with sulfur, which has a "loosening" effect, as copper sulfate (Cuprum sulfuricum D4, D6).

Mention should also be made of quartz, which has a special relation to the ego organization; through its function of bringing substances out of the vegetable state, it has a forming and structuring action on the metabolism and checks overflowing etheric life.

In the light of this discussion, it should not be difficult to understand the reason for the application of phosphorus. It stimulates the ego (ego carrier, light carrier) and gives it a foundation in the organism. We could also say that it appeals to the phosphorus process and the phosphorylation processes subordinated to this; it makes possible the engagement of sugar and its incorporation into the ego organization.

A reasonable, moderate diet is naturally also part of the therapy; its strictness will depend on the severity of the disease. Of course, the diabetic must keep to the diet; it is not at all beneficial, however, to extend his intellectual, abstract orientation to food consumption as well—for example, by turning it into an arithmetical problem with units of insulin and white bread. This has been pointed out quite rightly by G. von Bergmann. Besides the quantities, attention must be given to the qualitative origin of the foods.

A matter of great importance, which is not even discussed today, is prophylaxis. It is not hard to see, that the extremely high consumption of sugar today continually overtaxes the organism's regulatory capacity and its ability to control sugar metabolism. An equally important factor, which we have described above, is the diabetogenic effect of contemporary civilization. Intellectual education and premature orientation of the child around the nerve-sense system in many cases create the constitutional basis for a later outbreak of the disease. Thus, prophylaxis must not consist only in judiciously managed nutrition; it must begin in childhood with an education that is not exclusively intellectually oriented, but that promotes a harmonious development of the child, with consideration of what is appropriate to different phases of development.

The curriculum of the Waldorf schools was arranged in this way by Rudolf Steiner.

Fat Metabolism

In order to understand the significance and function of fat in the organism, one needs to explore the essence of this substance as such. The body substance of plants consists mainly of carbohydrates; that of animals, of proteins. Fat is found in both kingdoms. This is already an indication of the middle position held by fats, which we will meet with frequently, since it is characteristic of them. Their physical properties also suggest this. They never become hard and crystalline like sugar but always retain the viscous consistency of an ointment, which may approach the quality of wax. As oils, they never become as fluid as water, although they are lighter. This highly viscous aggregate state could be characterized as existing between solid and fluid if it were not that fats are lighter than water, their sphere lying above this element. Still, it could not be said that they have a looser inner structure than water or that their low weight represents an approximation to the gaseous state, as it would in other volatile substances, for example, ether or the essential oils, which, as simple fatty acids, chemically are not fats.

The immiscibility of fats with water indicates that the etheric element is foreign to them. Their behavior in congealing, their inability to harden in mineral form, shows that they also refuse to be pentrated by the physico-mineral laws. It has been mentioned repeatedly that the ego organization supports itself on the minerals, which is why sugar is a typical carrier of the ego organization. So we can say that neither the etheric body nor the ego organization plays a significant role in the formation of fats. Rather, it is the astral body that has a clear relation to the essential nature of fat. The astral body is connected with the star world, as even its name shows. Similarly, fat, as the bearer of the astral body, is so cosmically oriented that it has no direct access to the physical world of the earth. To be sure, the etheric forces also stem from the periphery, the cosmos, but this is just as differentiated as terrestrial substances. Earthly substances, after all, are really an image of cosmic forces. While primarily the etheric forces act in water and protein, the astral forces are active in air and in fat. Fat thus represents a step on the path by which the ego engages in the organism. The astral body stands between the etheric body and ego just as fat stands between protein and sugar.

The glycerine obtained from fat also shows the intermediate position that is characteristic of fat: it is soluble both in water and in organic fat solvents. In the splitting of fat into glycerine and fatty acids, however, this intermediate position disintegrates in a way. Glycerine has a strong ability to absorb water; it is hygroscopic. This ability is obviously lost when glycerine is combined with fatty acids, the rigidity of which is loosened through this combining.

The melting points of the fatty acids rise with the length of their carbon chains. The predominance of the fatty acids, C_{16} and C_{18}, is striking. They form the principle fats. Simply by their high melting point, the longer fatty acids show a rigid, lifeless behavior close to that of the chemically sluggish paraffin. It is characteristic of the nervous system that in it are found long-chain fatty acids (C_{24} cerebronic acid). This tendency toward rigidification is an essential expression of the nervous system; in other words, for its typical manner of functioning, the nervous system needs such lifeless, inactive substances.

Now we shall direct our attention to the unsaturated fatty acids. They distinguish themselves from other fatty acids with the same number of carbon atoms by a greater affinity for warmth. They are more heavily permeated by warmth, as their lower melting point shows. These qualities are expressed symbolically by the double bond. Their higher biological activity is based on their great inner content of imponderabilia. As examples, let us name just linoleic acid and linolenic acid, which occur primarily in linseed oil.[20] It should also be mentioned at this point that human body fat has an extremely low melting point, which is an expression of a strongly internalized warmth process. In this we can see an indication of the action of the ego organization, which works in warmth. The human metabolism in particular shows a strong inner activity in this respect. We cannot, however, explore the chemical nature of fats here.

The shortest-chain fatty acids, such as formic and acetic acids, are strong acids that display a marked volatility, and therefore odor. This property is an expression of the inherent capacity of these substances for dissolution. As we know, ants have the function in nature of taking formerly living substance, which has fallen out of life, and reincorporating it into the flow of life; for example, they bring wood toward rotting so that it does not go over to the inorganic state. Wood, however, is really sugar become "earth," since every particle of wood was once in the form of some sugar before solidifying. Formic acid formation is an essential part of the dissolving activity of ants, even if the acid itself does not participate directly in the dissolution of the wood. Through its corrosive properties it thus shows the essence of the dissolving activity in which it arises. The clear orientation of formic acid toward wood, a "mineralized" substance that has fallen out of the living process, leads us to this substance's relation to and action in the human organism. It opens the mineral realm once again to the action and control of the etheric body.

Acetic acid also shows this orientation toward the earth. In the section on metabolism, we described fermentation as a way of breaking down carbohydrates that ought not to occur within an organism but is only caused by the action of terrestrial environmental influences. Alcohol arises in this way. If the necessary influences remain, then the alcohol is finally oxidized to acetic acid, which is one step more earthly than alcohol.

It is also characteristic of the intermediate position of the fats that the physiologically "typical" fatty acids (palmitic and stearic acids) stand between the short-chain and long-chain fatty acids. The shortest-chain fatty acids, it is true, lose their fatty character and become acidic, while the longest-chain fatty acids approach paraffins or waxes in character.

A further characteristic of the fats that deserves mention is their low oxygen content as this illustration shows.

	Carbohydrates	Fat	Protein
Calculated for:	cane sugar	stearic acid	sundry
carbon	26.7	32.2	50–55
hydrogen	48.8	64.4	6.6–7.3
oxygen	24.5	3.4	19–24

Relation of carbon : hydrogen : oxygen, in per cent

The fats crave oxygen and in combustion they can take in a great deal of it. Oxygen is the element by which a substance first really gains a connection with the earth. It performs the same function in the human organism as well (see chapter on the lung, Vol. III). So we see that the low oxygen content and the immiscibility of the fats in water are an expression of their lack of connection with the earth; they prefer to conform to cosmic (astral) laws. For this reason, they are able to take in extraterrestrial impulses (imponderabilia), such as light and warmth, in large quantities. Their combustibility makes this manifest. The high caloric value of the fats is a clear indication of their pronounced affinity for warmth.

> 1 gram carbohydrate yields 4.1 cal
> 1 gram protein   yields 4.1 cal
> 1 gram fat   yields 4.1 cal

It can be seen that the fats store the most warmth in their substance. This warmth is liberated in the last step in their breakdown. The human being possesses a warmth organism and, as has been repeatedly said, the ego organization lives in it. Thus, all production and regulation of warmth depends on the ego organization. In relation to the fats, then, it can be said that, while fat metabolism is generally governed by the astral body, the last step of their catabolism, the metamorphosis into warmth, is a function of the ego organization.[21] Before the implications of this are discussed, we shall discuss the various steps in the organism's confrontation with fat.

The reason fat cannot be absorbed directly from food lies in its physical characteristics, its immiscibility with water. Mediating between fat and water is bile, by which the fats are emulsified. It is primarily by means of the bile acids (see p. 258) that fat is brought into a soluble and easily absorbable form. This ability of bile to engage actively in the turnover of substances is based on an iron impulse that is characteristic for the whole organ, the gall bladder (see section on the liver and bile, Vol. III).

This action of bile is prepared for by the stomach lipase, which brings the fats into an "oil phase," so that a better emulsification can be effected by the bile and a breakdown can be brought about by pancreatic lipase. This pancreatic enzyme is the visible result of the aforesaid active process that must always meet the flow of food. A deficiency here will be expressed in insufficient splitting of fats, which leads to steatorrhea (see above).

The breakdown of fats to fatty acids and glycerine or monoglycerides by pancreatic lipase in the small intestine is minor when compared to the protein catabolism occurring in the gastrointestinal canal. Furthermore, it does not result in any profound alteration in the nature of the fats; soon after absorption, fats, and not breakdown products, are found again.

Fat clearly does not bring much foreign etheric and astral material from the organism of its origin into that of the human being. Of itself, it could be assimilated more easily than protein, though not so easily as sugar, since it is not soluble in water. It must, therefore, first be brought into water. This occurs through emulsification, primarily by means of bile.

The further path of the fats beyond the intestinal wall is more significant than the initial stage. The relation of fats to the astral body has been described in detail, and we are also familiar with their relation to warmth. This relation is shown, on the one hand, by the high caloric content and, on the other, by the unsaturated fatty acids, whose double bonds show that they are inwardly permeated with warmth. This affinity for warmth, in turn, provides the connection to the ego organization, which lives in warmth.

The way in which the organism deals with fat must, of

course, reflect the quantity and quality of the fat consumed in food, but it is primarily dependent on the astral body and ego. In a healthy organism, these will manage the fat in such a way that the proportion of depot fat, organ fat, and cell fat is optimal for the given individual and the given organ. We can see the influence of the higher members of man's being on fat metabolism in the particular substances produced through their action in various organs. For example, thyroid hormones and adrenalin have a lipolytic action, and both are substances through which the astral body engages in the metabolism (see p. 272), whereas insulin, which originates from the activity of the ego organization, promotes the synthesis of fatty acids.

Disorders of fat metabolism can also be understood in light of the relationships described. The transformation of food into fat is above all a function of the astral body. If the astral body, though active, does not engage sufficiently in the metabolism, obesity will result; this is not at all so dependent on food consumption as it is commonly portrayed today. The opposite syndrome, emaciation, may well stem from an excessive catabolic process, but it can also come about when fat formation as such is too weak, that is, when the astral body is not sufficiently engaged. In addition, there can be an insufficient intake of food, which would point to the etheric body as the site of the primary disorder. It has long been known that arsenic can be used to promote the accumulation of fat. It has been indicated many times that the astral body can be specifically stimulated with arsenic. Arsenic effects a generally stronger incarnation of the astral body. Related is the fact that the accumulation of fat generally increases with age and also shows a typical distribution. This is a function of the gradual withdrawal of the higher members of man's being from the metabolism.

We see that the distribution of fat, as well as its formation, is primarily related to the astral body. Now we might ask, how much fat is transformed into warmth? This, as mentioned, is a function of the ego organization. If this transformation is too weak, then the fat cannot be processed further and remains in its normal state. With a too-intensive transformation, an excess of uncontrolled warmth arises in the organism. Rudolf Steiner called these places that are not incorporated into the warmth organization "parasitic foci of warmth."[22] In contrast, insufficient production of warmth from fat leads, through the insufficient action of warmth in the tissue, to a relative rigidity. The ego is forced to satisfy its hunger for warmth by taking the necessary warmth from the activities of the organs. "In this way, they become brittle and stiffened inside."[23] In these two cases, one of too-strong and the other of too-weak transformation into warmth processes, we can perceive a tendency of the organism toward inflammation or sclerosis. It is the influence of the higher members of man's being, particularly the ego organization, that creates this disposition.

These suggestions that one factor underlying sclerosis can be a problem with fats have been confirmed repeatedly in recent years. Especially the qualitative aspect of the fats has been recognized. In view of our discussions, it is easy to see that highly unsaturated fatty acids, which have taken in much warmth, can be managed more easily by the ego organization and are therefore more active in the metabolism. Saturated fatty acids, in contrast, are by their very nature the prototype of fixity and sclerosis (see section on diet, especially pg. 230 f.).

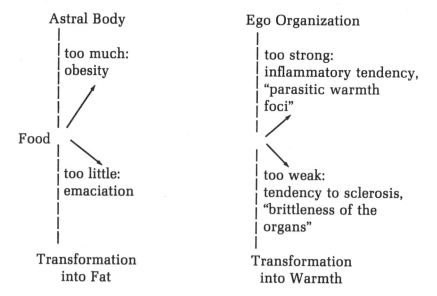

Astral Body	Ego Organization
too much: obesity	too strong: inflammatory tendency, "parasitic warmth foci"
Food	
too little: emaciation	too weak: tendency to sclerosis, "brittleness of the organs"
Transformation into Fat	Transformation into Warmth

Comparing fat to protein and the carbohydrates, we can say in summary that it assumes a well-defined intermediate position and also plays a sort of intermediate role. This function is performed perhaps in an even more pronounced way by the steroids, which are lipids.

Steroid Metabolism

There are a number of fatlike substances that are similar to fats in their physical behavior, but yet chemically are not fats. Of these, we will discuss one group of substances called steroids. They share the sterol framework as a "core," showing quite a uniform structure, and yet through quite minimal variation they manifest and act very differently.

One of these substances, cholesterol, has already been mentioned. It is found in all animal cells and body fluids. The highest cholesterol content is found in the adrenal cortex (5 per cent), nerve tissue (2.3 per cent), and skin. The single fact that this substance occurs exclusively in the animal kingdom and in man is a clear indication of a relation to the function of the astral body. Its abundance in the adrenal gland and nerves virtually gives us a key to understanding this substance. As is described in the chapter on the kidney (Vol. III), the kidney system has the function of "switching" the catabolic impulses coming from the nervous system into anabolic processes. This anabolism proceeds by way of the adrenal cortex, where the astral body is active within the etheric body, that is, anabolically. Accordingly, we can designate cholesterol as the carrier of the unspecific anabolic action of the astral body in the metabolism.

The fact that the highest cholesterol values are found in the adrenal gland and in the brain is an indication of the polarity between the nervous system and the urogenital system, which is described in greater detail in the chapter on the kidney (Vol. III). In the lower part of the human organism, specific differentiations develop on the "unspecific" foundation of cholesterol; these are described individually below. Most of them have a markedly anabolic character.

In the upper organism, in contrast, the same undifferentiated foundation serves the opposite functions. Brain substance consists almost exclusively of fats and lipids. Among the fatty acids found in the brain, however, are just those with the highest number of carbon atoms, that is, with the longest chains and the highest melting points. They are thoroughly rigidified. The whole structure of the sphingomyelins and particularly of the cerebrosides, manifests a process of extreme rigidification, which also underlies the formation of the brain and nervous system. Rudolf Steiner called this rigidification tendency of brain substance "ossifying," but it is interrupted at its very inception.[24] The cerebrosides show this in its most extreme form. These connections can be pursued in minute detail, but in this framework a few orienting indications must suffice.

Cholesterol is also included in this realm of rigidification and death forces in the nerve substance. Because of its unique character, it can participate in the dynamics of the nervous and the metabolic systems. Without such a mediating carrier substance, the astral body could not work anabolically in the metabolism but would have a catabolic action there as well. Cholesterol, however, gives the astral body the ability to penetrate either system, mediating a reversal of its catabolic activity in the adrenal gland. Through the nervous system, the astral body has an anabolic, consciousness-forming activity; through the metabolic system, its action is catabolic, organizing. Since we are dealing with a genuine polarity here, there must be a common element that has access to both poles. Cholesterol is the carrier substance here. In purely functional terms, however, it is the rhythmic system that stands between the polar systems; this makes it possible for the human being to experience the polarity.

At this point we will briefly discuss aspects of the cholesterol metabolism, the pathological alterations of which give indications of the higher members of man's being. The highest serum cholesterol values are found in genuine lipoid nephrosis. This disease, as we explain in the section on renal diseases (Vol. III) entails a disturbance in the formation of proteins that results in "excessive activity of the etheric body." This is manifested in the abnormally high cholesterol level. The astral body does not engage strongly enough from above in catabolism and structuring; rather, it tends to act anabolically from below, without this anabolism being founded on a sufficient preceding catabolism. In acute nephritis, however, hypocholesterolemia is generally found, expressing the excessive astral engagement from the nervous system.

Diabetics also show heightened blood cholesterol values, but as we have frequently mentioned, this is a matter of insufficient penetration and control of the etheric or astral body by the ego organization.

The alterations of the cholesterol level under the influence of the thyroid gland are quite characteristic, since it is through this organ that catabolic, awakening, consciousness-stimulating action of the astral body flows down from above. In Graves' disease this activity is pathologically exaggerated. Hence, we find a decrease in the cholesterol level in Graves' disease, while myxedema shows an increase.

It is unnecessary to go into the various alterations found in other diseases. The list could be extended, but from the examples presented it can be seen that cholesterol indicates the interaction of the astral and etheric bodies, and that in this respect as well, not only biologically, it represents a mediating, intermediate substance.

We have mentioned the differentiation of the unspecific action of the astral body in the lower organism, which takes place through cholesterol. As the structural formulas illustrate, this differentiation can be traced in the physiological steroids.

Of the structural formulas, let it just be said that they should be understood not anatomically, but rather in the way they were originally meant: as the shortest description of the properties of a substance. The formula H_2O, for example, says that this substance will yield hydrogen and oxygen in the proportion 2:1. In an analogous way, a double bond means that more imponderables, for example light and warmth, are active in the substance; or in the language of chemists, it possesses a greater energy content. Similarly, ring formations or steric differences must be understood as characteristics of a quite definite behavior of the given substance.

We see here that the differences between cholesterol and

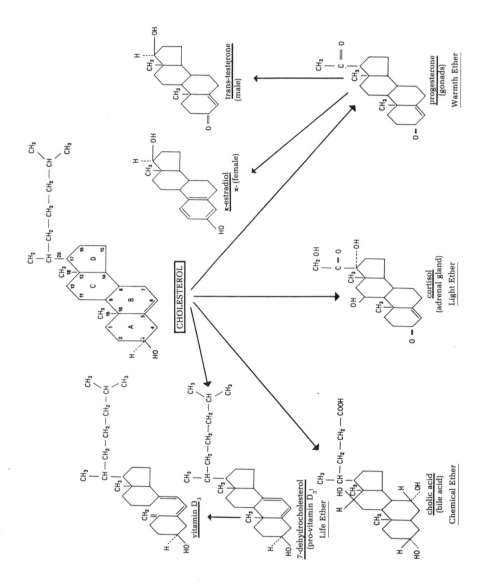

256

vitamin D are still minimal, but that they become greater as one approaches the sexual hormones; that is, the action becomes more specific as the substance becomes more "catabolized," more differentiated.

It may at first appear unjustified to regard the substances with simpler structures, such as the sexual hormones, as developments from the more complex cholesterol; in general, the more complicated molecule is seen as the derivative of the simpler one. Observation of the essential nature of organic development, however, will always reveal that the specific is derived from the general, the part from the whole, the dead from the living, never the reverse. To be sure, it is possible by synthesis to arrive at the complicated from the simple, but it will never be possible to build an organism from its parts. What Günther Wachsmuth showed for the whole earth and the development of organic life[25] also applies to the specific.

The differentiation already proceeds quite clearly in the adrenal gland, where the separate steps can be detected (see below and chapter on the kidney, Vol. III). This gland is the starting point of all differentiations of the steroids. About forty adrenal hormones are known today. Nevertheless, it is not so much the substance as the process visible in it that is important. The process can serve as the carrier for varied or labile substances, or it can be so fleeting that it does not manifest itself materially. In any case, the isolated active substance is the dead image of the process, though of course it still reveals the characteristics of the latter.

1. Cholesterol undergoes its smallest change in the transformation into physiological vitamin D_3 in the skin. This metamorphosis is effected by light. The skin, which is in practically continuous contact with light, stores 7-dehydrocholesterol (provitamin D_3). The transformation by means of light into vitamin D_3 can be traced chemically to the splitting of the B-ring. The creation of a second double bond in the molecule tells us that an imponderable—an immaterial quality, in this case, light— has been taken into the substance and has entered into it "substantially." Once the substance has assimilated the light, it enters in this form, imbued with a cosmic quality, into the body

and is stored in the liver, kidneys, adrenal glands, and brain. The activated vitamin is thus the product of the interaction of an inner and an outer light process, and by virtue of this it is a light-storer. If one of these two processes is disturbed, as when there is a lack of outer or inner light, then the basis for rickets is present. (The transformation of cholesterol into 7-dehydrocholesterol comes about through the activity of the human being's own light organism.) The cooperation of both processes is the precondition for healthy bone growth and normal calcification. This is the domain where substances leave the watery element and go into the mineral state, apparently dying. This is, in fact, the domain of the life ether.

2. The bile acids are essential components of bile. The metabolic action of bile is linked to the bile acids. These substances also conduct astral impulses into the etheric body; their action, however, is directed specifically toward the unlocking of the fats. On the one hand, they gain access to the fats by virtue of having fat-like bile characteristics without being fats themselves. On the other hand, their surface activity has the effect of mixing fat with water. This brings about a fine, emulsified distribution (cholic acid principle). Fat thus becomes accessible to the action of lipase and is capable of being absorbed easily. Hence, the bile acids are substances through which the astral body works in the chemical ether.

In the chemical formula this process is expressed in the three characteristic steps by which cholesterol is transformed into bile acids. The loss of the double bond shows us that an imponderable quality has been lost and that earth forces are engaging more strongly, which is typical of bile (see chapter on the liver, Vol. III). Next, there is a twofold hydroxylation, so that the cholic acid formed in this process has three OH-groups. This provides the relation to the watery element, which is a prerequisite for this acid's emulsifying capacity. Then, an oxidative shortening of the side chain takes place. Here we are dealing with the form of catabolism typical of the animal metabolism, as we have illustrated repeatedly in protein metabolism; in this case, it leads to a specialization. The acid character given by the carboxyl group is not strong, but it is also an indication of the astral action in its chemical nature.

The bile acids enter the intestine and are reabsorbed (enterohepatic circulation). A bacterial reduction takes place in the intestine; the secondary bile acids arise, deoxycholic and lithocholic acid, which have only two and one hydroxyl groups respectively. The solubility and capacity for specific functions is lowered in these compounds and approaches that of cholesterol.

Cholesterol, poorly soluble by itself, is held in solution by the chemical ether. The chemical ether, which holds the various (often poorly soluble) substances—for example, cholesterol, uric acid, etc.—in supersaturated solution, is manifested in the electrical charges and protective colloids that prevent the precipitation of substances from the unstable condition. (Bile is designated as a colloidal solution.) If the etheric body is too weak here, or if the astral body does not differentiate the cholesterol sufficiently into the bile acids, then these and other substances (cholesterol, calcium, pigment) fall out of the metabolism (precipitate) and are deposited. This creates the basis for gall stone formation. Moreover, the bile acids will be missing from the intestine for absorption of the fats; the fats then remain foreign bodies, since they cannot be taken in hand by the astral body (see the chapter on the liver, Vol. III).

3. It has been mentioned that the adrenal cortex is the starting point for the many-sided differentiations of the steroids. A knowledge of the essence of this organ, as described in the chapter on the kidney (Vol. II), provides the key to this transformation, and this insight shows us that the adrenal cortex mediates impulses that are formed when the astral body's catabolic action, which it possesses until it reaches the adrenal medulla, is switched through a "radiating" activity of the kidney system into an anabolic action. The close connection of the hypophysis and adrenal cortex (ACTH) shows that this action occurs by way of the etheric body. Cholesterol is an expression of the hitherto undifferentiated anabolic activity of the astral body within the etheric body (see above). More than any other substance, cortisol has concentrated in itself the life-

sustaining force that initially makes the entire metabolism possible and that flows from the adrenal cortex; it makes up 70 per cent of the total secretion of the adrenal cortex. Corticosterone, which was isolated earlier than cortisol, is also a carrier of this action. Its formula corresponds to that of cortisol, except that it lacks the hydroxyl group at C_{17}.

The clinical picture of an adrenal cortical insufficiency is Addison's disease; this syndrome includes abnormal pigmentation of the skin, adynamia, and metabolic disorders. The consequences of disorders in the higher members of man's being are clearly recognizable in this illness.

The dark skin indicates a disorder in the light metabolism (see p. 290 ff.). The inner light process is too weak, and the organism protects itself against the outer light, which is relatively too strong, by means of pigmentation; hence, this appears particularly at places exposed to the light. This disorder is a good indication that we are in the domain of the light ether. The diminished phosphorylation is also connected with the disturbed light metabolism, since phosphorus is the carrier of light. The decreased phosphorylation, however, like the hypoglycemia, shows that the ego is insufficiently active in anabolism, or that it has no adequate carrier in the blood. Its engagement in the body is hampered. The most striking symptom of adrenocortical insufficiency is weakness, lack of energy and buoyance. These symptoms reveal the general atrophy of the etheric body, which cannot regenerate itself because the astral body and ego organization are not brought into the anabolic process sufficiently. This is the case because the physical mediator of this process, the adrenal cortex, is destroyed (primary adrenal cortical insufficiency, Addison's disease) or because there is a primary constitutional weakness of the higher members of man's being, so that the adrenal glands cannot fulfill their function (secondary, relative adrenal cortical insufficiency or Addisonism).

Imbalance of the mineral metabolism is also characteristic of Addison's disease. Too much sodium is excreted, while potassium is retained. Sodium is the substance through which the astral body engages in the water organism. It is related to the capacity for consciousness, which is connected with the saline. In contrast, the steroids are substances of astral origin that participate in anabolic processes in the etheric body. The domain of the steroids is therefore completely unconscious, since consciousness is based on catabolic processes. Thus, if the etheric body is not structured suitably for the astral body, a function of the steroids, it will be incapable of providing the basis for sufficient conscious processes. This explains the psychic disturbances in Addison's disease.

In Addison's disease, sodium does not have a strong enough "hold" in the weak etheric body, and it is excreted; the retention of sodium is an active process, controlled by the astral body (see chapter on the kidney, Vol. III). Thus, in sodium deficiency, water lacks its organizing structure and cannot be kept in the body because the water organism is controlled through sodium. Finally, the high potassium concentration is an expression of the uncoordinated etheric body, whose impulses do not come from the astral body alone. To administer sodium is to give these patients a support, a buttress for their astral bodies, thus facilitating their engagement with the etheric.

In this light, one can also understand the hypotension from adrenal cortical insufficiency; it is a typical sign of insufficient incarnation of the astral body (see chapter on the heart, Vol. III).

Here we are confronted with the same phenomenon as in diabetes. In the latter, it was sugar that could not be taken into the metabolism because of weakness of the ego organization, and so it flooded the whole organism. In that case, however, the outer excess (hyperglycemia) replaced the inner process (insulin production) to a certain extent. In Addison's disease it is the astral body that cannot be brought to anabolic activity within the etheric body. Here, as well, intake of the carrier substance, sodium, can replace the active inner process more or less completely. It can be seen from this that both the blood sugar and the sodium level, and correspondingly absorption and excretion, come about through an active participation of the higher members of man's being. Predominance by one side will still permit functioning, but the true meaning of the actively maintained balance does not lie in the domain of the metabolism. The spiritual aspect of the human being can unfold only in an equilibrium of the inner and outer processes.

The adrenal cortex is pluripotent. In its peripheral layer (the zona glomerulosa) mostly aldosterone is formed, while in the middle region (zona fasciculata) the "real" adrenocortical hormones, cortisol and corticosterone, are produced; in the medulla (the zona reticularis) androgens are produced.

Aldosterone brings about a renal retention of sodium. Up to a certain point this is physiological. We have already spoken of sodium's role as the foothold of the astral body in the water organism. In aldosterone we can clearly see how the astral body engages in the water organism, the vehicle of the etheric body. From our description of the relation of the steroids to the higher members of man's being, one should understand that one of these substances acts as a mediator here. For this reason, the action of the astral body in water is always anabolic here, supporting the etheric body, and not excretory, which would speak of a dynamic of the astral body flowing "from above" through the nervous system. Secondary hyperaldosteronism can be seen as the organism's attempt to regenerate the etheric body by means of increased water retention, that is, through the retention of water in the tissue. We meet with this condition not only in chronic salt and water loss but also as a result of cirrhosis of the liver, cardiac insufficiency, hypoproteinemias, essential hypertension, burns, etc., that is, whenever the etheric body is weakened or damaged. Because of the weakness of the etheric body, the water taken into the organism cannot be vitalized and further processed. It becomes practically a foreign body and is "deposited" as a discharge or edema. Of course, this water retention can have secondarily harmful effects, for example, in ascites, pulmonary edema, etc. The fact that a healing measure taken by the organism does not lead to success, or may even be turned into its opposite, does not yet speak against its expediency in principle.

Cortisol as a physiological substance has been described. Replacement therapy of cortisol is possible. At present, however, such therapy is used chiefly not for replacement, but as a pharmacodynamic therapy in a dosage far exceeding its physiological level. Many diseases for which it is used, such as rheumatic diseases, asthma, skin affections, blood diseases, etc., are unrelated to adrenal cortical insufficiency. Cushing's syndrome therefore occurs as a typical side effect of this overdose. In this syndrome we can see directly the predominance of the anabolic process, which can lead to a constitutional transformation. The altered psychic disposition after the use of cortisone preparations also demonstrates the anabolic current, which the patient senses distinctly. It is characteristic of this effect that it is not associated with suppression of consciousness, as is the case with the anabolic process during sleep; in contrast, this kind of anabolism, which is connected with the activity of the adrenal cortices during the day, often involves the astral body more intensely in other areas as a reaction. This can lead to ulcer formation, since the stomach is an organ of the astral body (see p. 213).

In order to avoid the undesirable side effects of this high dose therapy, the basic substance is modified and substituted in a great variety of ways so that the effects can be controlled to a certain extent. These derivatives are naturally no longer physiological substances, so they bear no simple relation to the higher members of man's being. Another side effect of steroids is their ability to suppress mesenchymal reactions. This is why they are among the strongest specifics against inflammation, exudation, and proliferation. This effect can be understood in the light of the above descriptions; that is, even this suppression can be seen as an anabolic process, or at least as the prevention of catabolism. On p. 167 it was shown that inflammation is initially based on a catabolic process; this is reflected even in the substances involved, such as histamine (see p. 274). Inflammation is also associated with an intensified engagement of the astral body, but here it is in a completely different dynamic: dissolving, breaking down, and secondarily productive or proliferative. These substances of the cortisone group bring about a "switching" of the astral body in the sense described above.

The formation of the androgens in the adrenal cortex does not have a sex-determining action; it is also present in females.

These androgens are rather the specific expression of the anabolic action transmitted through the adrenal cortex. The anabolic influence on protein balance is connected with them, as is the growth spurt at puberty. These are processes that incarnate the human being more strongly, in the sense of increased development of the physical body. This can be recognized in the male hormones in a far more pronounced way than in those of the female.

4. The urogenital system forms a functional unit (see chapter on the kidney, Vol. III). The gonads represent a higher development of impulses that are already present in the renal system and suggested in the adrenal glands. The activity of the astral body within the etheric body is most differentiated in the gonads, where the male-female principle is at work. At the time of puberty it can be clearly seen that it is the astral body that totally changes its mode of action. This was described above (see p. 69) as the "birth" or "liberation" of the astral body. Until this time the astral body was active in forming organs. organs. This liberation in or for the soul realm is associated with a corresponding organic change that takes place in the gonads and also manifests itself in hormone production. It is a unique characteristic of the genital system that the freeing of the astral body in the soul realm is connected with a clear general growth spurt and with the beginning of productivity in the gonads. A new and different kind of growth commences, a new vitalization that bears the specific stamp of the astral body. One can see clearly how the astral and etheric bodies are closely interwoven here; soul and bodily processes are coupled; in fact, they are identical here. The members of man's being are active "sulfurically," to use the old nomenclature; the "imponderabilia" are internalized, active in the substance, bound in the metabolism. This is the domain of the warmth ether. The nerve-sense system stands in polar opposition to it; here, in the salt pole, the higher members of man's being are active in the salt process. Substance becomes permeable to imponderables; the members of man's being are free. Here, we see that the aforementioned polarity between the nerve-sense and urogenital systems is greatly enhanced in the sexual organs.

Since this polarity has the most critical importance for the nervous system and consciousness, it is understandable that these will be more strongly formed the greater the polar tension. This is the case in the male organism. The descent of the testes is the physical analogue to his physiologically stronger development of consciousness and emphasis on the nerve-sense system. Correspondingly, ritual circumcision appears as a measure whose significance is not primarily in the organic domain but rather in its specific influence on the nerve-sense function and consciousness.

Since the hormones originate from the action of the higher members of man's being in the body, the latter are reflected back in them. Progesterone has its greatest significance as a corpus luteum hormone in pregnancy. As a 17-ketosteroid it still shows a strong similarity to the genuine adrenocortical hormones, with which it has the anabolic function in common, though this is more specialized in progesterone. Both functionally and chemically, progesterone represents the connecting link between the adrenocortical hormones and the estrogenic and androgenic hormones.

Female and male gonadotropic hormones are formed by the man and the woman. This differentiation develops out of a relative unity that can be recognized in progesterone as well. It is the image of an evolutionary process, the development of the male/female polarity from an originally unified form. We have pointed out many times that the male is incarnated one step more deeply and is connected more closely with the earth than the female, who generally remains more cosmic. When we compare the structural formulae of estradiol and testosterone, as the typical estrogenic and androgenic hormones, we find that the relatively slight differences are nevertheless highly important. Estradiol has a threefold double bond in the A-ring, which shows that an "imponderable," a cosmic action, is more strongly internalized there. Testosterone, in contrast, has only one double bond; in this respect it is like progesterone and cortisol, and like them it also possesses oxygen at C_3. This provides the stronger earth connection than in estradiol and with it the stronger anabolic action. Testosterone, however, is still further broken down (at C_{17}) than progesterone and hence more differentiated. Here it also shows an earthly character.

From the description of the dynamic of the steroids, one will understand that the cardiac glycosides, of such great therapeutic significance, have a sterane derivative as the basis of their cardiac effect. Through it, the astral body is specifically brought into the etheric body of the heart with an anabolic action, so that the impulse to movement acquires a foundation again (see chapter on the heart, Vol. III).

In summary, the function of the steroids is to act as mediators of astral impulses and to convert their catabolic effects into anabolic processes. The steroids enable the astral body to work structurally, formatively within the etheric body. For this reason, a relative uniformity of the substances (sterane framework) is needed, although there still may be strong differences among them. Their action affects the entire human organism and reaches from the living reproduction in the genital region to the physico-mineral processes of the bone system (vitamin D). Thus, an anabolic process is proper to all of these substances, and linked with it is an effect that extends into the soul life; such is the particular nature of this astral action.

Protein Metabolism

Proteinaceous substance is distinguished from the carbohydrates and fats by nitrogen. Nitrogen is the principal component of air, in which it is nonreactive, dead. The astral body lives in the airy element, just as the etheric body lives in the watery element. Air, however, is not only active as the air organism, that is, in gaseous form in the human being. It also enters as nitrogen into certain characteristic substances that are enabled by their nitrogen component to be a vehicle for the soul or for astral effects. An ensouled being requires a "living nitrogen" as body substance; this is protein. As an astral body does not incarnate in plants, they need no nitrogen for their bodily substance. Only at those exceptional times when astral impulses are active in the plant kingdom do we find substances that are characteristic of astral action: the alkaloids, which accordingly contain nitrogen. Protein is the universal vehicle of life, and as such is found in plants as well. Through its manifold qualities (in contrast to the relatively uniform carbohydrates) and lability, it is infinitely malleable and accessible to the action of the formative forces. This is why protein is the real vehicle of life.

This living protein—as yet, it is "only" living—is then molded species-specifically by the particular animal. The "laws" of the animal's existence and its essential quality can then unfold in this protein.

In the human being, an individual stamp is added to the etheric and astral qualities of the protein. Each human being constructs his own individual protein as the specific forming substance of his bodily nature; this expresses his ego. Herein lies the essential difference between protein and the other body substances. All human beings have the same sugar in their blood, namely glucose. Only such a superindividual substance as glucose can serve as the vehicle for the ego organization, which every human being possesses. Human protein, however, is the expression of the etheric body, astral body, and ego.

Protein Breakdown

When protein is removed from an organism and subjected to the laws of the outer world, it rots through the action of bacteria. The sulfur compounds are released first, although protein's sulfur content is relatively small. The sulfur in protein is simply quite active and labile. Nitrogen compounds (NH_3, etc.) are not liberated until much later. This kind of catabolism does not take place within the organism, except in the colon, because protein is kept within the "laws" of the etheric body. The etheric body wages a constant battle against putrefaction.

The breakdown of protein in the stomach is initiated by pepsin in combination with hydrochloric acid, and results in peptone formation. These are then broken down in the alkaline medium of the intestine, by the trypsin from the pancreas, into the oligopeptides. The various peptidases of the mucosa cells of the small intestine carry out the last step of breakdown to the amino acids.

When we survey the modes of protein breakdown, we see that what takes place in the acid environment of the stomach is relatively crude. The purely catabolic character of pepsin in conjunction with the acidity points to the astral body. The stomach merely prepares and opens food; by far the more comprehensive breakdown of protein is effected by the pancreatic enzymes. They, however, cannot attack completely native protein, such as raw chicken egg or blood serum. These are still so strongly permeated by the etheric body of the animal that they are not susceptible to the action of another living creature. If they are denatured by cooking or by acid, destroying the etheric connection, then they will be accessible to the pancreatic enzymes. By means of the pancreatic enzymes and the intestinal fluids, protein is finally resolved into amino acids, that is, deprived of life. This kind of catabolism thoroughly removes the foreign etheric and astral qualities of the protein, stripping it of life. In this, we see an indication of the action of the ego organization. "Everything that comes within the domain of the ego organization dies."[26] We are inevitably reminded of sugar, the vehicle of the ego organization; it displays a markedly lifeless, mineral structure, although it shows the characteristics of something originating in life. It is not difficult to recognize this deadening, mineralizing tendency of the ego organization in the pancreas as well.

The Pancreas

The production of enzymes and hormones in the glands takes place through the etheric body. The type of the particular secretion, however, is also determined by the other members of man's being that act in or through the gland. Insulin, the secretory product of the β-cells of the pancreas, is a result of the action of the ego organization, which engages in the metabolism through it. As we have mentioned, fat metabolism is governed by the astral body. Hence, the lipase of the pancreas can be recognized as an enzyme originating in the activity of the astral body. Protein, as the vehicle of life, is governed directly by impulses from the etheric body, but all the higher members of man's being are active in protein, as we have stated.

The pancreas is a gland in which all of the members of man's being are active together and which has a dominating influence in the three types of metabolism. No turnover of substances takes place within the pancreas itself; the peace of the nervous system reigns in it, quite in contrast to the liver, which is the chief metabolic organ and the "showplace" of the turnover of substances. The pancreas is the "headquarters" of the metabolism, a sort of glandular brain in the lower organism. By virtue of the fact that it comprises all three types of metabolism, which is also true of the liver in another way, the ego organization is able to engage through it in the total metabolism and to structure the metabolism in a human way. Because of its control of the material foundation, the pancreas is of great importance for the development of man and the possibility of his spiritual unfolding; because it is a control center influencing the entire preparation of substances, disturbances in catabolism can have effects reaching into the anabolic side.

Such a knowledge of the essential nature of the organ permits a better understanding of pancreatic diseases; the range of these diseases, including acute necrosis of the pancreas, is continuously growing in importance. The pancreas is the organ through which the human being expresses his way of facing food, and thus the world in general. It makes incarnation in the metabolism possible. For this reason, pancreatic diseases frequently have a psychic component. Furthermore, the combination of pancreatic and bile diseases is not only mechanical (activation of the enzymes because of stasis, etc.) but indicative of a process governing both of the organs. After all, the bile is the substance whose formative impulse is governed by the iron process (see section on metals and the liver, Vol. II).

The character of the pancreas as an organ of incarnation also helps to explain the processes of several substances in this gland. Iron is most strongly connected with incarnation. Here it is not so active as a substance; it has transferred, as it were, much of its functioning to other metals. Iron itself is so versatile that some of its activities are also found in a special form in related metals of the iron group.

The pancreas (and the liver) is especially rich in cobalt and nickel. These two metals belong to the iron group; they are not merely related to iron; they actually represent specific individual characteristics of the all-encompassing iron. Nickel, for example, occurs about one hundred times more abundantly in the islets of Langerhans and in insulin than in the exocrine parts of the pancreas. Accordingly, less nickel than usual is found in the pancreas of diabetics. The exocrine gland tissue is specifically stimulated by nickel. Cobalt stands between copper and iron. It is no accident that cobalt and nickel are found in meteoric iron. Both represent, in opposite ways, the cosmic side of iron. These relationships are put to use in the application of meteoric iron in combination with pancreas.

Zinc is also found in insulin and is connected with its functions. Insulin without zinc is ineffective. Zinc in many respects is similar to iron, but it is unable to receive certain impulses that are characteristic of iron. As we have said, it is through insulin that the ego organization engages in the metabolism. Zinc can also be recognized as an important vehicle of this process. In contrast to iron, zinc cannot mediate conscious experience in the body. It therefore makes possible an activity of the ego organization that is undisturbed by the conscious ego. For this reason, zinc also has a generally calming action; the therapeutic use of zinc for local inflammations is also based on this (zinc shaking mixture, zinc eyedrops). Here it has the function of keeping the consciousness away from the metabolism, favoring a purely organic activity of the ego organization in the metabolism.

The Amino Acids

The amino acids represent well-defined intermediate products in the breakdown of proteins. The infinite multiplicity of protein resolves itself into the relatively uniform basic structure of about twenty amino acids. This is reminiscent of the circumstances in the carbohydrate metabolism in which the extreme diversity of kinds of starch and cellulose formed by the plant uniformly yields glucose upon breakdown.

A particular kind of protein rearrangement is transamination by means of transaminases. In this process, the α-amino group of an amino acid is transferred to an α-ketoacid (with the assistance of pyridoxal phosphate). These enzymes are especially abundant in the liver and in the myocardium. This is necessary because of their high metabolic rate. In severe tissue damage or cell death, transaminases are released into the blood and their serum level increases. Such pathological conditions are certainly a sign of increased protein breakdown; transamination, however, basically serves protein reconstruction, the maintenance that embraces anabolism and catabolism. The decisive step in this breakdown of destroyed tissue (myocardial infarction, cirrhosis of the liver) is the rapid deamination, whose significance will become clearer with the descriptions of the following types of catabolism.

Throughout the process of protein breakdown, until the formation of the amino acids, there is no alteration of the relation of the basic elements, carbon, oxygen, hydrogen, and nitrogen, to one another. At this point, this relation changes in a characteristic way. Oxidative deamination is quantitatively the predominant path of amino acid breakdown.

$$R-\underset{\underset{NH_2}{|}}{CH}-COOH \xrightarrow{-2H} R-\underset{\underset{NH}{\|}}{C}-COOH \xrightarrow{+H_2O} R-CO-COOH+NH_3$$

amino acid   ketoacid

Here we are dealing with oxidation, that is, with a type of breakdown that is typical of the heterotrophic animal metabolism, as opposed to reduction, which is typical of the plant.

Ammonia does not arise as a substance in man the way it does in the lower aquatic animals; instead, it enters the urea cycle by way of ornithine–citrulline–arginine. Urea is discussed below. The removal of nitrogen is decisive in this step.

There is yet another path of catabolism—less frequently used, it is true—but all the more significant, nevertheless: decarboxylation.

$$R-CH-COOH \xrightarrow{-CO_2} R-CH_2-NH_2+CO_2$$
$$|$$
$$NH_2$$

Here, the removal of oxygen in the form of CO_2 is decisive. The opposite of this process, oxidation, was described as the typical animal form of metabolism. This explains why oxidative deamination is found in the animal and human kingdoms but nowhere else in nature. Decarboxylation as a means of breakdown is found primarily in bacteria, in decay. It is natural that this process gives rise to products that are toxic to man and animal. An example of this is the formation of cadaverine from lysine.

Within the organism, catabolism by decarboxylation is held at a low level; it gives rise to the powerful biogenic amines, which are all toxic in large quantities, though in small amounts they are physiological substances. Among them are epinephrine, norepinephrine, serotonin, tryptophan, etc. Their production is increased in states of anxiety and excitement; they raise the synapse activity (neural transmitter substances). Both their manner of arising and their action point to the astral body, which creates these substances so that it can engage in the organism through the nervous system. This can be illustrated with the example of epinephrine. With modification, the same could be shown for other biogenic amines, but this would require a separate discussion. Similarly, at this point we cannot go into the problem of ring formation, which is essential for the action of these substances.

Epinephrine, or norepinephrine, to which the following discussion also applies, is the typical hormone of the adrenal medulla, which has a clear connection to the sympathetic nervous system and conducts its catabolic impulses into the metabolism (see chapter on the kidney, Vol. III). The action of epinephrine is clear; it produces generalized excitement, elevation of the pulse rate, increased basal metabolic rate, increased glycogen breakdown and hence elevation of serum glucose—in short, sympathicotonia. Applied topically, it leads to vasoconstriction. Bringing these actions together, one sees in them the dynamic of the astral body, which is mediated by the nervous system.

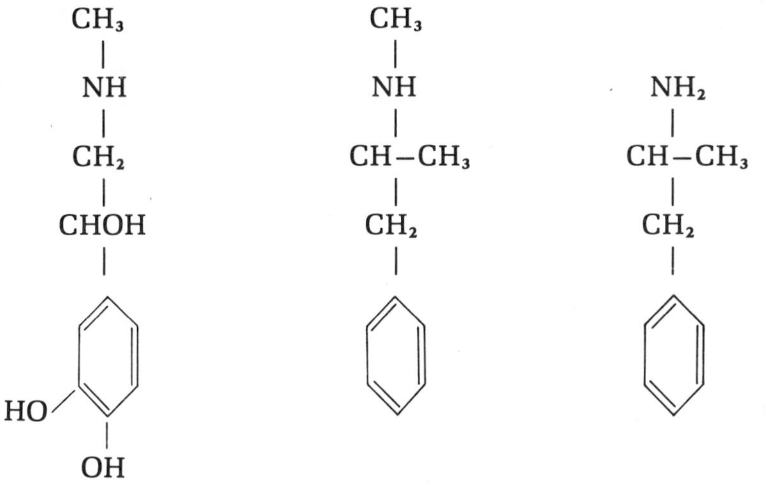

CH₃	CH₃	
|	|	
NH	NH	NH₂
|	|	|
CH₂	CH—CH₃	CH—CH₃
|	|	|
CHOH	CH₂	CH₂

HO

OH

epinephrine   pervitine   amphetamine
                                        (benzadrine)

The action is contracting, wakening, catabolic. In fright or shock, these astral impulses penetrate in an intensified form through the sympathetic nervous system into the adrenal medulla, where they bring about a more or less strong release of epinephrine. This is expressed in excitement; its catabolic manifestation, however, can even lead to death in shock.

These effects are enhanced in a one-sided way when oxygen is completely eliminated from the substance. This results in pervitine and amphetamine. These are amines with an arousing effect. They bring the soul into the body in the most intense way. Since the oxygen or the hydroxyl group is lacking, however, the connection to the typical animal oxidative metabolism is missing, as it is to the watery element through the hydroxyl group. Therefore, the effects of these substances are not so much physiologic-organic; rather, they are completely psychic, awakening.

An even stronger engagement of the astral body in the metabolism, in the sense described, is brought about by histamine, which results from the decarboxylation of histidine.

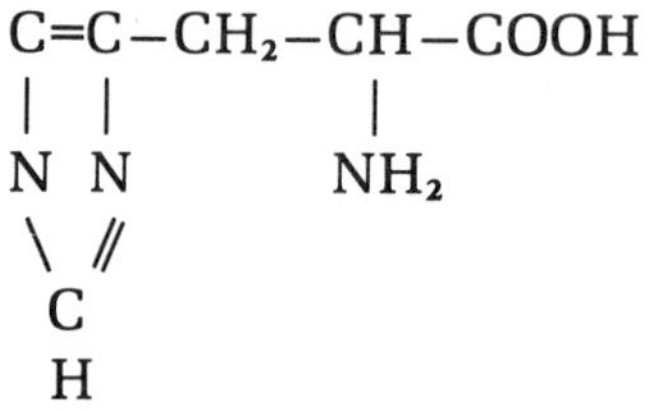

$$C=C-CH_2-CH-COOH$$

$$\begin{array}{cc} | & | \\ N & N \quad\quad NH_2 \\ \backslash & // \\ & C \\ & H \end{array}$$

histadine

$$C=C-CH_2-CH_2$$

$$\begin{array}{cc} | & | \\ N & N \quad\quad NH_2 \\ \backslash & // \\ & C \\ & H \end{array}$$

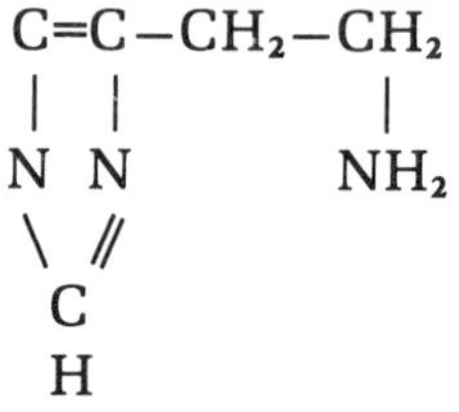

histamine

In the imidazole ring, oxygen is present twice; that is, the astral body is even more strongly internalized.

Though histamine is not abundant in the plant and animal kingdoms, it is found in many different places. It occurs in ergot, stinging nettle, bee toxin, and the salivary glands of stinging insects, as well as in animal tissues, especially the lungs, skin, and gastrointestinal tract. Histamine acts on the smooth muscle of the respiratory and intestinal tract, as well as on the uterus; it has a relaxing effect on the vessels, and brings about erythema and urticaria. For this reason, histamine is seen as the real inflammatory substance. Regarding the production of hydrochloric acid in the stomach, histamine is the most effective acid stimulator. From all this we can see in histamine an astral action penetrating deep into the metabolism and ultimately manifesting as inflammation (see p. 166).

Tryptamine, which arises from tryptophan (indolealanine) should also be mentioned in this connection.

tryptophan   tryptamine

Tryptamine has no "psychotropic effect," just as barbituric acid, as such, is not a soporific. Their derivatives, however, have quite specific actions. Both dimethyltryptamine and propyl-tryptamine are thus typical hallucinogens; their action is similar to that of LSD, but shorter in duration. Dimethyltryptamine is found, for example, in several South American legumes. It is also the active principle in the infusion of the roots of Mimosa hostilis. Similar derivatives can also be obtained from nutmeg.

Mescaline also has the structure of a biogenic amine even though it has no indole group.

mescaline

Lysergic acid is like tryptamine and barbituric acid, in that it has no psychotropic effects by itself. It is found as a component in all ergot alkaloids. The well-known psychotropic effect comes about only through substitution, that is, with a dialkyl compound such as LSD.

In all of these substances, nitrogen is the essential vehicle for the deep kind of astral engagement described. In every case, it

$$N(C_2H_5)_2$$

$$O=C$$

$$N-CH_3$$

$$N$$
$$H$$

LSD

is the decarboxylation, that is, the removal of oxygen, that first makes the specific action possible. Only in this way can the astral body engage with so strong a catabolic action in the metabolism (for example, histamine) or can psychotropic effects be produced.

Naturally, nitrogen is also present in amino acids; the effect, however, is altered by the presence of oxygen in such a way as to create the basis for living protein and anabolism. This is symbolically expressed in the formula—where oxygen is "near" to nitrogen—or in the unit of COHN. This should not be understood atomically but pictorially, that is, as the shortest description of the fact that the forces of the four protein forming substances are working together harmoniously. This provides for the typical animal form of anabolism.

If oxygen is taken from this harmonious grouping, then, briefly in concise terms, HCN is left. To be sure, cyanide does not arise as a substance; still, a modified cyanide process can be recognized in all the biogenic amines. Though this process does not go so far as to produce the substance cyanide, the individual substances arising represent steps on the way to it.

We can thus trace, on the level of substance, how our consciousness, wakefulness—that is, our soul presence—is linked to a particular form of nitrogen; this is a mild inner intoxication process that goes in the direction of cyanide formation.

The organism must be capable not only of forming these substances, but also of detoxifying them again. In the light of what has been said, it is understandable that the chief part of this detoxification is accomplished by the introduction of oxygen. The biogenic amines are practically always broken down by oxidation, which is initiated by enzymes (monoamine oxidase, diamine oxidase, among others). Here, as well, the detoxifying, life-sustaining form of oxygen in the animal and human organisms is clearly recognizable. For this reason, any substance that lacks oxygen but has carbon and nitrogen in a "close" bond represents a certain danger for the organism. For example, this is the case with porphyrin, which is discussed in detail in the section on light metabolism. In this case, iron replaces oxygen as the detoxifying factor. We need hardly elaborate on the fact that oxygen and iron are closely coupled in animal physiology in the respiratory function. Iron is also the specific antidote to cyanide, and cyanide, by blocking iron, can cripple the entire process of inner respiration. The universal healing function of iron is connected with this.

Along with oxygen and iron, a third factor in the detoxification of the cyanide process, which manifests in different degrees, is sulfur. The end result of this is rhodan formation, the elimination of potassium thiocyanate (KCNS) in the saliva, for instance.

The end product of the general protein metabolism is urea. It is the most compressed, most catabolized form of protein, that is, the "closest" combination of the four elements COHN.

$$H_2N$$
$$\diagdown$$
$$C=O$$
$$H_2N \diagup$$

urea

Here we can see how the organism always strives to keep the four protein forming substances together, even in this simplest form. Since oxygen continues to play a part up to this point, urea has no toxic properties. Although ammonia is formed intermediately on the way to urea, there is no combination with the ubiquitous bicarbonate ion to form ammonium carbonate; instead, urea is formed, which as an organic substance, in contrast to ammonium carbonate, does not bear a trace of a salty character.

Uric Acid

In the human being, the final breakdown product of a particular form of protein, the nucleic acids, is not urea but uric acid. We will devote a separate discussion to this, since it permits us to see how spiritual processes are connected with specific properties of substances.

In birds and reptiles, uric acid is excreted as the end product of the entire protein metabolism; they do not excrete urea. This is related to the lack of separation of the intestinal and renal systems in them; the significance of this is indicated in the chapter on the kidney (Vol. III).

In mammals, uric acid is broken down to allantoin by means of the enzyme uricase. In the human being (and some humanoid apes), this step beyond uric acid does not take place, so that he excretes uric acid in addition to urea. Uric acid thus has a special place in the human metabolism. The fact that the human being does not possess uricase and therefore cannot break uric acid down further is certainly no precise answer to the question why the human being excretes uric acid and the mammals do not, even though, in general, comparable types of metabolism correspond in most points.

The occurrence of uric acid alone in birds and reptiles gives us an indication of its significance in the human being. By their essential nature, birds are "far from the sphere of the earth forces." Nevertheless, they are "even more earthly than the mammals in respect to their substances."[27] The bird is totally formed by the head forces, which always have a catabolic, mineralizing character. In contrast, their metabolic processes in the intestinal system—the digestion and its differentiation, for example—are quite weakly developed, unlike in the cow, which is an example of a typical metabolic animal.

Thus, we can understand the occurrence of uric acid in man, as contrasted with the mammals, as a stronger action of the head forces. These, however, represent the salt process, as we have indicated on several occasions. The fact that the substance uric acid actually is derived from the saline head forces is shown, for example, by its strikingly poor solubility and readiness to crystallize, in contrast to allantoin and urea. In the blood and organs it is always on the point of precipitation and is prevented from it only by the colloids. It is in this capacity to precipitate easily and enter the crystalline state that we can find its significance for the human being; this we intend to demonstrate.

We have seen that uric acid points to the head forces. Now these, or the nerve-sense system, form the foundation for processes of consciousness. It is true that these also occur in the animal; the human being, however, possesses an ego consciousness, a consciousness of his self, which is made possible by an ego organization. This is, in turn, the prerequisite for the thought process, that is, for the ability to join the contents of consciousness by means of an activity of the ego. Hence, we can make a connection between uric acid—specifically, that part of uric acid that goes over into a crystalline, practically inorganic form—and the thinking process. According to Rudolf Steiner, such a uric acid secretion takes place "in a finely distributed manner in, for example, the brain.[28] In the final analysis, thinking is really a salt process connected organically with the brain and functionally with the crystalline, mineral element. More exactly, objective thought is based on the crystallizing uric acid.

Rudolf Steiner also referred to the consciousness aspect of uric acid. "The uric acid excreted through the urine produces, by such an inward counterpressure, the right disposition of the organism for sleep. Too little uric acid in the urine and too much in the blood produces such short sleep that it is not sufficient for the health of the organism."[29] We find that insomnia is accompanied by a parallel decrease in uric acid excretion; this can also be found in semi-conscious epileptic states.

Besides its decrease in insomnia, a disorder of uric acid elimination is also present in gout. If the ego organization is too weak to control the uric acid metabolism, then astral activity gains the upper hand. The astral body causes the uric acid to be excreted, but excreted inward, and it is deposited in the joints.[30] It happens that Sydenham, the first great clinician of gout, provided an indication of the connection between uric acid and thinking; he had his attacks of gout particularly while working with great exertion on his classic work on gout.

The relation of uric acid to consciousness can be recognized in an especially instructive way in the examination of the "relatives" of uric acid. Caffein, whose stimulation of consciousness is well-known, is quite similar to uric acid. Related to this are its diuretic and analeptic actions. This involves better structuring and excretion in the water organism, brought about by the higher members of man's being. Mention should also be made of theobromine, the most important alkaloid of the cacao bean; it has the same diuretic action and dilates the cardiac vessels, but it does not stimulate consciousness; the same is true of the isomer theophylline.

uric acid   caffeine   theobromine

When uric acid is broken down in a certain way by splitting off urea, the result is barbituric acid. Alone, it possesses no sedative properties, but its countless derivatives are sold as soporifics.

diethylbarbituric acid   urea

Here, two opposite directions can be recognized; one leads to stimulation (caffeine), the other to quieting (barbituric acid derivatives) of the thought process, which requires healthy formation and excretion of uric acid.

Disorders of Protein Metabolism

Even in the gastrointestinal tract, protein is broken down further than any other nutrient. No other food substance undergoes such a radical change there. If breakdown does not occur or does not go far enough, then pathological symptoms appear. If the disturbance is of a rather crude nature, so that the protein as such is not processed sufficiently, then it rots in the intestine, resulting in putrefactive dyspepsia (described above). The finer disturbances are often difficult to recognize as belonging to the protein metabolism.

We have already discussed the fundamentally oxidative metabolism in intermediate protein metabolism. Any kind of catabolism different from this leads to toxin formation and hence to pathological symptoms; this, however, is necessary to a certain extent in man's life.

The decomposition of protein by heat or in burns also gives rise to highly toxic breakdown products from the bodily substance. More severe damage is sometimes caused by these than by the actual destruction of tissue and loss of protein. This pathologically catabolized protein is eliminated through the kidneys, another source of organic damage. Fever is also associated with increased "melting down" of protein. This, however, is not caused by the temperature increase alone; a body temperature of 41° produced by external application of warmth (bath) can be tolerated without any damage, while a fever of 41° is most dangerous. Furthermore, hyperthermia from outer warming does not bring about increased nitrogen excretion, while infectious fever brings about an increase in creatinine and uric acid excretion in the urine as an expression of an increased endogenous protein catabolism. Even in chemical action we can perceive that warmth is only a vehicle of the ego and not the active principle itself. The ego, however, lives in warmth, and through it penetrates into the bodily substance during fever, melting it down and "recasting" it, that is, primarily the protein, of course. Protein is the vehicle of life, but in it lies the potential to form highly toxic substances.

First, however, the questions arise just why protein must be broken down so far in the gastrointestinal canal, and why no protein, not even larger components of it, passes into the organism. This is related to a certain pathological reaction that will be discussed here because of its increasing importance.

Allergy

When von Pirquet introduced the concept of allergy (1906), he conceived of it as an altered (different, as the name says) reactivity of the organism. He understood the phenomenon comprehensively, however, in its significance for the whole of life and in connection with polar illnesses, especially cancer. For this reason, he entitled his last work *Allergie des Lebensalters* (*Allergy and Age*)[31] and gave it the subtitle, "Malignant Tumors."

In current usage, allergy is now understood only as hyperergy, that is, as specifically induced heightened reactivity. Its opposite, anergy, is the expression of a nonreactivity, but attention is largely diverted from it by the imposing hyperergic phase. The reason the concept of allergy, which once comprehended hyperergy and anergy, is now used only for the hyperergic reaction, is connected with the customary way of conceiving disease today. In order to avoid misunderstandings, we will follow the customary usage and use the designation allergy only for the hyperergic reaction. It is only through the recent investigations in immunology that attention has been turned again to the fact that not only allergy (in the sense of hyperergy) but also anergy is a pathological reaction that plays a decisive role in the growth of tumors.

The phenomenon of excessive reaction is most clearly presented in anaphylaxis. When an animal is injected with a primarily harmless antigen, in the form of protein, for example, there is no reaction. A second injection of the same substance after several weeks, however, leads to violent reactions, even death under some circumstances (acute anaphylaxis, serum anaphylaxis, hypersensitivity reaction of the immediate type). In these conditions there is a serous inflammation with heightened capillary permeability, blood stasis, hemorrhage, and circulatory collapse. The clinical picture can be imitated particularly by histamine, which is released, along with serotonin and bradykinin, from sensitized tissue by the antigens. Certain details of these processes have been thoroughly studied. The ability to recognize the same substance is linked to an intact immune system. The small lymphocytes originating in the bone marrow, in particular, are responsible for this. The thymus (discussed on p. 25 ff.) plays a special role in this process, the development of immune cells. In this framework, we shall present only the phenomenon as a whole, and its sense and significance for the understanding and conception of disease.

The central elements are the organism's ability to "notice" the specificity of the first contact with an antigen, and that the "remembering" is manifested in the inflammatory processes. It is interesting that in order to describe these organic elements accurately and realistically, one is practically forced to use soul-spiritual concepts. We speak of "memory cells," "immunologic memory," "recognition" of self and non-self. Thus, this is clearly a matter of the soul, a remembering on the organic level. In fact, the phenomena found in allergy can also be found on the soul level: a human being, or also just an opinion, a desire, a form of expression or habit to which someone at first reacts neutrally, on repeated "action" can cause a sensitization and the psychological allergy to arise, that is, a defense. The lack of reaction, anergy, also has a counterpart: a psychological dullness in which a person does not react, or no longer reacts, even to strong psychological stimuli.

This evident connection of organic process with soul faculty is comprehensible when we remember that a step in human development is the transformation of organically bound forces into the basis for the acquisition of higher faculties. The development of the memory is based on a partial freeing of the etheric body (see pp. 16f., 30). In a wider sense, man can do mathematics and grow to wisdom only because his whole organism is constructed with wisdom according to mathematical laws. In the final analysis, both allergy (or immunity) and memory are phenomena of the etheric body. It is the bearer of memory; in it, all experiences are inscribed. To be sure, the astral body is needed for memory to become conscious. Once again, this is true not only on the soul plane. On the organic level, the phenomena of itch, reddening, release of histamine (see p. 274), and increased catabolism generally are expressions of the astral body, while the "memory cells," the lymphocytes and the thymus, represent the etheric body (see p. 27).

The possibility of inflammation is an immanent function of the human organism and can be understood only in connection with its counterpart, sclerosis; in the same way, every human being is capable of allergy. Without this capacity, he would not possess the capacity for immunity; he would be anergic and would be subject to another group of diseases: on the one hand, the infections—foreign life that overpowers the organism; on the other, the sclerotic diseases, particularly cancer. Recent research shows increasingly that the cancer patient is in an anergic phase; his immune system is not in a position to "recognize" the foreignness of the cancer cell. In any case, this situation results in the destruction of the organism of the "self" by the dominance of foreign formations (bacteria, viruses, cancer cells, mineral deposits).

This shows that health is a state of equilibrium and does not consist in the absence of a reaction. Hyperergy and anergy are the polar deviations from the healthy state and both are pathological.

From this we can draw the therapeutically important conclusion that an excess may safely be limited, but a further displacement—for example, in the direction of immunosuppression—must promote the opposite disease tendency, in this case, especially infection and cancer.

It may be surprising that infection and cancer are considered together here, whereas infections are usually grouped with the inflammatory diseases, which stand in polar opposition to cancer. The present classification applies only to immunodeficiency, which is under discussion here, and for the atypical disease course resulting from it. In the "healthy" course of an infectious disease, fever appears along with antibodies, leukocytes, etc. These reactions are the expression of an intact immune system and ideally result in healing. When the immune system is not functional, however, foreign substances (bacteria, viruses) overwhelm the organism, because it is too weak to defend itself. Fundamentally, the same process occurs in cancer, although in this case the cancer patient does not defend himself against the bodily cancer tissue because he is "blind" to it and cannot "recognize" it as foreign. In a certain respect, the autoimmune diseases represent the opposite of this situation; the organism senses itself or parts of itself as foreign and acts against itself with inflammation, which ultimately leads to dissolution and destruction.

We have seen that the organic capacity to react allergically is not only the basis for higher functions, but also the expression of constitutional health. Beyond this, however, this reaction fulfills another task, which we shall describe.

In principle, an allergy can exist or develop toward any substance; most often, however, it is protein or protein-like substances. This is understandable in the light of our description above of the essential nature of protein, since the etheric and astral bodies of the particular animal, for example, live in its protein; in man, protein is the carrier of his individuality. The sense for the "recognition" of such a substance as "foreign," that is, the sense for self and non-self, can only be the sense for preservation of one's own self from becoming foreign.

Here we have the significance of the fact that protein is the substance most thoroughly broken down in the gastrointestinal tract and that nothing of its essential quality is taken into the organism. If this mucosal boundary of the gastrointestinal tract is transgressed, then an allergic reaction sets in to make up for the missing breakdown of foreign protein on another level; so it is really a form of self-preservation. The fact that this reaction in excess (anaphylactic shock) can lead to destruction of the individual does not contradict its fundamentally higher purpose. If the reaction is suppressed repeatedly or for a long time, however, then the organism loses the ability to recognize foreign material, which is the case in cancer, or it forms foreign protein as its own body substance. Then the human being can no longer live properly as "I" in his organism; it has become foreign to him, and it is no longer possible for the spirit to unfold in accordance with the ego.

Protein Anabolism

We have seen that the breakdown of protein takes place primarily through the ego organization and that correct catabolism of food protein is the prerequisite for the formation of body protein. This formation takes place through the etheric body, which, as we know, is the source of anabolic and formative processes. It has been mentioned that the activity of the etheric body is individually determined in each human being; that is, impulses from the ego organization and astral body guide the formative processes. Rudolf Steiner indicated that human protein is the result of the interaction of four organ systems: kidney, liver, lung, and heart. They are not active merely in the formation of protein; a substance so labile as protein is permanently and wholly open to such forces and would change immediately if it were left to its own resources.

> For this reason, human protein in its structure is unthinkable in our earthly sphere. . . if it is not under the influence of these four organ systems. We must conceive of the inner construction of protein as resulting from that which proceeds from these four organ systems.[32]

Often today the conceptions reached on the basis of isolated organic activities stand in the way of an insight into the whole picture, such as spiritual scientific research has provided. It is quite possible, for example, to obtain information on details of respiratory or cardiac functioning from a heart-lung preparation; the picture of these organs' functions obtained in this way, however, must necessarily be one-sided. These organ functions can only be recognized in their mutual interaction in the organism, since a single organ extends its sphere of activity far beyond its anatomical boundaries. It can be understood only when it is seen as a part of the whole organism and when its domain of action is recognized in the rest of the organism.

Functional connection between organs are, in fact, quite well-known, which helps to overcome the one-sided conceptions of the organs. The close connection of respiratory and cardiac functioning has more than an anatomical or mechanical basis. It may also be mentioned that the adrenal cortex, belonging to the renal system, clearly influences the liver (aldosterone), the lungs (asthma), and the entire protein metabolism (anabolic hormones). Concepts such as hepatorenal syndrome, hepatogenic myocardosis, etc., point to the connection of two organs. By means of blood protein research (electrophoresis), alterations have been discovered in the plasma protein that place the protein metabolism in the center of organic research.

The anabolic activities of the liver have long been known. Similarly, the capacity of the kidneys for ammonia formation, hippuric acid synthesis, etc., has been shown; the formation of a particular, chemically definable substance, however, is not the essential aspect of the organic activity to which we are referring. It would be a mistake to search for partial syntheses in the individual organs that then might yield protein in a way analogous to the construction of an apparatus from individual parts.

Rather, we are interested in the formation of protein as a living substance that issues from the etheric body as a whole. The four organs are only the gates for various effects of the etheric body, whose harmonious flowing together results in protein. Protein, as a living substance, cannot be thought of in the cus-

tomary way as constructed from building blocks, any more
than the human body can be thought of as the result of fitting
together the head, trunk, and limbs. They both originate from a
whole. The etheric body must thoroughly overcome the strong
individual tendencies of the four basic substances found in
protein—carbon, oxygen, hydrogen, and nitrogen—before
these can be the vehicle of the formative forces. Protein has
"the capacity to lose whatever form it has by nature of its
material parts when it is called upon in the organism to serve a
form that the latter requires."[33] This is accomplished by the
four organs, each of which has a special relation to one of the
four substances. This occurrence in fours—the four organs
and the four elements—is really a reflection of the four
members of man's being: physical, etheric, and astral bodies,
and the ego organization. True, it can be said that there are
preferred relations, for example, between kidney and astral
body, liver and etheric body, lung and physical body, heart and
ego (see corresponding chapters on the organs, Vol. III), but
these should not be taken schematically. In the same way, the
substances can be connected with both the members of man's
being and the organs, but this is always true only from a particular viewpoint. For harmonious interaction, every organ has
its own relation to each substance. An expression of this opti-
mally harmonious interaction is the striving of the organism to
keep the four elements together even in urea, the last stage of
protein breakdown.

From our discussions, it will be clear that the more harmonious and finely balanced this interaction of the organs or members of man's being is, the more undifferentiated the protein
will be; in this way, it is made universal, plastic, labile. The
more differentiated and defined the protein, the more one-sided
and lifeless it is.

Since the liver is the chief metabolic organ, it is evident that
most of the transformations of substance necessary for protein
formation take place in it. It would be wrong, however, solely
on the basis of the fact that the liver is the scene of this activity,
to draw the conclusion that the impulses leading to it come

from the organ itself. The other organs are of equal importance in this process.

Nephrosis was mentioned above as an example of a typical disturbance of an organ's activity in protein formation. Nonetheless, disorders of the activity of one of these protein-forming organs need not present themselves as clinically detectable disease affecting the particular organ. The consequences of the disturbance of an organ in protein formation sometimes are manifested in quite another organ, for example, in the skin; after all, the skin is also an organ of metabolism and discharges or reflects inner processes. Finally, the dysfunction of these higher organ activities can project into the soul realm, for human soul life supports itself on these organs, just as consciousness requires the brain as an organ of reflection (see chapter on psychiatry, Vol. III).

These results of Rudolf Steiner's spiritual scientific research open us to cognition of the essential nature of various organs; the physiologically or clinically describable functions of these organs form only a part of their significance for human life. The same is true of protein metabolism and its connection with the organs. These indications are of fundamental and far-reaching help in gaining an essentially correct understanding of the human organism and its organs and in finding appropriate therapy. Furthermore, they represent only an initial and partial application of these ideas.

Protein Metabolism

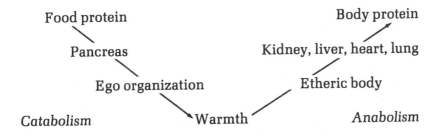

Light Metabolism

In both clinical practice and research, metabolic processes are known that have a clear relationship to light (see below); it is not customary, however, to speak of a light metabolism. Rather, the transformations in the organism tend to be seen as the transformation of various forms of energy into others, for example, chemical into kinetic energy. Despite the knowledge of various forms of energy, however, it is still not possible to explain their qualitative nature. For this reason, in our consideration of the life processes in the organism, we must not start with "energy" as such, but with the origin of all life, namely, light.

Only light is able to create living substance. An essential knowledge of light is a prerequisite for an understanding of life. In a broader sense, every living substance has arisen from a light process. This is why every living substance is also burnable. In combustion, the internalized "energy," the life, is freed again and appears as light and heat.

Today, science knows of many examples beyond the photosynthesis of plants that show that not only the autotrophic plant but also man and animal require direct light and are affected by both its presence and absence. An example is the transformation of 7-dehydrocholesterol into vitamin D^3. Beyond this, there are clear connections between light and the autonomic nervous system and metabolism, as the investigations of Hollwich[34] have shown. These impulses pass through the eye, but not by the familiar path of sight. Besides its optic function, the eye also possesses a "biological function." In this function, light impulses are conducted not only to the visual cortex but also to the "autonomic headquarters," the mesencephalon, and thus also to the hypophysis. Hollwich therefore describes, in addition to the optic, an "energetic portion of the visual path." This light effect directed at the autonomic nervous system is dependent on an intact, healthy eye.

In this way there is a stimulation of gonad development in birds (especially from long-wave light). Hemoglobin values decrease in the dark; light, however, accelerates the regeneration of the red blood cells only when it can act through the eye. As is known, the eosinophil levels follow a circadian rhythm: the highest values are found in the early morning hours, the lowest between 11 a.m. and 4 p.m. These values are dependent on adrenal activity. Countless studies, however, have shown that both functions are guided by the daylight rhythm, but in opposite ways. Intensive ocular light stimuli cause an increase in adrenocortical activity but also cause a fall in the eosinophil count.

Accordingly, the blind show clear disturbances of the vegetative functions. Particularly the water balance is disturbed. The physiological rhythm, which shows a greater excretion of urine with lower specific weight in the day and a retention and concentration in the night, is destroyed, so that enuresis occurs in the blind. We may recall the relationship of the water organism to the etheric body, which has been mentioned frequently. In addition, the blind show disorders in the regulation of the carbohydrate balance: they show an abnormally low rise in the blood sugar curve under loading. These deviations are related to a dysfunction of the hypophysis. Finally, persons blinded early in life also show a retardation of development and growth of the sella turcica. This represents a part of the disorder in the mesencephalon-hypophysis system.[35]

It is also significant that in toxicity tests with acetonitrile, test mice kept in the light displayed up to a 50 per cent lower mortality than animals kept in the dark. If the daily light rhythm is changed repeatedly, neoplasms may even result, as tests on insects have shown.

These findings indicate that light has a fundamental importance for the vital processes in man and animal. In particular, it is primarily anabolic processes that are stimulated because they are governed by the etheric body: the water organism and the hypophysis, as well as the adrenal cortex, whose relation to the anabolic processes of the etheric body is plain and has been mentioned more than once (see p. 259 f.). So it is really the etheric body that reacts to light. Rudolf Steiner also employed the terms "life body" or "light body" for the etheric body. Life is transformed light.

The purely anabolic process of assimilation in the plant, which proceeds by way of photosynthesis, meets with a new process that reverses it, a kind of dissolution, in the higher animals and man. As we have shown many times, the anabolic process, which is naturally also present in animal and man, is linked with a preceding catabolism in them.

Representatives of these two processes in the kingdoms of nature are found in chlorophyll and hemoglobin, which have a polar relation to one another. One of the milestones of chemical research has been the clarification of the connection between chlorophyll and hemoglobin. Both substances have a porphyrin framework of the isomeric type; in chlorophyll, however, it is connected with magnesium, while in hemoglobin it is connected with iron. Like all polarities, this one also can have arisen only from a common original state. This state, which lies before the separation of the animal and plant kingdoms, was repeatedly described by Rudolf Steiner.

The polar relation of hemoglobin and chlorophyll can be seen even in their color, and it becomes especially evident in relation to light. Manifestly, it is chlorophyll that first makes possible the assimilation of light by a plant; it brings light into the substance and reduces carbon dioxide and water to carbohydrates. The carbohydrates have just such a configuration as to be inwardly permeated with light. The more intense this process, the more light becomes manifest as life. To a certain degree, and for a certain length of time, light can also be stored in the dormant form of starch, or it goes over into the rigidified form of cellulose in which it is completely fixed in the dead state of chemically bound "energy."

The reversal of this process of assimilation takes place in man and animal. The respiration process, totally based on iron, releases the light qualities taken in by the plant. It is significant that small quantities of iron are necessary for the action of chlorophyll, just as the human organism requires magnesium.

Today, the transformation of light in the organism is not recognized as such, since the process is only regarded calorically, and such calculation cannot take into account the quality of the transformed imponderabilia. Even if the light released in the human organism in the process of oxidation and catabolism cannot be perceived with the eye, we must still recognize it in its transformed state; otherwise, we are closing off the possibility of understanding the disorders connected with it.

Since hemoglobin (or hemin) and chlorophyll differ from one another in their metals, we may take these as the basis of their polar relation, whereas the porphyrin framework shared by both points to light. While this relationship is quite clear in the plant, it can also be immediately recognized in man and animal when prophyrin is administered or arises in the organism. Immediately a strong photosensitivity will be noticeable; depending on the quantity, this can even lead to death within minutes in animal tests. If the test animal is kept in the dark, however, there is no reaction whatever. Hence, prophyrin is not a poison; it simply sensitizes the organism specifically to light, which then leads to severe damage or even "light death." These tests also show that hemoglobin possesses a connection to light, though this is hidden from direct observation by the combination of porphyrin with iron. The combination of porphyrin with iron (hemin) no longer causes a sensitization.

Iron has a "light-detoxifying" function. This is based on the fact that iron, like magnesium, has a definite relation to light, though of a different kind (see below).

Porphyrin displays a strong affinity to the bone system. It can be detected in the skeletons of growing animals. After injection, it is stored in the zones of most intense growth but also wherever calcifications appear (in the cartilage and teeth). Potassium salts easily bind porphyrin. Thus the most mineral part of the human organism comes into intimate connection with light. This relationship has already been mentioned regarding the "light mineral," vitamin D, on p. 36. In this way, the ego organization can send its structuring force even into the structure of the bones, so that the bone system becomes an image of the ego organization. The extent to which this light process extends even into the bones is shown by the finding that immature erythrocytes are particularly rich in porphyrin. Their membrane is distinctly photosensitive.

Closely connected with porphyrin's light effect is its relation to oxygen. No oxygen is present in the relatively large porphy-rin framework. This feature cannot but have a considerable influence on its capacity to bind oxygen, which is the basis of the respiratory function of the blood.

In sum, we can say that the affinity of chlorophyll and hemo-globin for light is due to their porphyrin component; without it, light could not connect itself with a substance. In contrast, the metal determines the direction in which the light is active. Magnesium internalizes the light and brings it into a substance, where it becomes life; hence, magnesium has an anabolic func-tion (which is found also in enzymes, for example, and in its therapeutic action), whereas iron again releases the light from a substance. The metamorphosis of life to an inner light pro-cess, which is the ultimate basis of thought, occurs via iron.

By their natures, magnesium and iron are suited for this mastery over the light process. It is unnecessary to elaborate on the fact that magnesium has an extraordinarily great capac-ity to store light and to liberate it again in combustion; that is, it can emit light. Iron also has a unique relation to light, how-ever, since it forms sparks like no other metal.

In specific ways, spark formation is enhanced by the so-called rare earth metals. Particularly in cerium, we find an isolated development of one aspect of iron: the light aspect. Neverthe-less, iron is needed for optimal spark formation (70 per cent cerium + 30 per cent iron makes the optimal spark-metal). It is characteristic that iron, like magnesium, gives off a white light in combustion, while other metals show a specific coloration. The phenomenon of spark formation shows that iron, in con-trast to magnesium as well now, has an active process in it. A particle of iron bears light actively into the darkness; it perme-ates the dark with light. This is a typical expression of the essen-tial nature of iron. Each spark is a little meteor, as meteors also consist of iron. Most substances, of course, will give off light in combustion, but none can scintillate, none can carry light sub-stantially into the darkness like iron. This tells of the light effect of iron in the organism as well. Iron not only metamorphoses light; it permeates the whole human being with light, thus acti-vating him and illuminating his very thought.

Rudolf Steiner indicated that the human being, in contrast to the animal, possesses an "original light-forming" capacity. This is related to man's spiritual activity, because only man has an ego consciousness, enabling him to act spiritually and creatively, independently of outer stimulation.[36]

Light-bearers in Man

We have already become acquainted with porphyrin as a substance that mediates light. Magnesium and iron have likewise been mentioned as substances related to light.

Another important vehicle of light in the human being is phosphorus, whose function is already expressed in its name. No one will dispute the propriety of this name for yellow phosphorus. Nevertheless, the role of phosphorus today is also seen only from the point of view of energy. It is seen as an energy transmitter in adenosine triphosphate or in high-energy phosphate bonds. It is also possible, however, to see an inner light process in this effect of phosphorus in the organism. Phosphorus is only capable of being a vehicle of the ego because it is a vehicle of light. Phosphorus has the same relation to light as sulfur to warmth. Phosphorus levels in the blood are typically decreased by insufficient action of light in the organism, as in rickets.

Another substance that could be named as a light bearer is quartz. Inwardly, it is structured by light through and through, and it is transparent. It could be said to represent an ocular formation in the mineral realm. Just as the eye is "formed by light and for light" (Goethe), the mineral quartz has an inner configuration corresponding by essence to light, so that it offers no resistance to it.

Of the organs, the adrenal gland manifests the clearest relation to light. We have already mentioned the direct influence of light on adrenocortical activity by way of the eye. We are familiar with the phenomenon of heavy pigmentation of exposed portions of the body in Addison's disease. In addition, the participation of the adrenal glands in the phosphorylation processes shows the effect of this organ on the light metabolism.

As is explained in the chapter on the kidney (Vol. III), the anabolic processes of the organism pass through the adrenal glands. The light ether in particular has a preferential site of activity in the adrenal glands (see the section on steroid metabolism). This is why tuberculosis poses such a threat to this organ; it entails a marked disturbance of the light metabolism (see below).

Of the bodily substances, sugar and protein show a special relation to light, in that they are optically active. In regard to the highly interesting phenomenon of optical activity, we can touch on only a few points here. In the same way as a living substance can arise only from a living body, an optically active substance can be produced only by another such substance. In the final analysis, however, all optical activity is derived from the life processes of an organism. This is the basis for the preference of one direction of light rotation for a physiological substance. Racemization does not occur within a healthy organism, but it may well occur outside the organism or in pathological states. Thus, $1^{(+)}$-lactic acid that arises physiologically — in the muscle metabolism, for example — has a dextrorotatory structure; in fermentation, however, just as in stomach cancer, racemic lactic acid arises. The discovery of racemization of the natural amino acids in cancer tissue has not yet been fully confirmed. In this regard, it is of interest that the particularly effective antibiotics contain d-amino acids and 1-sugars — just the opposite of the naturally occurring substances. Certainly a part of their function, which is directed against life as the name says, is based on this fact. The human being is constructed symmetrically, but closer examination shows that the symmetry is purest in the outer form and in the head region. The metabolic system, in contrast, is arranged totally asymmetrically. This is reflected even in the inner structure of the substance: optical activity is an essential expression of the asymmetrical configuration of the metabolism. Furthermore, daylight, as well as starlight, is polarized.

Optical activity is linked to carbon. It is the carrier of the structure of living substance. It is primarily responsible for the fact that light in substance can be life, that the life body is a light body. Any bit of burning carbon in a flame shows that carbon is able to transform warmth energy into light more easily than other substances. Carbon is a representative of organic, living substance only by virtue of the fact that it is inwardly permeated with light.

Here, again, the close connection of light and life can be recognized. Through the optical activity of protein and sugar, the whole of the living body substance acquires a polar structure. The entire human organism has a polar arrangement in its dynamic. This is true also in its relation to light. Since the polar construction of the organism is a prerequisite for the engagement of the ego and for the "physiology of freedom," we are justified in saying that an ego, as a being of light, can be joined with bodily substance only by virtue of the fact that this is also organized in a polar way with respect to light.

Disorders of Light Metabolism

In the preceding section we referred to a deficient inner light process in rickets, which is expressed in low phosphorus levels in the blood. On p. 34 ff., it was described how in rickets there is either a lack of outer light or insufficient formation of the provitamin (7-dehydrocholesterol) that takes in light.

In porphyrinuria, there is an inability to deal further with light that has been taken in; this can appear symptomatically after abuse of soporifics (barbiturates) or lead poisoning. Chronic use of soporifics has a crippling effect particularly on thinking—that is, on an inner light process—so that the human being is no longer able to live in this process. In lead poisoning there is also a paralysis and destruction of the formative forces, which, as we know, release the inner light process by means of their transformation.

Porphyrin can occur congenitally as a syndrome in its own right, bringing severe damage through the action of the unguided outer light. Xeroderma pigmentosum should be mentioned here. Its sufferers are subject to the action of outer light because they cannot supply iron, with its "light-detoxifying" function, to the porphyrin in their organism.

Beyond this, the light process is disturbed in other ailments in which the connections are not immediately recognizable. In depression, the clinical picture of the patient already points to an inner light deficiency. The inner darkness can be experienced directly. The hopelessness and the inescapability of the situation in which these patients believe themselves trapped correspond to their state of being cut off from the living, acting spirit. They experience the weight of matter too strongly. During the pathological stage, these patients lack active, creative, and uplifting forces to overcome this heaviness through their connection with light. On a purely empirical level, it has been found that depressions improve when the patients are treated with photosensitizing substances. Both porphyrin as well as hypericum, which also causes a strong photosensitization, have proven themselves therapeutically. Such substances open the organism to the action of light that is lacking. Magnesium (hepar-magnesium) and iron work in the same way.

Cancer also shows clear relations to the light metabolism. Ninety per cent of all skin cancers occur on exposed portions of the body. Melanosis circumscripta praeblastomatosa (pre-malignant melanotic changes) affects especially the head and face. In the United States, the Negro population has a ten to twenty times lower incidence of skin cancer than the white population. The incidence of skin cancer also arises going from north to south, in accordance with the exposure to light. The protoporphyrin increase in the blood of cancer patients, discovered by von Euler, points to an insufficient iron process. The light cannot be utilized (see above). The insufficient respiration of the cancer cell is also a result of this deficient iron process. Instead of respiration, fermentation takes place in malignant tissue. Thus we see that both light and carbohydrate metabolism are subject to insufficient control and processing; they are allowed to take their own directions. This, however, is the characteristic trait of the growth disorder in cancer in general: the higher members of man's being cannot keep the growth forces completely within their sphere of influence. Parts are left uncontrolled and lead to separate functions (see pp. 27, 81f., 285ff.). The discovery that carcinogenic substances are fluorescent is given new significance in this connection. It is on the basis of this property that they were first discovered and concentrated, but this means that they are capable of transforming light. Obviously, the matter hinges on how this transformation occurs. Of course, it also occurs by means of porphyrin; properly, however, the transformation must occur in that the light stream is taken up and continued directly by the iron process. Through the action of carcinogenic substances, the transformation of light seems to occur in such a way that it no longer can be controlled and transmitted to the higher functions. Hence, it begins a forming activity of its own without connection to the rest of the organism.

It has been mentioned (p. 79 f.) that a light deficiency plays a causative role in some forms of anemia. Heilmeyer indicated that "the old knowledge through common sense, that sunlight promotes blood formation, becomes clearly apparent in regeneration tests, that is, when greater than normal demands are made on the bone marrow."

The light metabolism plays a special role in tuberculosis (see chapter on the lung, Vol. III). According to Rudolf Steiner, the behavior of the ubiquitous tuberculosis bacilli is determined by their photosensitivity. If the human being does not get enough outer sunlight or is incapable of transforming light within, then an inner light process is lacking and tuberculosis bacilli can thrive. It was shown above that this transformation of light from life is a function of iron in the organism; this also explains iron's therapeutic use in tuberculosis.

Addison's disease was mentioned above as a disorder of the light metabolism.

Therapy of Disorders of Light Metabolism

As we have shown, man is dependent on light. Light cannot be replaced and therefore must be supplied in certain diseases, such as rickets, tuberculosis, anemia, etc., each in a suitable form for the particular disease.

Therapy of systemic lupus erythematosus with Finsen light is also based on stimulation of the light process. The treatment of lupus with Vitamin D should also be mentioned here. It has already been shown that physiological vitamin D_3 is the product of an inner and an outer light process (see pp. 36, 257).

Of course, it is a prerequisite for physiological or therapeutic light effects that the organism possess the capacity to assimilate and transform light since, improperly assimilated, light can lead to severe disorders. It is possible, however, to improve "light utilization," especially with phosphorus, which appeals to the ego and thus to the inner light process. Hence, phosphorus is indicated in rickets as well as in tuberculosis. Magnesium has a clear relation to the etheric body and therefore not only works anabolically, but, especially as hepar/magnesium, it also has a specific action as an inner disseminator of light, as in exhaustion depressions, for example. Iron possesses the active quality of the light process and therefore is especially indicated in the later phase of depression. The general application of iron in anemia needs no further comment. The stimulation of inner activity through the administration of iron stems from this stimulation of the light process.

In an isolated form, one can use the light effect of iron as cerite (D4, D6 as trit., D6 inj.), its natural cerium compound, for stimulation of the light metabolism in anemia, cancer, and depression.

Carbo deserves special mention. Stimulation of the light organism with it becomes possible only in the higher potencies (D20, D30). The effect reaches the etheric body as a sort of "refreshment"; it is indicated especially when the etheric body threatens to dissociate itself, which may be expressed in serious states of circulatory collapse with danger of death (carbo D30 is indicated here). The action goes by way of the renal system, especially via the adrenal gland, whose connection to light and the anabolic aspect have already been discussed.

Among plants, Hypericum in particular shows the capacity to form photodynamic substances (hypercin). The latter activates the effect of light as porphyrin does and is used with success as an antidepressive medication (in a tincture or in Hyperforat®). Phosphorus works in all cases by stimulating the light process, and by this means it appeals to the ego.

This is also the domain for a comprehensive therapy such as

curative eurythmy; this enables the patient to find his proper place in the force relationship of light and heaviness. Since thought formation is really an inner light process, man can influence his organism in this way. What is meant here, however, is not abstract thoughts joined in a schematic way, but the active engagement of thought in creative activity. This ultimately works back on the configuration of the whole organism.

The course of man's life is an expression of the confrontation of the spiritual world with the material world; they meet one another in man. In Greek antiquity the connection of the light-filled spirit of man with the dark earth in the incarnation process was still immediately perceived. *Melainesthai* means to ripen, to become earthly, but literally to become black, dark. Today, knowledge of the light nature of the human being must be added to our knowledge of his material nature; the latter can only be understood through the former. As a "citizen of two worlds," the human being embraces both realms. He may not fall to either extreme but must hold the two in balance within himself through the strength of his ego.

Chapter X
Pharmacodynamics

The extended image of man that can be gained from anthroposophically oriented spiritual science also provides new guidelines for pharmacodynamics and the preparation of remedies. Apart from certain principles, the indications of Rudolf Steiner in this connection were given not in the sense of a fully developed pharmacology or pharmacopoeia but usually in the context of concrete cases of disease and preparation of remedies. It remained for his students to take these indications as working hypotheses, to grasp them in their inner relationships, and to accept them as suggestions for further pharmacologic-therapeutic practice.

In view of the fact that many of the resulting preparations require foundations not customarily used in the pharmaceuticals and that different means of processing are also used, new pharmaceutical establishments were needed. To accommodate this need, appropriate laboratories were added to the clinical-therapeutic institutes that came into being in Arlesheim, Switzerland and Stuttgart, West Germany in immediate connection with the advisory activity of Rudolf Steiner. Later, still in collaboration with Steiner, these laboratories were united as a single enterprise, the Weleda AG (Weleda-Heilmittelbetriebe), with the task of producing the preparations based on Steiner's indications and also of serving the further needs of his medical students. In the Weleda pharmacopoeias, the individual preparations, as far as necessary, are marked as to place of origin and mode of preparation. An exact knowledge of these facts is important for the doctor so that, to use an expression of Steiner's, the remedy becomes wax in the hand of the medical artist. More extensive explanations of individual problems and descriptions of the significance of the modes of preparations by means of practical examples are found in the publications of the Weleda as well as in many places in the literature.

Substances from all the kingdoms of nature are used as bases for the pharmaceutical preparations. The pharmaceutical techniques applied to them serve to unlock and develop the active processes in the animal, plant, and mineral, and to bring the remedies into relation with definite processes in the human organism. These techniques are not aimed at isolating single active substances out of the whole complex. The use of substances provided by nature guarantees an immediate and comprehensible relationship between what is inside and outside the human beings. Man, the microcosm, is a mirror of the macrocosm, whose substances and forces all find their correlates in the human organism and display a kinship to it; this, after all, is what makes it possible for them to have a healing action.

According to the dynamic configuration in a given remedy, processes or organs that are too weak are stimulated, or functions that are too strong are weakened. To apply a medication means to bring into the organism a process to which it is unaccustomed, one that differs from the normal processes; such a process is "different," while foods are essentially neutral.

In plant preparations a rather large complex of substances is generally used (aqueous, alcoholic extract; volatile oil distillate; oil extract, etc.), and under some circumstances two or more plants are combined to form a new therapeutic whole. The use of isolated alkaloids, glycosides, hormones, etc., was recommended by Rudolf Steiner only in exceptional cases; still less often did he advise the use of synthetic products such as the customary chemotherapeutic agents, most of which completely lack any genuine relation to the human organism, in the sense of man's mirroring the macrocosm.

Pharmacodynamics, in Rudolf Steiner's sense, is not to be found in crude chemical or physical effects such as chemical reactions; rather, it must be sought in higher forces that arrive at efficacy through the substances. These forces are derived from the processes underlying the formation of animal, plant, or mineral. When a patient is given a remedy, the forces contained in it act in such a way that the corresponding activities and processes are stimulated or evoked in his organism.

Rudolf Steiner described the medicinal action in the upper organization of man as "homeopathizing"; that is, the process locked and fixed within the substances are released by the organism. This dynamic quality released from the substance is actually the effective principle in both medicinal and food substances. The organism itself carries out a preparation, a sort of potentization, on everything it takes in; if, in the preparation of the remedy, this is done beforehand, then the organism is relieved of this additional activity and can assimilate the remedy more directly.

For numerous plants—for example, arnica, chicory, horsetail, chamomile, etc.—Steiner adduced a series of effective substances whose consonance, so to speak, results in a dynamic complex. For others, such as mistletoe and Christmas rose, he directed attention not so much to the substances as to other things like the course of the year and, for mistletoe, the different host trees. In other cases, he made the essential nature of a plant accessible by pointing to elements of its form and color and to other phenomena. All these things are important for a genuine understanding of a plant and its curative effect, although in our times they are not yet given much attention because of the one-sided, excessive emphasis placed on the component substances.

The fact that the essential quality of a curative plant is also manifested in its outer appearance was quite obvious in former times, even for Paracelsus. He was referring to the training needed to recognize these connections when he said that the physician must "go through nature's examination." For such a perception, however, a deeper, intuitive insight is needed into the nature of the forces of the plant. With the disappearance of the faculties for more intimate contemplation of natural phenomena, this old "science of signatures" inevitably fell into decadence. The natural scientific approach to substances, as found in chemical analysis and so forth, lies on a different plane. Nonetheless, when the scientific picture of man and the world is complemented and deepened by spiritual science, a new way is opened for looking into the inner dynamic of the medicinal plant, both as a natural phenomenon and as something active in the human organism.

Continuing the Goethean approach, Rudolf Steiner showed how important it is to let phenomena speak, because when they are not simply grasped with thought but are experienced with a feeling eye—what Goethe called an intuitive power of judgment—then they form a bridge between the outer and inner worlds. Understood in this way, the "signature" can once again become a legitimate key to understanding medicinal plants.

A significant guideline for the relation between the plant and the human organism is given in Steiner's reference to their "threefold structure" (see the chapter, "Toward a Science of Healing Plants"). The correspondences between the three-membered plant and the three functional systems of the human organism represent the naturally given connection of a member of a plant to one of the human systems. With appropriate preparation, particularly differentiated applications of heat, plant preparations can be oriented toward one of the three systems in an intensified way. Specific modalities of preparation result from this. In order to understand them, it is necessary to begin with the differentiated warmth organism of the human being. The metabolic-limb region represents the warmth or sulfur pole. In the sulfur process warmth and other imponderable forces are connected with the substance, which makes it flammable. Its polar opposite is the nerve-sense system, which represents the cold or salt pole. In salt formation, warmth is eliminated, resulting in a qualitatively "cold" substance. The rhythmic organization stands between the two as a mediator. Accordingly, parts of plants intended to act on the metabolism in the broadest sense are subjected to heating; a warmth-sulfur process is added that directs them to the metabolic organization. The plant substance is altered by exposure to warmth; in this way the warmth action of heating is preserved in the medication. A characteristic example of a metabolic effect is represented by menodoron; its components, mainly blossoms, are processed as a decoction or infusion. This preparation serves to regulate the menses, explicitly metabolic processes.

The root as well can be opened by treatment with warmth for action on the metabolic system. Examples of roots prepared in this way are those of gentian, iris germanica, chicory, and others.

Typical remedies for the promotion of rhythmic activity are digestodoron, which is made from leaves of ferns and willows and helps to regulate rhythmic functioning in the gastrointestinal tract, and the cardiac and circulatory specific, cardiodoron, and others. For them, Steiner indicated heating to 37° C. In contrast, when influences are intended in the nerve-sense area, as with arnica and aconite, the corresponding preparations are produced in a cold process without heating.

The differentiated warmth processes—cold preparation (maceration), heating to 37° (digestion), and cooking (decoction, infusion, and distillation)—are not applied primarily in relation to the substance to be processed but to guide the action of the substance in the threefold human organism.

Heightened exposure to warmth beyond cooking leads to the formation of roasted products, coals, and ashes. This brings about extensive alterations in the substances, initially leading further toward the "sulfuric" side. In this way, colorless and tasteless cane sugar becomes caramel, still soluble in alcohol but colored and aromatic. Elastic and extremely absorbent sponge substance becomes the brittle, heavily colored, and aromatic spongia tosta, which serves for astralization of the thyroid gland. Further examples could be mentioned.

As the next step, by shutting off the air supply, we obtain charcoal from wood, etc., and as the final product of complete combustion we obtain mineral ash at the border of the inorganic, the purely mineral image of plant substance.

In plant coals, we have the substance that forms the framework of all vegetable life: mysterious carbon with its enigmatic properties. Some of its especially significant properties are its great desire to take in the airy and gaseous, its insolubility in any fluid medium (except perhaps melted iron and the like), and its identity in substance with the noblest and hardest of all gemstones, the diamond. The strong power to absorb the gaseous points once again to a special connection with the "air organism" and the astral body of the human being. Hence, the sphere of action of coals is particularly efficacious in deficient respiration. Organically, this can be the case from the lungs to the kidney region. Plant charcoal also has a connection with inner processes of light permeation. Carbon is first worked into the organization of plants through light forces; these are then captured in the black coals that are formed in the absence of air and they are freed again in the pharmacologic process in order to activate an inner light activity in the organism. The therapeutic range of this activity extends from treatment of improper putrefaction processes in the intestine to stimulation of the light metabolism (see p. 300) as the higher function of the kidney (see chapter on the kidney, Vol. III). Specific applications are presented when we consider different species of plants such as carbo cichorii in relation to the liver-gall system, carbo equiseti for the kidney-bladder region, etc.

In the process of ash formation, unlike that of coal formation, which is produced by shutting off the air supply, the carbon is burned without leaving a trace. The correlate to ash formation is the breathing process. The formation of carbon dioxide in respiration is a process corresponding to that of complete combustion. Incineration (ashing) gives an action "aimed" at the pulmonary respiration process. Salts in general will appeal to the head region and also to the lungs, since the formative head forces are dominant in them. Cinis glechomae, for example, has proven itself in the treatment of bronchiectasis and emphysema, and also as an adjuvant in the treatment of pulmonary tuberculosis (see p. 333).

The modes of selection and preparation described here make it possible to unlock and enhance specific qualities of a plant that otherwise remain inaccessible. These procedures concentrate in the medication, not active substances but the dynamic contained in the plant. This provides not only an intensification of but also a large variation in the therapeutic effect.

The season of year that roots, bark, etc. are harvested is also significant for the therapeutic effect of plant preparations. If a vitalizing, anabolic effect is intended, or a counteraction against deposition, then spring, with its abundance of budding and sprouting, is the appropriate time of harvest. This applies to birch leaves that are to be used against rheumatic ailments, celandine root against indurative processes in the liver-gall region, gentiana lutea to promote vital processes in gastric digestion, etc. In the opposite case, when primarily nerve effects are desired, harvest takes place in the autumn when plant processes strive toward an inner consolidation and gathering, for instance, with aconite bulb and valerian root.

As mineral remedies, Rudolf Steiner often recommended ores and other minerals in their natural form, such as pyrite, chalcopyrite, cinnabar, corundum, quartz, etc. As to the objection that natural minerals often contain secondary components ("impurities"), we may note that just these "trace elements" often have an extremely positive significance for organic life; of course, each single case requires careful examination. Besides natural minerals, in numerous cases Steiner recommended the use of laboratory preparations, such as plumbum chloratum, cuprum sulfuricum, barium citricum, tartarus stibiatus, etc.

A special process, whose pharmaceutical application traces back to Rudolf Steiner, is the mirror preparation of metals. The metals are vaporized and only after precipitation in fine form as a mirror are they processed as remedies. In this way, the metallic-mercurial state of the metals is brought out in a particularly pure form; this use of pure metals represents a principal area of therapy in anthroposophically oriented medicine (see chapter on the metals, Vol. II).

The process or way in which a substance arises, or the state in which it is found in nature, is always essential. Thus, to give another example from the realm of nature, calcium carbonate in the forms of the oyster shell and crab stone are not necessarily the same in their medicinal qualities. In the crab stone there is a repeated deposition of calcium in the stomach mucosa of the crab that is dissolved again after each shedding, while the clam shell represents a final deposition of calcareous substance. These properties go into the therapeutic quality of the remedy.

Potentizing occupies a special place among the procedures for preparation of a substance as a remedy.[1] This procedure was introduced into medicine by Samuel Hahnemann (1755–1843). There are, however, indications that the principle as such was known in much earlier times.

The procedure in brief is that one part of an original substance, for instance, sulfur or a plant extract, is thoroughly ground or shaken with nine parts of a medium such as lactose, water, or alcohol. From the 1:10 "dilution" formed in this way, one part is taken and processed again with the same medium. Since the proportion here is always 1:10, we are dealing with a decimal potency; the preparation thus created is designated D1, D2, etc., depending on how often the grinding or shaking is repeated.

Potentizing is at first a simple dilution, and in the lower potencies the original substance is still recognizable or detectable. In the higher potencies, however, to look only for the original substance or its action is to miss the essence of potentizing. The action of this sort of remedy will inevitably remain incomprehensible if approached in this way. It can easily be calculated that in potencies higher than D23, not a molecule of the original substance can be present. What is crucial in potentizing is the rhythmically repetitive treatment of a substance so that in this way the dynamic of the substance being processed can imprint itself on the medium.

In summary, we can say that this rhythmic treatment (shaking or grinding) has the effect of releasing those processes latent in every substance that first produced the substance through the interaction of cosmic and terrestrial forces and that remain in its condensed state; the released processes are then communicated to the medium. Their effects change in definite rhythms with rising potency and their action at some points is actually reversed. This is true, for example, with lead, which, as is known toxocologically, calls forth symptoms reminiscent of sclerosis when consumed in large quantities.

High potencies of lead (D20–D30), however, have an antisclerotic action. Thus we can see that low potencies, in which the original substance has been only slightly "unlocked" by the potentizing process, affect the metabolic system of the human being; this, after all, is where the turnover of substances takes place. The more "unlocked" medium potencies (ca. D8–D15) act on the rhythmic system, and high potencies (ca. D20–D30), in which the substance is no longer active but only a transmitted dynamic of the substance, act on the nerve-sense system. With increased potentizing the initial substance is wholly worked into the potentizing medium, gradually and increasingly giving it a new kind of configuration, as a seal does to sealing wax, where there is no question of transmission of substance from one to the other. Similarly, the nervous system, unlike the metabolic system, is oriented not toward the assimilation of substance but toward "impressions" gathered through the sensory organs without direct material communication with the environment.

Remedies produced by rhythmic potentizing are generally designated as "homeopathic." This is not quite right, in that homeopathy in Hahnemann's sense refers to a method of finding remedies, that is, to the similarity rule (*similia similibus curentur*). In order to put this principle into practice, Hahnemann made use of the method of potentizing for the preparation of substances; he called it "dynamization."

Homeopathy presents us today with a voluminous literature and a wealth of accumulated experience, and also with therapeutic possibilities that can be achieved in no other way. It is a tragedy of the medicine officially taught and accepted today, which is oriented only toward orthodox natural science, that it takes no notice of this therapeutic principle. Above all, this is because such effects cannot be understood by contemporary thinking or its concept of substance. In the higher potencies, it is simply not the "diluted" original substance that is active but the specifically modified medium. Homeopathy is a project of great genius, but it is in danger of being forgotten today because it can no longer be understood within the confining established natural scientific forms of thought, which are pure empiricism. Spiritual science offers concepts and fosters insights according to which an old spiritual inheritance, in all its greatness and significance, as well as the natural scientific approach, can be understood, credited, and united with one another in a certain way.

Potencies higher than D30 were recommended by Rudolf Steiner only in rare cases—belladonna, for instance, is used occasionally as D60 for psychic disorders.

For experimental proof of the efficacy of potentized substances, Rudolf Steiner recommended that plant seeds be germinated under exposure to a series of potentized substances, and that the resulting plants be compared. This suggestion was taken up by Lili Kolisko, and her results were recorded over many years with numerous "potency curves" of leaf and root lengths of correspondingly treated wheat plants.[2] Kolisko's comprehensive work, *Physiologischer und physikalischer Nachweis der Wirksamkeit kleinster Entitäten* (Stuttgart, 1959), contains no less than 379 such growth curves, the majority of them going up to D60. The reproducibility of these growth curves in dependence on the original substance was proven statistically significant in these voluminous tests.

As for the route of administration, Rudolf Steiner gave the following rule of thumb: injection, the immediate introduction of the medicine into the fluid circulation, penetrates the organism through the middle, rhythmic member; oral administration takes the path of the metabolism; external applications such as ointments, poultices, baths, etc., take effect by way of the nerve-sense system. It has been found repeatedly, however, that injection, as an unaccustomed mode of application for the organism, makes for faster action than oral administration, especially in higher potencies such as argentum D30 and arnica D20.

A transitional stage from plant to metallic-mineral remedies is formed by the "vegetabilized metals." The principle of their preparation was presented by Steiner in his second medical course.[3] Metals, ores, or other mineral substances are subjected to a special "unlocking" procedure and added in fine dilution to the growth medium of certain medicinal plants; the growing plants are composted and once again added to a fresh growth medium in which a new generation of plants is raised, etc. In this way, the basic substances are obtained for the preparations ferrum per urticam, cuprum per melissam, stannum per taraxacum, and others. These remedies help the disease-weakened organism to overcome the strong metallic-mineral forces, and they can be of service in introducing a later therapeutic application of metal.

Another group of remedies that arose in response to a suggestion of Rudolf Steiner are the "compositions on the model of curative plants." The principle behind them is that after appropriate analysis, the composition of essential mineral components of certain medicinal plants is imitated in a pharmaceutical process. This involves the manipulation of corresponding functional association. It is not so much a matter of definable chemical bonding. Rather, the original substances must be mixed with binding agents in such a way that something more like a "cementing" of the components occurs. For example, equisetum arvense was the model for solutio siliceae comp., consisting of flint, sulfur, and the salts of potassium, sodium, and calcium; likewise, corresponding to the urtica dioica, solutio ferri comp. was made up of iron, sulfur, and potassium and sodium salts.

These synthetically produced preparations represent a sort of counterpart to the synthetic imitation of individual "active substances" such as alkaloids, vegetable acids, vitamins, etc. Here, however, the effective principle of the remedy is sought, not in a single component, but in such a way that the plant unites various mineral substances in itself into a specific effective complex; it is this, in its essential components, which must be imitated. In contrast to the plant remedies, these concentrated preparations are without the roughage substances that are needed for the life of the plant but not for its healing action. The action is thus enhanced, concentrated, and shifted from the vegetable to the mineral domain, which gives it a greater affinity for the innermost ego member of the human being.

A unique remedy within this group is solutio alkalina, which was developed by W. Cloos. Since this represents an independent continuation of indications given by Rudolf Steiner and touches the oldest wisdom of mankind as was present in genuine alchemy, the effective principle will be described in brief. The starting point for this, as for the other pharmaceutical procedures such as vegetabilizing metals, was Steiner's exhortation to "work in accordance with becoming nature, not with nature that has become."[4]

In this sense, we can recognize germination and ripening as two basic principles of creative nature. In germination, the seed must die, as it were; it must be decomposed, dissolved, in order to make way for the formative forces that now take effect. The critical intermediate state that makes this possible is the dissolution of starch to dextrin or maltose, for instance; that is, a state of formlessness, chaos, is the prerequisite for the reorientation of the substances. A corresponding process can be found in cell division as well as in fertilization. Even in the mineral world, we find this principle of dissolution and reorientation proceeding by way of a chaotic and, in this case, colloidal, state.[5]

In the growth that follows, the essential nature of the plant manifests itself. In the blossom, however, and in the whole ripening process, this unadulterated growth meets with a reversal, an involution. Now an astral impulse enters into the etheric growth. For this reason, ripening also signifies limitation and transformation of growth. This ripening finally leads to the seed, now only a representative of the plant, which has withdrawn from manifestation.

If we pursue these two opposite processes of germination and ripening further into the inorganic realm, we are led directly to decomposition and combustion. If we direct these two processes in an appropriate way at plant substances, then we are working with the inorganic models of the processes of germination, growth, blossoming, and fruiting. The product will then contain the essence of the original substance, just as the ripe seed represents the involuted "essence" of the mother plant.

Solutio alkalina is thus based on a universal principle. It does not represent a therapeutic specific, but acts on the human organism in the same way as humus does on the soil, by making it receptive to the seed. For the human being, this means that the seed of the ego organization can develop harmoniously in the correct balance of anabolism and catabolism. Ordinary clinical diagnoses cannot comprehend this action. According to medical experience, however, the indication extends primarily to all hardening tendencies in the organism, from arthritic processes to depressive conditions.

Regarding remedies from the animal kingdom, Rudolf Steiner indicated, besides apis, formica, aranea, etc., various organ preparations from higher animals. In part, these are aimed at promoting the functioning of the corresponding organs—for instance, pancreas for stimulation of the activity of the pancreas—and in part at guiding other curative actions to particular organ regions—for instance, arnica D20 + medulla oblongata in order to guide the arnica effect specifically to the medulla oblongata.[6]

We shall describe another pharmaceutical principle that consists in a practical application of spiritual scientific insights. There exist concrete relationships between the individual organs and certain metals that can be recognized on the basis of an essential knowledge of the substances and organs. These relationships are founded on a common connection to individual planets. This is discussed in greater detail in the chapter on metals (Vol. II). It has long been customary to administer a metal along with the associated organ preparation, which serves as a sort of "live rail." It has also been found that the effect can be intensified considerably if the metal is joined directly to "its" organ. Here, the metal must be used in a form appropriate to the organ or the desired effect. This is the origin of such preparations as hepar/stannum, in which fresh liver is combined with zinc hydroxide, and ren/cuprum, in which copper is used in a nitrogen complex, the nitrogen appealing to the astral body and binding it in the kidney region. This pharmaceutical principle has also led to a number of other preparations.

For individual diseases, preparations from the three kingdoms of nature can be combined with one another as needed. The use of mixtures, including those of potentized remedies, as well as the alternating administration of different remedies, is not rejected in the curative method represented here. Differing medications can add to one another and also potentize one another in the pharmacologic sense.

If this practice is not sanctioned in the classical school of homeopathy, it may be because of the classic homeopathic principle of determining the choice of remedies according to the sum of individual symptoms and then choosing just one remedy as the best suited. In the anthroposophically oriented approach to healing, the symptoms serve purely to direct attention to the relationships of the supersensible forces and the members of the human organism as a whole. The medication is intended to normalize their interaction, which is quite feasible with simultaneous effects from different angles, as in the combined preparation of arnica/betula comp. for the treatment of cerebral sclerosis. In this preparation, plumbum mellitum addresses the sclerotic process as such, arnica restores the functioning of the nervous system, and betula stimulates dissolution and excretion.

A completely distinct group of medications are the so-called "type remedies," which go back to Rudolf Steiner. Outwardly, these may appear like mixtures. They are based, however, on a conception, not of specific diseases, but of basic processes of the human being or of individual organs. They are not directed against a disease but appeal to an organ in its archetypal functioning. This type of medication can be called primordial, and remedies like cardiodoron, cephalodoron (biodoron), hepatodoron, digestodoron, and others each form a whole. In them, a certain antagonism between plants (in cardiodoron and hepatodoron, for instance) or between the minerals sulfur and flint (in cephalodoron), is brought into equilibrium by means of a pharmaceutical process or a substance (iron, in cephalodoron), and combined to form a higher unity. It is this that enables cephalodoron to be an image of the threefold human being and to have a harmonizing action on his functional metabolic, rhythmic, and nerve-sense systems.

Corresponding explanations could also be given for other "remedies for typical diseases" given by Rudolf Steiner. Most of them are intended to act as harmonizing stimuli in order to restore equilibrium in the event of a disproportionate inter- action of forces of one of the supersensible members of man's being.

At bottom, when we succeed in letting the necessary stimuli take effect, the healing agent is really the human organism, that is, the etheric body.

In conclusion, it has been possible in these brief descriptions to sketch the intended relationships and circumstances only in their roughest outlines. In a more thorough presentation, these general guidelines and suggestions would be made much more concrete and would be developed in elaborate detail.

Chapter XI
Toward a Science of Healing Plants

Man and Plant

We propose to draft the outlines of a science of medicinal plants[1] that can be called rational in the pure sense, since it is based on original relationships between plant and man. It must succeed in throwing light on nature in man and on man in nature, and particularly in making visible the real dynamics between the patient and medicinal plants.

Any such attempt will have to look toward the Goethean theory of metamorphosis as its foundation, because the laws of life revealed in this theory are, according to Rudolf Steiner, the "Kepler's laws of the organic world." As it has usually been presented, however, it is not yet adequate as a science of medicinal plants. It does not incorporate knowledge of the original relationships between plant and man, which were first discovered and presented in their full context by Steiner.

The Rhythmic System in Plant and Man

A primary phenomenon of such original relationships is the relation of plant to human breathing as is expressed, for example, in the formation and function of leaf pigment, chlorophyll, and blood pigment (hemoglobin). Here, a primal polarity in earthly existence visibly confronts us (see p. 292). The basic organ of the plant, the one through which it appears in its purest nature, is the leaf; the original relationships between plant and man are therefore to be sought in the leaf.

The foliage, built up node upon node in regular repetition, represents, in its very form, the middle member of the plant entity, its rhythmic system. It can be compared to the middle system of the human organism, which is also supported anatomically on a rhythmic articulation: the spine with the ribs springing from it in regular succession, enclosing the chest cavity in their curve. Plant respiration and assimilation follow the light rhythms of day and night; they represent a complete polarity to human respiration and the processes of exhalation connected with it. Both activities take place between the fluid and airy spheres, but in an opposite way. The plant's carbon dioxide-condensation process, in which oxygen is exhaled, bears the same relation to human respiration, with its inhalation of oxygen and exhalation of carbon dioxide, as that of a seal to the impression it makes. It is truly a revealing "rune" of nature's process that chlorophyll is extraordinarily similar to hemoglobin. Furthermore, in both of them a metal is the "vehicle of respiration"; in the plant it is magnesium and in man it is iron. Despite their great similarity, these two respiratory substances show a polar relationship even in their appearance: chlorophyll is green and has a red fluorescence; the reverse is true of hemoglobin. Also, the opposing roles of iron must not be overlooked. It is true that the plant requires iron for the formation of leaf pigment, but still the iron remains outside the chlorophyll and represents something external to it. Man, however, internalizes iron.

It can be seen that chlorophyll and hemoglobin, in their functions in plant and human respiration, represent the primordial phenomena and relationships of the two organic domains. At the same time, this shows that a hidden unity really stands behind this polar opposition and that the polarity must represent a genuine "divergence." This insight forces us to far-reaching conclusions. It says that the more highly developed creature, the human being, cannot have developed gradually from the lower vegetable form of existence, but that an original state of existence cast off the plant form of existence through "divergence" in order to set free the human form. The two cannot even be thought of separately, since they are mutually dependent and incapable of existing alone. The air the plant breathes must come from the human and animal spheres, and vice versa. These are two mutually dependent forms of existence. One of them alone could only exhaust its life-sustaining sphere of respiration and, being unable to recreate it, would quickly destroy itself.

Plant and man are a complete polarity not only in their rhythmic systems. In each kingdom the rhythmic element is placed between two polar opposites. The animal does not belong in this comparison, since man and plant have chosen the vertical as their formative motif, while the animal has chosen the horizontal. The human being is the complete reverse of the plant, while the animal is so only partially.

In the human being this rhythmic system, including breathing and blood activity, is situated between the head, in which the nerve-sense system is concentrated—though it extends throughout the body—and the abdomen, in which the metabolic system predominates, though it also permeates the entire body, including the activity of the limbs. The knowledge of the threefold nature of man and plant is a foundation of the spiritual scientific knowledge of man (see chapter on the heart, Vol. III). In the plant, the leaf process has an intermediate position between the root and blossom regions. The threefold nature of man and plant demands an investigation into the relationships between the two.

The Root Process and the Nerve-Sense System

Through the root, the plant belongs to the earth and its sphere of forces. At the same time, it is through the root that the plant confronts the kingdom of nature below it, the inanimate, mineral world. The root is sensitive to the earth (geotropic), the sprout to the cosmos (heliotropic). The root is also receptive to the substances of the soil, to water and salts. It not only "perceives" but also grasps them in active growth. In this, it displays a specific selectivity, such that one species of plant selects just these, another species other substances from the soil, enlivening and joining them together in a new way. (Ash analysis gives only a dead impression of this union.) The salts and water are then vitalized and thus lifted out of the sphere of gravity and conformity to the mineral structure of the earth. In this way, a finer salt process permeates the plant and makes it an earth organism.

Man, however, does not share the plant's outer relationships to the mineral kingdom, though he does have inner ones; these are an inversion of the corresponding plant processes, just as we have seen in respiration. While minerals in the root of the plant press toward vitalization, the head and nerve-sense system in man devitalize what is organic and bring it to mineralization in a subtle way. The head is the most hardened part of the body; processes of solidification and salt formation emanate from it and from neural activity. In contrast to the plant's unconscious perception, selection, vitalization, and anabolism that is carried out by means of the root, stands the human being's mineralization and catabolism, individually activated by the conscious human entities, the ego and astral body. Numerous root drugs, with their pronounced relationships to the head and nerve-sense processes, testify to the relationships between the lower pole of the plant and the upper one of the human being.

The Blossom-Fruit Process and the Metabolic System

Their obvious connections to the sexual organs are already a reason to associate the upper parts of the plant with the lower part of the human body. This association is even more broadly applicable to the entire metabolic region. Nevertheless, it is the *how* of these connections that we must consider most exactly. The plant is a being that is open to the world. This is indicated simply in the form and function of its principle organ. The leaf can be conceived as surface tangential to an infinitely great sphere that belongs to it. Out of this surrounding cosmic world flow in the activities that cause, affect, and order the plant's metabolic processes. The results of these activities are embodied in the plant, but their motivating centers remain outside in the universe. In contrast, the human being, and to a certain degree the animal as well, has incorporated these impulse centers in the inner world of his metabolic organs. The lung, liver, kidney, heart, gall bladder, etc., carry out autonomous activities, working together with the whole human organization. The plant can carry out these same activities only in conjunction with processes of the whole universe. For example, the building up and breaking down of carbohydrates in the plant follows rhythms of sun and earth; in man, however, they conform to the will impulses active in his organism.

In the blossom region, the plant form approaches that of the animal. In flowers we find butterfly, throat, and lip forms, etc. In fructification, the plant passes as food substance directly into the human metabolism.

Recalling the threefold nature of the human organism in connection with the unfolding of the faculties of the human soul, we will mention that the capacity for conscious thought is based on the organic processes of catabolism and devitalization connected with the nerve-sense system. The soul faculty of feeling is based on the manifold rhythmic processes of the middle organism, and the faculty of willing on the metabolic processes.

From what has been presented above, it follows that the plant's roots are related to the human head and nerve-sense system, the leaves to the rhythmic system, and the blossoms and fruit to the metabolic-limb system. This is true of the "normal" plant and the healthy human being. We must also discover, however, the relationship between the sick man and the medicinal plant, which has something "abnormal" about it that removes it from the ranks of the "normal" plants.

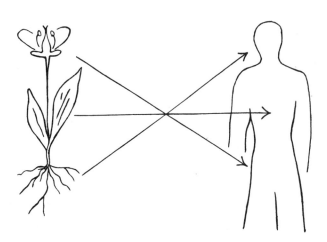

The "Idea" of the Disease Process
and the "Idea" of the Medicinal Plant

It is among the great insights of Goethe that pathology cannot be ascribed to outer causes but must be thought of from the point of view of health; that is, it has inner causes. A healthy organism has an internal equilibrium involving all its members, so it is also in balance with the world around it. A sick organism, according to this view, contains in itself the same forces and impulses as the healthy one, but they are no longer able to remain in equilibrium. When this harmony is shaken, certain members of the whole are favored and others neglected; the neglected atrophy, and the favored develop excessively. Because of the lost inner equilibrium, the outer is lost as well; the forces of the outer world push in too strongly, or they are too weakly managed, and then damage from without is added to the disturbance within. The lost inner equilibrium can be seen as the diseased constitution, the outer as its secondary consequences as seen in bacterial infection (see chapter on infectious diseases, Vol. III).

The idea of the threefold structure of the human organism explains and illuminates such a whole with all of its polarities and balances. The nerve-sense system is, of course, indispensable for the whole human being, yet it must suppress its own life in order to serve as the organ of consciousness. This occurs through breakdown and mineralization, processes that are pathological in the rest of the organism and that must be healed by compensatory impulses coming from these other regions. In contrast, the metabolic system also causes disease when it acts of itself alone, because, with its powerful anabolic processes, it can develop overvitality only at the expense of a dimming of consciousness. The rhythmic system balances the polarities; in it lies the essence of health (see the chapter, "The Second Epoch of Life"). Thus, health can exist only with harmonious cooperation of all three systems. Like man's upright posture and his gait, this balance is highly unstable, but it is also the basis for the human being's potential to be a self-developing creature who can at any time sacrifice an old equilibrium in order to gain a new one. This is why each stage of life has a different foundation of health.

Such an "idea of disease" leads to two polar archetypal diseases. If the lower organization grows too vigorous, this can become manifest in inflammatory, febrile states with their processes of dissolution and "melting down." If the upper organization grows too powerful, this will be expressed in stagnation of metabolic activities and in excessive breakdown and hardening. Inflammation and tumor are the "archetypal phenomena" of disease founded in the essential nature of the human organism (see the chapter, "Inflammation and Sclerosis").

Plant life is also structured by the opposing forces of dissolution, characteristic of blossom activity, and hardening, characteristic of root activity. Leaf activity in the middle system mediates rhythmically between the two poles. In the vegetable processes, however, the predominance of one or the other polarity is not a source of pathology but represents a creative structural principle in the world of plant forms. One-sided development results, for example, in plants that are almost all root, with leaf and blossom formation stunted. Bryony and mandrake can be mentioned as examples. Other plants develop enormous blossoms, showing hardly any root or leaf development, such as rafflsia and the flowering fungal growths of the tropics. Otherwise another organ develops immoderately, the stem perhaps, as we find in equisetum (horsetail), etc. We find an exclusive dominance of the cotyledons in the welwitschia, native to South Africa. A predominance of the stamens can be found in the hypericum plants. Here, the flower forms are imitated by the anthers. There are plants that hypertrophy in giant fruits, such as the pumpkin and the melon; others become all leaf, like the fern and bryophyllum. Finally, in some trees we can observe a preponderance of bark formation, as in the cinchona and the birch. It is just such distortions of the archetype and tendencies to emphasize the development of a single part or process that make "normal" plants into medicinal plants. It is necessary to see this clearly. The possibility of a

truly rational science of medicinal plants is based on the discovery of the direction in which a plant can act to be a medicinal plant.

But why does man become sick with "distortion of his archetype," and not the plant? Why does the principle of distortion
call forth new and thoroughly healthy, if peculiar, forms in the
plant kingdom, while in man it produces pathological states
and not, say, a race of men with giant heads or barrel chests,
big feet, or long arms, etc.? Why does the human being experience such tendencies as a threat to his existence and as discomfort and pain?

The possibility of falling ill lies in man's spirit and soul activity. He has a different relation to his formative forces from
the plant. It is quite evident that another sort of claim is made
on his etheric body; his life is not spent in limitless, perpetually
active growth. The plant keeps its formation in a constant flux.
When a plant's growth is stopped, its life is over. The human
being has concluded a process of development when he is
"born" in a completed form, and only then does his form of
existence as a human being begin; the plant, in contrast, ends
its existence when its formation ceases. In man, this flowing
formative force is sacrificed to a higher principle and transferred to a region of the spirit. Thus the fundamental difference
between plant and man must be seen clearly in order to solve
the questions we have raised.

The Four Members of Being and the Four Elements in which They Are Embodied

Man is surrounded by three kingdoms of nature, of which he
forms the center as the fourth terrestrial being. He is connected
to these three kingdoms of nature through the most intimate
relationships. The inanimate mineral world contains all the
substances found in his body; the world of formative forces
participates in him just as in the plant; soul properties belong
to him as to the animal; he is a human being in the full sense
only in grasping himself as spirit. Man stands in the midst of
the other kingdoms, and in addition he has internalized them
in himself.

When we proceed from medicinal plants to medicinal remedies, we must remember that these no longer represent the living nature of the plant but are substances derived from it. Hence, we must learn something of the relation of the substances to the processes that form them. Ultimately, these are the activities of the members of being and the spheres corresponding to them. Such archetypal relationships of the material world to that of the four members of being were revealed by Rudolf Steiner.

The mineral, composed of dead physical substance, best expresses its essential nature in the solid state.

The plant, in contrast, requires another element for its embodiment, the fluid, because it must "incarnate" not only a physical, but also an etheric element. Its form does not result from the physical structure of the substances composing it but from its etheric nature. Its essential nature is not stamped on an immutable form but manifests in continual metamorphosis. This fluid transformation of forms, with its metamorphic laws, requires a state of matter that is just as ready to assume a form as to give it up again, immediately and without resistance, when the life principle of the etheric body demands this. The solid creates no form in the plant but merely becomes a preserving vessel of the life form. In its truly solid parts, the plant has already carried out a devitalization process. It has extracted life and water from its bodily substance and brought them to rest. Examples are wood, bark, and seed formation.

It is the animal that first succeeds in incorporating the gaseous, airy element by means of its own respiratory organism; that is, it has developed an air organization. This development becomes more complete as we rise from the lower to the higher animals; in the human being, however, it is closest to perfect. The most important aspect of the incorporation of air is that the soul element, the astral body, penetrates the body along with the airy element. In this way, a bodily organization with inner organs is formed. The body is an organ cosmos that assumes on the inside those activities that the outer cosmos performs for the plant. The essential nature of air is fully manifested for the first time in the breathing of an animate creature. It attains its highest form and definition in the air-forms produced by the sounds of speech. These are the best physical expression of the inner life of the soul.

The plant is no more able to receive warmth as an organized element than it is able to have an air organism of its own. Depending on its species, it seeks out the appropriate climactic zones and conditions of warmth, but the center of warmth always remains in the far-distant sun. The lower, cold-blooded animals are also determined by outer warmth conditions. Only the human being raises himself out of dependency on these outer factors. He has developed his own, inner warmth organism and therefore is able to inhabit any place on the earth regardless of the conditions of warmth. Man has gained control of fire within himself and he alone, of all terrestrial beings, also controls fire outwardly. With the power of warmth, he has control over every state of matter on earth; he can form and reform it as he will. It is through union with warmth that the human spirit, the ego, finds it possible to inhabit a material body and to control all states and all levels of being; warmth has the same power materially over the air, the water, and the earth. In this way, the ego lifts itself out of the bondage associated with the forces and laws of the earth, since the strength to master them lives in warmth. The blood process in man is its bearer. The opposition between blood and leaf pigment, which was so strongly emphasized in the first part of this section, is also an indication of the opposite directions in which the human ego and plant spirituality are to be sought, most particularly in respect to the centers of their warmth impulses. This is why the human blood process so stubbornly maintains in itself a temperature of about 37° C. The vegetable assimilation process must conform to the outer warmth conditions, though it proceeds most intensively at about 37° C. The highest form of warmth, however, is the fire of enthusiasm living in the human will.

In conclusion, we present a diagram summarizing our brief discussion relating to the four members of being of the four kingdoms of nature and to the elements they employ for their incarnation. This will be important for the special section to follow. The abnormal ways in which a plant may relate to the solid, fluid, airy, and warmth elements can teach us much about its nature as a medicinal plant and especially about its influence on the individual members of man's being.

Mineral	Physical body	*Solid*		Head organization
Plant	Physical body Etheric body	*Solid, Fluid*	Root	Rhythmic organization
Animal	Physical body Etheric body Astral body	*Solid, Fluid, Airy*	Leaf	Metabolic organization
Man	Physical body Etheric body Astral body Ego	*Solid, Fluid, Airy, Warm*	Flower	

Typical Healing Plants

The action of the four states of matter—the warm, airy, watery, and solid—leaves an extremely vivid stamp upon certain plant families. A brief summary may be given as a survey.

```
          Warmth . . . . . Labiatae
    Sulfur
          Air . . . . . . . Umbelliferae
    Mercury . . . . . . . . . . . . . . . Ranunculaceae
          Water . . . . . . Cactaceae
    Sal
          Earth . . . . . . Chenopodiaceae
```

The Chenopodiaceae are not typical medicinal plants but serve as dietetic and general foodstuffs; they are treated quite briefly here (p. 351 ff.). In contrast, the Labiatae, with their affinity for warmth, possess the character of typical medicinal plants.

The Labiatae

Many of our indigenous medicinal herbs, such as sage, thyme, lavender, marjoram, lemon balm, rosemary, teucrium, etc., belong to the family of plants with labiate flowers. Most of these herbs appear outwardly insignificant. It is noteworthy that in all of them the stem is square and the leaves wrinkled, often appearing dried up. All properties of the Labiatae indicate that they overcome the watery element through their strong air and warmth processes, which determine their being. The air and warmth processes do not remain limited to the blossom, as in other families, but permeate the entire plant right to the root. In this way, the leaves receive something of the character of the blossom; they become the bearers of the volatile oils that give the Labiatae their characteristic odor and represent their really curative principle. These volatile oils represent an enhancement of the fatty oils brought about by concentration of hydrogen.

These medicinal herbs need the sun's warmth for their development. They take it up readily, permeate their whole form with it, and become bearers of warmth in the truest sense of the word. This also expresses what is essential in their therapeutic application; that is, they support the warmth process in the human organism. This process is intimately bound up with the ego organization and it also forms the foundation for the "airing through" of the organism.

In view of this, the Labiatae are of importance as remedies where permeation with warmth or air is impaired in the organism, as from the cold, and where catarrh is present, or where the warmth process proves too weak in the organism's development, as in menstrual troubles in young girls.

Characteristic of the labiate type is a predominance of processes that assimilate cosmic warmth activity. In contrast, there is a dearth of the forces that flow into the plant from earth and water. This group of plants seems to be ruled by an inner fire that dries out the plant's body and defines the forms sharply, so that the leaves become small and needle-like, as rosemary and thyme illustrate in a particularly characteristic way. This inner fire causes the whole plant to be thoroughly permeated with aroma and spiciness, which normally occurs only in the blossoms and fruit, but it also causes a withdrawal of the juicy and plastic tendencies.

An abundance of flowers on tightly formed foliage held close against the stalk is the result of this dynamic, which brings forth a variety of medicinal and spicy plants such as hardly another family contains. It makes impossible, however, a large accumulation of such substances as are characteristic in food plants. The labiates thus produce no fleshy, juicy fruits but rather tiny, dry nuts full of oil.

This essential character explains their preference for dry, warm soil—indeed, they are all native to the Mediterranean region—as well as their abundant growth at the height of summer. These plants also form nectar that is especially treasured by the "warmth animals," the bees, whose bodies are adapted to the form of flowers.

Rosemary (Rosmarinus off.) is the ideal representative of the Labiatae; the contracted form of the foliage and the aromatic permeation of the whole plant have been taken farthest in it. The leaves seem to be almost needles, and the plant's content of volatile oils is higher than that of any other labiate. This oil also has the highest hydrogen content of all volatile oils and it is genuinely volatile. It has a pleasant, spicy smell, and a wakening rather than a dulling effect. The blossom process is held within the leaf region. It does not separate itself as an isolated inflorescence, but enters again and again into the rhythmically superimposed leaf stalks.

In folk medicine, rosemary is still commonly used in the form of leaf decoctions for skin problems, chronic stomach catarrh, and menstrual disturbances. Good results have also been seen in the states of exhaustion following typhus, fever, influenza, and in liver ailments, etc.

The use of oils (in the form of an emulsion) in the bath and as an injection, indicated by Rudolf Steiner, is an innovation. A rosemary bath has a strong inner warming and mildly stimulating effect on the nervous system; hence it should not be used late in the day.

Rosemary oil works favorably in all cases in which the ego cannot incorporate itself adequately in the organism, as is the case in all states of exhaustion and in the constitutional disposition to diabetes. The beneficial effect of rosemary baths in diabetes, which was first recommended by Rudolf Steiner, has been confirmed by many doctors. Successes are also reported with injections of rosmarinus D4–D5 in diabetes. For weakness of the ego manifesting only in the soul region, injections with rosmarinus D25 may be tried. States of unrest at night, and also in psychoses, are often quieted by this.

In *lemon balm* (Melissa off.), we observe a stronger involvement of the plastic-fluid element, whence its more herbaceous character. The aromatic permeation of the plant is not so great as in rosemary. There is only a gentle lemon scent, and the content of volatile oils is correspondingly low.

Melissa (infusion or "spirit of melissa") brings about a mild, highly beneficial "airing through" of the whole organism. It provides the correct relation between the water and air organism and, with its gentle character, it is especially suited for women and children.

It is used in all complaints stemming from insufficient airing through of the organism, such as mild stomach and intestinal disturbances resulting from heavy foods or a cold, flatulence, deficient and painful menstruation, leukorrhea, as well as related "nervous disorders" such as cramps, palpitations of the heart, asthmatic complaints, insomnia, migraine, hysteria, and melancholy. It is especially valued for its antispasmodic action in the area of the upper respiratory passages (convulsive coughing) and "replaces codeine." (For individual gynecological indications, see the chapter, "Gynecology," Vol. III.)

Thyme (Thymus vulgaris and T. serpyllum) could be called slightly unsuccessful rosemary. In it, however, the blossom process is separated from that of the leaf and placed at the tip of the shoot. The scent is mustier than that of rosemary, the oil thicker, and it produces thymol as a solid component.

The action of thyme rises higher into the rhythmic system. It stimulates a strong inner airing through of the organism and consequently is effective in rickets and exudative diathesis. It relaxes convulsive states in coughs and whooping cough, and for country people it takes the place of an entire apothecary. Furthermore, a diuretic and nerve-strengthening quality is attributed to it. In all forms of thyrotoxicosis, thyme appears to be contraindicated, since it acts like iodine in these cases.

Sage (Salvia off.) seems to be a metamorphosis of thyme. The leaves become broader, more akin to the watery element and to shade, and they allow these forces to enter into them more. The plant also has an inner affinity to warmth, however, just as its range is almost identical to that of rosemary.

In accordance with the more leafy character of the plant, its oil is less spicy and fiery. Some kinds of sage even seem to degenerate in the watery, herbaceous direction, becoming sweaty and musty in their odor, even producing volatile aromatic substances in solid resin. Meadow sage is almost odorless. There is, however, a significant new component added to the volatile oil in sage: the intensive tannin formation, which is an expression of a strong incorporation of formative forces.

The stimulating effect of the tannins on the formative processes is an additional factor in controlling the warmth forces; this is shown in the inhibition of sweating. In people with little tendency to sweat it will act to stimulate perspiration, and in those who sweat heavily, it will act as an antiperspirant. Consequently, its action is altogether equalizing. The profuse night sweats of the tubercular patient are treated beneficially with sage, making the customary atropine unnecessary. Sage is also used to restrict lactation. The tea is a good gargle for inflammations of the oral cavity (sore throat, teeth).

The leaf of *marjoram* (Origanum vulgare), like that of sage, is broadly developed, and the blossom process is pushed out of the foliage to the tip of the shoot, where it pulls together in a green, oblong form resembling a beehive. On the whole, the plant remains more herblike and softer than sage, but more akin to warmth. While in rosemary the flower is drawn into the leaf region, here the leafy element is drawn up into the sphere of warmth and therefore no oblong panicle is formed as in sage.

For this reason, we may expect this plant to influence the rhythmic processes in the metabolism. Marjoram has a regulating and promoting influence on menstruation, strengthening the uterus and aiding the digestion when it suffers through chilling of the lower organism.

In *wood germander* or wood sage (Teucrium scorodonia), the labiate takes a unique turn: it goes into the moisture and shade of the woods. There, it shoots up like other etiolated plants and sends up a narrow, pale yellow panicle of flowers from the corolla. Below, the plant defends itself against excessive upward penetration of the watery element by the formation of tannins and bitter substances. Above, it struggles for adequate intake of light and warmth forces. The odor of the oil formed in this struggle is correspondingly musty, heavy, aromatic, but sweat-like, as if the plant would bring itself to sweat. A similar odor is found in hedge nettle, another labiate that lives in the woods.[2]

In accordance with the dynamic of this plant, we may expect it to have the effect on the rhythmic system of permeating it with light and warmth. Like many labiates, it is able to help pulmonary patients in their battle against the upward penetration of metabolic processes. For ages, tuberculosis and bronchial catarrh have been treated with teucrium. This remedy is also of use in pediatrics. From the ages of three to seven, a boy had recurring attacks of fever with sudden onset and a threatening aspect, lasting from two to three days and defying every treatment. Teucrium tea eliminated the symptoms in a short time. Rudolf Steiner called germander "a specific for balance in the uterus." This is also the basis for its use in climacteric disturbances (see chapter on gynecology, Vol. III).

The indications for *peppermint* (Mentha piperita), which contains the volatile oil of peppermint from which menthol separates in chilling, are so well known that they will not be presented here in detail. The characteristic cold feeling that the tea and the oil leave on the tongue follows after the burning, aromatic taste and adds a special note to the labiate character of this plant.

In *ground ivy* (Glechoma hederaceum) the labiate type is drawn completely into the earth region, specifically into the water processes of spring, in which the forces of light and warmth are still weak. The predominance of the earth forces is expressed in the strong vitality of the shoots, which creep over the ground and propagate through runners. As always when the watery element dominates, the leaves become broad, herb-like, rounded, and indented. The warmth nature of the Labiatae struggles into this watery-herbaceous condition with more difficulty than in summer plants. No defined inflorescence is formed, but leaf and flower are repeated rhythmically as the plant creeps along the ground. Nevertheless, the plant does become aromatic and spicy, and it is a favorite addition to "spring herb soup." Here, the warmth process of the Labiatae is inwardly permeated by the vital processes of the root. Ground ivy could be called a springtime teucrium. It is indicated in catarrhs of the inner organs, when these stem from insufficient "airing through," and its sphere of action includes a disposition to tuberculosis from this origin.

The Umbelliferae

The extensive family of plants with umbel-shaped blossoms (about 2,600 species) shows, as its most striking characteristic, such an enormous range of leaf forms as can scarcely be found elsewhere in the plant kingdom. Simple, unindented forms are found in species living in water (marsh pennywort) as well as in the high mountains (hare's ear). Notched and indented leaves are found in such shade and moisture-loving forest plants as sanicle and astrantia. The meadow and prairie plants of this family have bi- and tripinnate leaves (chervil, wild chervil, hemlock, giant fennel). Finally, species living in especially light-filled air, such as fennel and dill, seem to dissolve into the air with their foliage. To a considerable extent, the umbellifer goes out of the watery element, which it loves, into the airy element. Parallel to this, it forms volatile aromatic substances that become finer the more the plant allows the airy element to participate in its formation.

It is the root, however, that first claims this air-suffused foliage. In a powerful life-systole, the root sucks into itself all that can be grasped from the cosmos through the foliage, and from the earth through the roots. The cosmic forces are first breathed deep into the earth pole of the plant. Following this systole, which usually lasts one year, there is an equally powerful diastole the next year. The blossom process shoots up and passes into umbellate rays until, like a cloud of stars, countless tiny blossoms float over the shoot, loosely held together in the form of an umbrella or dome. The flowers are completely flat and open, and the stamens spray out of them. The fruits are dry and are often formed like small stem parts. In this, they are true to the principle of linear spray-formation.

Not only leaf and blossom formation strive into the realm of the air. The plant also seeks to embrace and incorporate the airy element with hollow stems, stalks, and fruits, air-chambered rootstocks and ventricose, inflated leaf sheaths. In this development, however, the umbellifer is seeking to grow beyond the plant realm, since the normal plant is given only the solid and fluid for its formative force organization. Only animate beings form an air organization of their own and maintain it through a breathing process. In permeating themselves with air to such an extent, the umbellifers are striving to incorporate an astral sphere that ought to remain only an outer envelope for them.

The aromatic substances arising as a result of this "aeration" and astralization are joined by gummy and mucilaginous substances sent from the fluid nature of the plant's lower organization, so that the two come together as "gum resins." These are quite characteristic of umbelliferous plants. What in other families moves toward the dead, mineral realm with the formation of hard wood, in the Umbelliferae remains within the realm of the etheric, which always lives in the organic and fluid. It is transformed into gummy substances, and what in "normal" plants blooms fragrantly toward the surrounding astral world is here drawn down and held fast in this mucilaginous region.

Through this abnormal assimilation of airy and astral processes, this family of plants produces some highly poisonous plants. The toxins arising in this way are the image of such astral processes. For this reason, they have an effect on creatures endowed with astral bodies: animals and human beings. Their action can be turned to therapeutic use when it is necessary to regulate the relation of the astral body to the other members of man's being.

This brief sketch of the essential nature of the Umbelliferae provides us with the range of its therapeutic indications:

1. An organic area that is remarkably susceptible to the action of the Umbelliferae is the glandular system. They promote the activity of the various digestive glands and the lacteal glands; some species, however, inhibit it. The glands are organs of the fluid organization and hence also of the etheric body, which maintains their anabolic processes; the engagement of the astral body in them produces secretion and catabolism. In these organs, which serve life and not the development of consciousness, the astral and etheric bodies act in a plant-related way. Their formative principle shows all possible varieties of ramification and distribution, from the simplest to the most complicated, as the structural plan of the Umbelliferae demonstrates in the plant kingdom.

2. The effect of the Umbelliferae is also applicable wherever the astral body engages in the fluid organism. They strengthen it in relation to the etheric body; they promote secretion, have a diuretic and diaphoretic effect, and also increase expectoration.

In bloating of the intestinal region, as well as "cramping" of the astral body in the respiratory and circulatory systems, these plants act directly on the air organization, which is penetrated by the astral body. Asthma, seizures, whooping cough, and angina pectoris are treated with certain members of the Umbelliferae. Pain is always experienced by the astral body, and their pain-relieving action is also connected with this.

A brief presentation of a few important medicinal plants of the umbelliferous family follows.

When the formative tendencies of the watery element enter strongly into the umbelliferous nature, then air and warmth come into conflict with the fluid element. In the *water hemlock* (Cicuta virosa), the airy element conquers the watery. It refines the leaves, makes room for a spraying flower system, "aerates" the stem, and fills the rootstock with hollow spaces. The displacement of the airy element all the way to the root region is characteristic of the water hemlock. The intoxication picture of this plant (dizziness, sleepiness, dilation of the pupils, seizures, inflammation of the digestive organs, difficulty in swallowing, and paralysis of the tongue) indicates its therapeutic uses. Lockjaw, tetanus-like symptoms, angina pectoris, and whooping cough give an idea of curative action of Cicuta virosa. It tends to decrease the pathological overactivity of the astral body. Thus, the pain-relieving effect of Cicuta ointment in gouty, rheumatic, and even cancer-related tendencies is also understandable.

In *celery* (Apium graveolens), the therapeutic action extends to the astral organization in that this plant stimulates the activity of the digestive glands. Celery is beneficial in bladder and kidney ailments, stone and gravel formation, as well as in gout and rheumatism. This curative action is to be expected from an umbellifer that is also a halophyte. In its wild form, celery inhabits salty swamps and the seashore. Its ash has a high salt content. The enhanced light and air effect produced by reflection on water surfaces is carried by the plant into the root process, which is influenced by the salt effect.

In the *healing sanicle* (Sanicula europaea), the permeation with air is more moderate, as we can see in the leaves, which are round and divided only in a hand-shaped fashion. The sanicle is rich in calcium and silica and contains saponins, volatile oils, resins, and tannins. This medicinal herb of ancient fame was used in a way similar to arnica, since it promotes the healing of wounds, cleans purulent ones, stops bleeding, and is also effective in treating internal hemorrhages of the lung, stomach, intestine, and kidney. It also heals inflammations of the gastrointestinal tract. The center of gravity of the plant is in the rootstock. By means of the silica process and the tannins, the vitality of the rhizome is impressed with what the leaf, in the manner of the umbellifers, has absorbed from the surrounding light and warmth realm, and that is manifested in the formation of the saponins, volatile oils, and resins. The root element of this plant is able to support the formative forces of the nerve-sense organization in their balance with the activity of the blood and metabolic system. In injuries of the physical body, it shows the etheric body the right paths by which it can counteract the inflammation and the chaotic tendency of the blood process with its formative forces. In accordance with the moderate involvement of the astral sphere in this plant, the antispasmodic and gland-stimulating effects of the Umbelliferae mentioned earlier are not so pronounced in it.

The *carrot* (Daucus carota), as the harmonious mean of the Umbelliferae, represents among them approximately what the rose represents in the rose family. It favors a soil in which light, silicic acid, humus, and warmth interact in a balanced way. The pinnate leaves, which open to the light-filled air with their fine articulation, build up in the first year the root, rich in sugar and nutrients, which the carotene pigment gives an orange color. Carotene also occurs in the leaf, in the immediate vicinity of chlorophyll, which covers it up; it plays an important role in the plant's assimilation of the light forces. It is a real light-substance. In the human organism it is transformed into vitamin A, which is connected with vitalizing processes of the sensory sphere and of the ectoderm in general. Its strongest concentration is in the eye, the organ of light (visual purple). Carrot ash, with its silicic acid and iron, also points to the light connections of the carrot. By means of its silica content, the carrot draws the surrounding cosmic sphere down into the root with special intensity and there interweaves it harmoniously with the earth and water realms. Following this breathing-in process, the expiration in flower and fruit leads, through the fine articulation and harmonious gathering of the multitude of flowers, to the hemispherical umbel structure. Often, a purple central umbel emphasizes this as the mid-point, demonstrating the love of balance and moderation of this umbellifer.

The carrot root, with its light-silica processes, is the ideal food plant for the child; it stimulates the head and the sensory sphere. Furthermore, the ego and astral body can make use of the formative warmth and light processes of this plant in order to engage powerfully in the anabolic etheric activities of the child's metabolic region and to promote structured growth even in bone formation. The well-known antiparasitic action of the carrot root is understandable from its permeation of the metabolic system with light. The blossom-fruit pole also helps the astral body to engage more strongly in the lower organization. The fruits of the carrot promote menstruation and conception, and also have a dehydrating and diuretic effect.

In *caraway* (Carum carvi) as well, the high content of silica, iron, and manganese speaks of the strong light relationships of this plant. Caraway extract can successfully overcome debility of the astral body in the digestive tract and atonia of the etheric body. Its antispasmodic and antiflatulent property, its emmenagogic action and influence on gastric and uterine cramps, hypochondria, and hysteria, all lie within the range of the Umbelliferae.

Anise (Pimpinella anisum) varies the basic umbelliferous pattern in such a way that the systolic inspiration and root-forming process occur during the short spring rainy season, while the diastole, with its loose, airy white clouds of blossoms, proceeds with the increasing air, light, and warmth of summer in the same year. The fine iron-salt process is essential here, according to an indication of Rudolf Steiner.[3] This is also found in other Umbelliferae, but in a coarser and more substantial form, while in anise it is effective in a much more dynamic way. Therapeutically, anise has the antispasmodic and antiflatulent property, but in a more pronounced way and with a mild narcotic effect. Furthermore, its effect of soothing coughs, loosening phlegm, and even overcoming asthmatic states is greater than that of the Umbelliferae already mentioned. Anise helps to "air through" and astralize the fluid organism in manifold ways.

Fennel (Foeniculum vulgare) especially manifests the airy. A fennel field offers the airiest impression imaginable. In this medicinal plant, the umbelliferous effects on the air organization (astral body) and on the endocrine system, as a tonic for the fluid organization, are especially enhanced. Its relief of pain and release of mucus in stubborn cases of bronchitis are sufficiently well-known, as is its use in bloating in small children. Its action on the sensory sphere, in connection with the significant silica content of the ash of its seeds, is noteworthy, especially in disorders of vision and eye inflammations.

In *hemlock* (Conium maculatum), the astral principle, active in "airing through," has grown so strong in comparison to the etheric forces that dwell in the fluid element that it overwhelms the etheric element and breaks directly into the physical realm. The root, built up in the first year of growth from the elaborately divided foliage, draws the forces of the astralized surroundings deep into the formation of its milky juice. In the following year the plant breathes out vigorously into the periphery. It evaporates the ether-bearing watery element so intensely that the plant stands there limply on hot days. A musty, animal-like cloud of vapor, smelling like mouse urine, surrounds it like a poisonous cloud. The alkaloid conine, growing more and more concentrated toward the upper organs, takes on the volatile nature of an essential oil in hemlock. The general umbelliferous curative action is altered in a characteristic way in this plant. Endocrine activity is inhibited by Conium maculatum; lactation is also decreased or even stopped. Compresses or ointment of hemlock will soften abscesses, glandular indurations, and tumors. It fights nerve, skin, and testicular inflammations, and its effect on the testes can be similar to castration. Its effect on the astral body, however, is the strongest. Its analgesic property, even in cancer, far exceeds that of other Umbelliferae. The Teutonic tribes knew of the spotted hemlock, the "rage herb," as a tranquillizing remedy for states of agitation. Of equal importance is its antispasmodic action in spasms of the stomach, intestine, and bladder, as well as in asthma, whooping cough, epilepsy, even chorea, mania, and delirium tremens. The capacity of various Umbelliferae to release the astral body from excessive bondage, from "cramping," becomes the dominant principle in hemlock; by way of the airy element, the astral sphere engages excessively within the plant. Even in lethal poisoning, consciousness and heart activity are retained to the last; the victim lays aside his physical body calmly. The death of Socrates provides classic evidence of this.

Lovage (Levisticum officinale) does not spend itself completely in flowering, as many Umbelliferae do, but after blossoming it sends its life down into the root. The root contains a yellow milk, fluid balsam gum, abundant levulose, thick volatile oil, protein, gummy substances, malic and angelic acids. Lovage engages powerfully in the fluid organization in disturbed diuresis, cardiac edema, and edematous swellings; it promotes kidney activity and is useful in cystitis, albuminuria, nephropathy, and migraine resulting from deficient kidney activity, as well as for foul-smelling sweat due to these conditions. It also stimulates the activity of the digestive organs. In indurative diseases, such as gout, rheumatism, kidney stones, spleen and liver ailments, it helps the astral body engage in the catabolic processes. Its tonic action on the astral body is the basis for its therapeutic power in menostasis and amenorrhea. In general, lovage has an invigorating effect on the whole abdominal area (see chapter on gynecology, Vol. III). The root decoction, as a bath, strengthens the abdominal organs. An important use of lovage is in otitis media. The ear, an "air organ," is meant to serve only the astral body and the ego through hearing. In this disease, however, etheric processes become too strong and lead to inflammation and proliferative swelling.

One of the best representatives of this large family of medicinal plants is *angelica* (Angelica archangelica). This plant also encloses the airy element in its inflated, saccular leaf sheaths, hollow lower stems, and seeds. It bears an aroma that is the finest scent an umbellifer can produce. It has something spicy and volatile about it along with the freshness of the delicate spray of an alpine waterfall; it is fluid refined through the air. The curative action described for the umbellifers above comes forth in a comprehensive and characteristic way in this plant. A most impressive angelica therapy is the treatment of swellings, inflammations, and glandular indurations, particularly of the head and neck region, and above all in children with an adenoidal constitution. These are diseases in which the astral body cannot incarnate from the head into the metabolism, or is diverted back toward the head. Here, the etheric forces are left too much to themselves and proliferate, particularly in the glands, which are primarily etheric organs. The proper curative plant for such processes is angelica. It astralizes the watery element, bringing it completely out into the airy element, and it lives in the "head region" of the earth, that is, the cold zone.

The Ranunculaceae

As a type, plants of the crowfoot family display a plastic, changeable formation, an overflowing character little restrained in number and form. Above all, they require water to unfold their essential nature forcefully, but they also need air and light to bring their character to full manifestation. The earthly, solidifying element is of as little consequence for them as warmth. So we find in this large family of the plant kingdom primarily succulent herbs and shrubs, but not a single tree and few fragrant or aromatic plants.

Ranunculaceous plants thrive where water and air come together in the full light of spring. The organ of water, air, and light—the green leaf—manifests its essence most clearly in these plants; its formative tendency readily takes on the characteristic form that gave them their name, crowfoot. Here, the metamorphosis of the leaf is lived in all its fullness and variety, as we can perceive in the individual plant as well as in the whole family. We see the work of the formative forces of the fluid element in the plastic, rounded form; it slowly becomes indented, extended, and divided into hand and foot forms. Then, however, the more that light and air participate in its formation, the leaf form rushes irresistibly toward pinnation, toward an airy dissolution into the finest laciniate fringes and threads.

What is seen in the metamorphosis of form also has its image in various transformations of substance. The watery juices of these plants are permeated with sharp, inflammatory, yet very volatile substances that often disappear when the plant dries up. This all speaks of the intensively penetrating blossom process proper to this family. Dominance by this process can lead to production of alkaloid substances that fix themselves more strongly, binding themselves to acids in a salt-like manner. While it is the etheric forces that first express themselves in the luxuriant sprouting, the cosmic-astral forces are invisibly active first. It is they who impel the formative forces to continual transformation and thus generate that varied metamorphosis of form. Ultimately, they also find visible expression in the rich flower formation. The cosmic astrality also works in transformations of substances, however. At first, it acts fleetingly, as in the formation of glycosides (anemonin-like substances), but with more intense involvement it produces alkaloids, such as the poison of aconite.

In the following paragraphs we will discuss several therapeutically important plants of this family.

In the pasqueflowers, a dark, noddingly heavy quality still lives in the blue or brown-violet flowers. The *common pasqueflower* (Pulsatilla vulgaris) shows its healing force in delicate, nervous people with scrofula, a susceptibility to colds, an insufficiently astralized, too-moist and cold organism, a melancholic temperament, and a tendency easily to cry.

Of the many ranunculaceous species exhibiting similar behavior, we will mention only the lesser *celandine* (Ranunculus ficaria), which nestles its leaves to the ground under shady, moist hedges, expends its vegetative forces in offset-bulb formation under the earth, and yet strives upward toward the sun with slender-petalled yellow flowers. In folk medicine, an ointment made from the fresh herb is used for hemorrhoidal complaints.

The *helleboraster* (Adonis vernalis) has taken in the air element's articulating and feathering tendency especially strongly, thus paving the way for a powerful blossom element. The delicate spring flower, which is restrained by the damp and therefore also prefers drier, hilly meadows, unfolds in a sunny radiance. In it there is a strong tension between etheric and astral forces, which also comes to expression in the formation of the glycosides, effective in heart conditions.

The *peony* (Paeonia off.) is connected more with the formative forces of water. Here the plant element is coarser, more material. Growth is still herbaceously luxuriant but formed more by the warmth processes, giving the "farmer's rose," as the peony is also called, its rough beauty. There even occur varieties with a fragrance like that of lily of the valley or, in the most finely articulated Chinese species, that of the rose. Our red peony has coarser leaves and a bulbous rootstock. The summer's flow of warmth forces does give the plant a more fiery quality, but it remains a "fire that burns in water." Seeds and roots of the peony are considered effective in inhibiting epileptic seizures. Primarily, however, the curative action of this plant works through the soul-spiritual realm to order and control the fluid organization when this has withdrawn from the impulses of the etheric body with its cosmic lightness and has fallen to the earthly forces of gravity, as in edema and ascites. To combat such affections that appear along with cardiac insufficiency, Rudolf Steiner recommended a preparation from peony root together with blessed thistle.

The blossom process of the *columbines* shows a new thrust. Out of the cup, bell-, and shell-shaped flowers, radiating like stars, these plants produce, through various invaginations and enclosures, forms with a throat, jaws, a helmet, etc. The blossom stretches out horizontally, becomes symmetrical, and takes on, in form and direction, qualities that remove it from the realm of true plants and bring it nearer to that of the animal.

This process is enhanced in *larkspur* (Delphinium), which begins to bloom around St. John's Day (June 24th). Here we have perennials of high summer, with strongly articulated, structured leaves and animal-like flowers. The posterior sepal has a horizontal spur extending behind, into which two spur-like nectaries are deeply sunk. This enhanced astralizing element is expressed in the formation of its own alkaloids. To this plant was formerly attributed the power to heal wounds rapidly; in fact, the "sensory-moral effect" produced on looking at the flowering plant was felt to be healing for the eyes, especially in Delphinium staphisagria.

Monkshood (Aconitum napellus)is the summer culmination in which the ranunculaceous archetype is made manifest. Aconite develops its blossom when the outer cosmic astrality has reached its height. This tall and yet compact plant probably shows the most formative forces among plants of the crowfoot family. Strict definition structures the leaves. The watery, swelling element is dammed up below in the tuber and therefore does not have so much significance above. The bilaterally symmetrical blossom stretches out horizontally in its characteristic helmet form, fashioned out of the enveloping blue, which seems to be a mold of the insect's head that it is waiting to receive. In the nectaries, opening like throats and winding backward in spiral convolutions like intestines, it has adapted itself completely to the proboscis. Its favorite sites are primitive rock and mountain streams flowing over siliceous earth through mountain meadows or pasture land, where some shrubbery on the banks has damped the excessive light and where there is a balance between light and dark, moisture and airiness. In this way, the elements of its environment harmonize with the plant's inner formative forces.

Each plant must be seen against the background of a definite landscape that is the expression of the interaction of specific cosmic and terrestrial entities. The plant fashions its being from the forces of this background. When a remedy is obtained from it, when the plant is taken out of nature into the world of men, it by no means has a uniform action on the whole organism; rather, it favors certain regions, inner landscapes of the microcosmic man, just as the plant itself comes not from the whole earth, but from characteristic individual landscapes. From this point of view, we can look to the human counterpart of the outer "aconite process." When the upper organization and its formative forces have been weakened, from a febrile cold, for example, and the metabolic processes, and with them the fluid organization, overflow their banks and break through into the upper organization, then the warmth organization defends vigorously against the invading cold outer world and loses its harmonious interaction with the fluid organization and the metabolic region; in such cases, aconite can be a powerful remedy. Pneumodoron 1 contains aconite as well as bryonia, and both are also found in the combination preparation Inludo. It has also proven effective in night terrors and tachycardia.

The *Christmas rose* (Helleborus niger) completes the round of the Ranunculaceae. It is a mountain plant at home at medium altitudes on the moist, bushy, stony limestone cliffs of the eastern Alps, mainly on their southern slopes. The plant holds on to this cool and moist, lightly shaded environment with its strong rootstock that releases leathery, perennial leaves divided into a foot shape. It blooms at an unusual time, in later winter, when cosmic activity exerts the least influence on the plant world. The devitalized blossoming forces are accordingly much weaker than in normal plants. This is shown by the fact that the gleaming white blossom, into whose realm the sepals are drawn, as in most ranunculaceous plants, does not completely wilt and die after blooming but outlasts the blossoming process. The snow white turns to purple and then green; the blossom continues to live as a proper leafy element. Such a weakened astrality, which is always contrasted in the Ranunculaceae to an etheric element highly active in the fluid-plastic domain, does not lead to alkaloid formation in the hellebores, though it does to glycosides formation.

Therapeutically, the Christmas rose has a tonic effect on the fluid organization. Indications of this are, on the one hand, the raising of blood pressure, the digitalis-like effect of diuresis, and a digitalis-like effect on the heart; or on the other hand, oversupply of blood to the meninges and spinal cord, dilation of the pupils, tinnitus, dizziness, numbness, decrease of brain fluid, and symptoms of psychic agitation. Helleborus extracts combat both the sequelae of nephritis—especially scarlet fever nephritis—and meningitis-like signs and symptoms. Meningitis arises, according to an indication of Rudolf Steiner, through too-strong engagement of certain cosmic constellations in the lower organization and a convulsive defense against these lower processes by the upper organization.

A new use of this plant in the supportive treatment of cancer in male patients was indicated by Rudolf Steiner. In this connection, he referred to the perseverance of its blossoming against the normal course of events, much like that found in mistletoe, the chief remedy against cancer. In the Christmas rose, however, this process is closer to the earth. It permeates the leaf and blossom element with the strong vital forces of its root and carries the action of life-ether into a winter blooming, that astrally caused activity that mirrors the cosmos. The malignant tumor arises when the upper organization's formative tendencies, which are proper for formation of the sense organs, penetrate into the lower organization, which responds with abnormal growth processes in which the etheric body withdraws from the normal formative impulses of the astral body. The abnormality of the Helleborus process corresponds to that of cancer, but we must forego further discussion of these connections here.

The Cactaceae

In this plant family, which has such a distinct character, two formative principles are struggling to gain the upper hand. The watery element would swell into a sphere and isolate itself as a living drop. The airy and warm elements, however, strive in vain to segment, break up, and attract this drop into their realm. They flow around it spherically but can only dry its periphery and harden it into spine, thorn, and bristle. What in a "normal" plant becomes leaf, shoot, etc., is only hinted at in cacti in the form of tubercles, areoles, ribs, and spines but is not developed further. Strong life-potency is dammed up without being used in outer formation. This is the source of the tremendous vitality of these plants. Life reigns in them unformed, and for this reason it is enormously strong.

Discs, spheres, and columns are the basic forms of the most typical cacti. Their growth is slow and the living change of form that is so essential to true plant life is practically brought to a standstill. The leaf is entirely suppressed and the rhythmic middle system is as if extinguished. The stalk can extend the sphere to a pillar or to a snakelike form. The "leaf cacti" widen and flatten out their stem members, betraying in this way something of their swallowed leafiness. Only a few species of this family freely develop true leaves so that they represent normal plants but abnormal cacti. The law of the spiral arrangement of the foliage manifests in ribbing and channelling of the spheres or columns. It has taken on a permanent geometrical form, however, thereby assimilating something of the structural laws of the mineral world.

In the spine of the cacti, there lives the extraordinary variety that a plant family can bring to leaf formation and formal differentiation, but in the cactuses this is simply held back at its very inception and rigidified.

The blossoming process often explodes suddenly and unexpectedly in great fullness after many years of dormancy. The intensity of its appearance corresponds to the short life span of the individual blossom, which sometimes lasts only a few hours.

The fruits bring the watery element, which in the blossom region occurs only as nectar, to swell within them; usually they are berries or juicy, edible fruits. Many are appealing to the taste, so that this represents an important fruit family of the plant kingdom.

The phenomenon of watery accumulation, succulence, normally occurs temporarily at two points in plant development: during germination and fruit formation. The first swelling occurs at the beginning, the other at the end of the growth process; between the two come the elongation of the stem and the formation of foliage. In the cactus, this intermediate stage is suppressed; the plant goes from one pole directly into the other, bearing leaf-life in itself as a manifestation only in time and not in space.

The bodies of cacti do not become woody; the lignification process in them is softened to strong mucilage formation; here, mucilaginous substances are transformed cellulose. Moreover, they contain much vegetable acid, which arises through a repressed expiration process; that is, when sugar is broken down in the life process, in normal plants this leads to the formation of carbon dioxide and water as the end products of their metabolism. In the succulents, however, this catabolic process stops halfway at the formation of plant acids (malic, tartaric, oxalic, and citric acids). Such acids are noticeable in the taste of unripe fruit. Ripening leads not so much to an increase in the sugar content as to a combustion of the vegetable acids.

Plant mucilage has a strong capacity to retain absorbed water. It helps to turn the stage of watery swelling into a permanent life form. The body of the cactus forms much vegetable wax on its surface, as is usually found on the surface of fruits, and sometimes also resins.

Rudolf Steiner provided a key for the understanding of these strange forms that are so full of character. He indicated that in the cacti, solar and lunar qualities are in conflict, while in the Ranunculaceae, sun and moon forces are harmoniously united. All that shares in the living fluid element is associated with the moon. This is shown crudely and obviously in the ebb and flow of the tides, more subtly in the growth rhythms, and especially strikingly in the process of germination. The hypertrophy of the watery element and the maintenance of the power of reproduction through all stages of growth point to the lunar nature of the cacti.

While the moon affects the fluid element, it is primarily air and warmth that are receptive to the action of the sun. Plant metamorphosis is set in flux by the interaction of the solar and lunar forces. In cacti, however, this is missing. The water element draws together in a sphere, and the life forces do not unfold but are congested; air, light, and warmth flow around the congested structure and can take hold only on its periphery where they make everything hard and thorny. The cactus relates to these cosmic forces as though it were a fruit, although it is basically just a giant, spherical embryonic leaf. From this point of view, the cactus fruits forming from the blossoms are only cactus bodies raised one level; they are spiny, vital, and virtually capable of reproduction from each cell.

The strong etheric congestion, which is released in a short and intense blossoming process, in which it submits to the astral realm, is reestablished immediately after this explosion into blossom. Consequently, the cacti are characterized not only by a conflict of sun and moon forces but also by a strong tension between the etheric and astral forces. It is this dynamic that can be used for healing purposes.

In his book *Magische Gifte* (*Magic Poisons*, 1938), Reko describes how, in northern Mexico in a region of unspeakably desolate, brown-gray hills covered by only a little sparse grass, one can find the *peyote cactus* (Lophophora lewinii). On a turnip-shaped root there sits a spineless, gray-green, flat sphere, somewhat wooly-haired on top, from the middle of which the reddish or yellowish flower breaks. The plant, about the size of a small apple, is classed as an echino-cactus. Dried slices cut out of the middle zone contain drugs of singular effect, that is, mescaline and related alkaloids.

The cacti are plants that prevent their etheric organization from actively engaging in the physical in such a way as to unleash growth. They cause to desiccate what in other plants unfolds and sprouts in fresh life. Since this concerns precisely their rhythmic organization, it is understandable that, as an image of their abnormal life processes, they form toxins that affect the rhythmic system in man by pressing out the higher members of man's being active in it, that is, the astral body and also, in part, the etheric body. This part then "vitalizes" the sensations of the astral body and calls forth distorted imaginative images. Since the ego has not produced them in full consciousness, these images sweep the person experiencing them into their current by force. This results in states that are similar to certain mental illnesses. The use of the peyote cactus as a remedy is conceivable in states of loosening of the higher members of man's being in the rhythmic system.

The largest number and the most typical of the plants of this family are raised up into a column; some, however, creep or struggle against the force of gravity by propping themselves against rock walls. In these cases, the etheric forces engage more strongly in the physical, bringing the rigid form into flux, if only linearly. The *queen of the night* (Selenicereus grandiflorus) is a good representative of the species that climb on limestone walls in the West Indies. The spines have disappeared; air roots push out of the ribs everywhere so that the whole stem element seems like a rootstock above the earth. The tropical air, pregnant with moisture, is more earthy than the air of our climes, and branches and twigs spring out of the roots above ground. In the high mountains, of course, only the light and air organs, the leaves and blossoms, can exist. In the West Indian habitat of the queen of the night, the air is permeated by fine salt processes in addition. At first, Selenicereus grandiflorus cannot free itself from the earth; it must raise itself with great effort.

When the many-branched, bloated trunk has reached a certain age, a thick bud forms on a green branch. It swells as if a little spherical cactus were going to grow on this stem-cactus, but does not grow longitudinally. The growth that cannot occur longitudinally comes out in thick spine formation; the spherical formation, however, is actually the ovary of a developing flower. This develops horizontally to the length of a hand or more, seeking the mean between the forces of lightness and gravity, and uncertainly groping its way toward the sunlight. It is the setting sun that brings its hour of blooming; throughout one night the giant flower unfolds. Clouds of aroma gush out of this enormous blossom in waves; the scent is reminiscent of jasmine, benzoin, vanilla, and violets. The (astral) blossoming force takes hold of the etheric organization of this plant so intensively that a few hours' time brings complete wilting, leaving a limp sack hanging there in the morning.

Conflict between levity and gravity and between etheric formative forces and astral domains is the signature of this plant. It is significant that this is an astral force that manifests at night. The dynamic described is also expressed in the formation of certain substances of an alkaloid-related nature. Prepared appropriately, as a remedy it affects the organic region of the heart, since rhythmic interaction of etheric and astral impulses is essential in the heart, which assumes a middle position between light and gravity in the living topography of the human body. It is here that the harmonization takes place between the upper system, removed from the earth forces, and the lower, which deals with these forces most intensively. This dynamic, however, is that of all plants with an effect on the heart. The rhythmic system of the human being has its existence in the rhythmic encounter of etheric and astral effects; at the same time, this is where the rhythmic joining and separation of airy and fluid processes takes place.

Etheric loosening and excessive "physicalization" in the heart area, on the one hand, and astral cramping on the other, as is shown in angina pectoris, for example, are the conditions that can find their remedy in preparations from the blossoms and young sprouts of Cactus grandiflorus.

The Chenopodiaceae

With the presentation of a plant family in which salt processes are particularly significant, the relationship of the plant kingdom to the mineral kingdom standing below it can be made clear. Such a family is the Chenopodiaceae or goosefoot plants, which are halophytes, that is, lovers of salt.

It is instructive to see how the predominance of the salt pole shapes the type of the archetypal plant. The leaves draw together, in some species swelling into sausage-like forms or round discs that surround the stem, or else they shrink to scales and surrender the leaf function to the stem, which is swollen with green juice. Stem and leaves put out water-filled bladder hairs. True wood formation does not occur. The root can swell up like a turnip; in contrast, the blossom process atrophies. When sal becomes so strong, then sulfur is neglected. The blossom parts have a greater vitality, however, since the astral blossoming processes cannot have such a devitalizing effect. The vitality of the root pole penetrates into the blossom region. The petals are retained in some species and continue to grow after blooming is done, becoming fleshy like fruits or changing into winglike or thornlike structures that give the fruit to the wind or attach it to animals. No aromatic substances are formed. The high potassium or sodium content of the whole plant made potash or soda extraction possible in earlier centuries. The roots store sugar; the beet and sugar beet belong to this family. The fruits often contain starchy seeds.

Two plants of this small but interesting family may be mentioned briefly here.

A wild seashore halophyte is the ancestor of the cultivated *mangold* (Beta vulgaris), *beet* and *sugar beet*. They fruit in their root region, as it were; the sugar, which the leaves form abundantly, is stored there. By being drawn into the root-salt region, the sugar process is made earthly. In addition, the whole plant contains large amounts of saponins, and the root contains a great quantity of pectins.

Rudolf Steiner made reference to the curative effects of the beet. According to these indications, the moon has a certain influence on the growth of plant roots. Particularly in childhood, a root diet may be of significant benefit, above all for children who grow too slowly. Childhood growth is still dynamically much related to the head forces, and root foods stimulate these forces. Specifically in children who have a tendency to intestinal parasites, a diet of beets at the time of the full moon will be beneficial. The control of sugar through the root-salt processes, a characteristic capacity of the beet, brings the digestion more under the ordering influence of the head forces. Carbohydrates, which are not permeated by such root-salt processes, are known to promote intestinal worms. As we know, the Chenopodiaceae withdraw from their fruit region the forces that normally come to this area in plants in which the sal pole does not suppress the sulfur activity. The child infested with worms allows etheric forces to proliferate in the intestinal area and does not send enough forming, ordering forces from the head to the digestive breakdown of food. The use of the root at the time of the full moon weakens the reproductive powers of the parasites, which are subject to lunar rhythms.

In *spinach* (Spinacia oleracea), root and leaf processes, sal and mercury, cooperate harmoniously and actively. This is expressed in a high chlorophyll and iron content. In addition, the root contains much saponin. This is a mercurial substance whose strong capacity for foaming speaks of processes that rhythmically combine the fluid with the airy. Saponins act on the life of the glands, including that of the digestive glands. Furthermore, spinach contains secretins that particularly stimulate the secretions of the pancreas. A number of vitamins

–provitamin A, vitamin B_1, B_2, B_6, vitamin C, and in summer some vitamin D–are also contained in this nutritious plant. A considerable amount of oxalic acid expresses mastery over congestive processes in the etheric realm. In addition, spinach contains folic acid in amounts not usual in plants. Deficiency of folic acid is connected with certain forms of anemia, so spinach can be expected to produce a strong stimulation of the digestion, orienting it toward the iron processes, which culminate in blood formation, as we know. The patient with pernicious anemia allows certain tendencies to decomposition of the digestive metabolism to penetrate into the blood-forming processes. Appropriate preparations from the spinach root are able to counteract this. Rudolf Steiner introduced spinach root into the treasury of remedies for the first time. Besides other remedies, he recommended it together with a decoction of sassafras wood for the treatment of pernicious anemia.

The Solanaceae

In the introductory chapters on the original relationships of the plant to animal and man, it was stated that the plant, through which all higher life on earth flourishes, also depends on the kingdoms of nature that stand above it. Plants "need" animals, but the fact that there are poisonous plants would seem to oppose life's law of give and take.

Although these plants are toxic to animals and are removed from this general law of give and take, to the normal plant world they are not toxic; every manner of non-poisonous growth flourishes in their vicinity. There must be a relationship to the animal world built into the essence of the poisonous plants that opposes the normal relationship of the plant to the animal world. The life process of the poisonous plant produces toxins, but only to excrete them. The alkaloids are waste products of the metabolism; bound with vegetable acids into salts and insoluble in dying cells or tissues, they are eliminated. They fall out of the anabolic stream of life. Thus, it is not these substances that the plant needs but the processes whose by-products they are. They are connected with catabolic activity. These plant toxins separate out of the anabolic metabolism;

this can also occur through a "misdirected" anabolism. Some amino acids are remarkably similar to the alkaloid vegetable toxins. This indicates that we are dealing with natural processes of dying—or at least of devitalization—that eliminate substances as refuse from the living protein, or disturb the anabolic process in such a way as to form such "dead" substances as the alkaloids represent. Such substances cannot be formed by anabolic plant life; they can be formed only by something that inserts itself as an antagonistic, crippling, and finally killing element.

Deficient flowering signifies nontoxicity; excess leads close to toxin formation. In order for a poisonous plant to result from a normal one, it is necessary that a process that takes place in each blossom of the plant should increase beyond the normal measure. This process is connected with the animalic principle, since the blossom represents a gesture of the plant toward the state of being of the animal; it is the organ through which the plant "acknowledges" that there is an animal world. Since the animal surpasses the plant in that it has not only a physical and etheric organization but also an astral body, the blossoming and toxin formation must generally reveal the connections of plants to the world of astral being. Poisonous plants deviate from the norm of the plant world in that they develop one-sidedly and permeate themselves excessively with a basic pattern that is present everywhere. The astral principle impresses itself into the body of the plant.

The nightshade family is composed of plants that are hardy and rapidly growing, bursting with vitality. Their strong growth stops suddenly and is seized by the blossoming process before it has a chance to develop fully as an herb. We see a conflict of two principles, in which there is a unique concrescence of the sprouting nature of the foliage with the excessively powerful inflorescence that is pressed into it. This struggle demonstrates the statement that in poisonous plants the astral element becomes too strongly connected with the plant. It actually bores into the plant "visibly." The more intensively this occurs, the more poisonous the species of plant will be.

The blossom forms of the Solanaceae are the result of invagination processes that are often quite deep. Cups, bells, deep and slender tubes, and narrow, dark gullets are typical of the vigorous and highly poisonous species of this family. In many of them, a dusky tint rises up from the root or diffuses outward from the depths of the blossom's throat. The darkness of night has embodied itself in this family. This is also manifested in the time of flowering (at night, for example, in tobacco and thorn apple species) or in the flowers' tendency to seek out the dark.

Not all nightshade plants are subject to such strong astral penetration. In the numerous members of the genera Solanum, Physalis, and Capsicum, to which the tomato, potato, bittersweet nightshade, eggplant, red pepper, and winter cherry belong, their stronger etheric forces push back the astral principle; the blossoming process, though still intense, appears more at its "right place." Sprout and foliage are allowed to develop fully. The blossom is no longer such an involuted structure. Related to this is their formation of much weaker poisons; in fact, fruits and tubers actually become nontoxic in ripening and are important foods.

Accordingly, the nightshade family can be divided into two large groups. In the first, "strongly cramped" kind, we find the typical poisonous plants with the specific nightshade alkaloids; the second, not so strongly affected by the astral principle, contains the much weaker poison, solanin, and related substances.

The abnormal invasion of the astral sphere into the solanaceous nature produces the alkaloid poisons through its catabolic action in the life of the proteins. These toxins, in turn, have the power to affect the human astral body, specifically where it is connected with the sense organization. In the most various ways the astral body is pushed out of its healthy connections with the physical body. The soul life is not filled with sensory perceptions but with abnormal content, that is, with pictures that do not correspond to any outer reality and are experienced as hallucinations and visions.

The healthy way to the development of higher stages of consciousness, however, leads forward, not backward. It leads out of the spiritual emptiness of sensory consciousness, which comes about only through the mortal body with its death forces, and into a new spiritual fullness. By strengthening the waking, ego-conscious day-consciousness, such a path provides access to a world of living, weaving images whose contents are "true images" (imaginations) of spiritual realities. The book, *Knowledge of the Higher Worlds and Its Attainment,*[4] in which the path to true imagination is described, represents at the same time a great therapeutic deed.

Some of the most important healing plants of this family will now be described briefly.

The *mandrake* (Mandragora off.), a typical nightshade plant, is oriented chiefly around its root, whose fleshy body has taken much from the blossom process, which presses close to it. From the root flows a strangely sweet, narcotic fragrance. In earlier times both berry and root were used as a soporific, one that works even through its scent.

Its medicinal use is ancient. Hippocrates described how it is possible to cure anxiety and deep depressions with quite small doses of mandragora. Somewhat larger amounts lead to dilation of the pupils, an effect characteristic of many nightshade plants. The eyes become "night eyes"; they behave in bright daylight as though they were in deep darkness. Sense impressions are felt as too strong; unrest and overexcitement appear. Blood rushes into the head, just as it does, to a lesser extent, in sleep. Stronger doses produce a sedative effect, which increases to a deep sleep. Still more powerful doses bring about anesthesia. External application as a liniment causes soothing of pain to the point of anesthesia. Finally, internal administration leads to complete loss of sensation and deathlike sleep, which formerly permitted extensive cutting and burning of the body and limbs, and can be seen as an anticipation of our anesthesia. Besides these physical effects, there are also the psychic, which can appear in visions, hallucinations, even delirium.

All of these symptoms show how the supersensible vehicle of the soul life is expelled, step by step, from the physical organs of sensation, depending on the amount used, and how the mandragora effect takes its place.

When the astral body engages too strongly in certain organic areas that ought to be subject to its normal activity, then mandragora acts as a spasmolytic, a stronger one than belladonna or hyoscyamus. Colics, stubborn tenesmus in hemorrhoidal ailments, as well as asthma, hay fever, and whooping cough have at different times been indications for the application of this medicinal plant. Mandrake is also an ancient aphrodisiac; the roots in particular were believed to promote conception.

The effects, however, for which mandragora has been taken into the pharmacopoeia of anthroposophical medicine lie in different areas from those that have been touched on so far. Here it is used as a remedy against certain forms of rheumatism, but particularly against gout.

Rudolf Steiner indicated[5] that catabolic, not anabolic, processes are the material foundation of conscious experiences. An especially noteworthy catabolic process is the formation of uric acid. It is caused by the consciousness-developing members of man's being, his ego and astral body. The ego directs the exceedingly fine secretion of uric acid in the brain, while the astral body guides the coarser secretion throughout the body, as well as the excretion through the urine. It is through the impregnation of the organs with the right proportion of inorganic material that "man can be the conscious being that he is." In the healthy organism, the right balance of distribution of uric acid to the different regions must be maintained. This reveals whether the ego organization and astral body stand in a healthy relation to one another in any particular organ or organ system.

The mandragora effect under consideration is based on the fact that the plant presses its blossom process to the root pole, and in this way conducts excessive astral impulses in alkaloid formations to the very tip of the root. In the normal plant, the root is a region in which it deals chiefly with the mineral, salt processes of the soil. It masters the mineral element, enlivens and orders it in all its multiplicity, in accordance with the formative laws of the particular species. In the mandrake root, however, the control of inorganic, mineral nature and the overly strong astralization meet with one another. For this reason, the mandragora process, as it is manifested in the root, is well-suited to counteract the overactivity of the human astral body in relation to uric acid formation and distribution in the gout patient. It allows the ego organization to become again the leading and mastering force in relation to the total organization of the uric acid balance, which is so important for the development of consciousness.

The entire structure of the *deadly nightshade* (Atropa belladonna) is the expression of the struggle of light and dark forces of being. It is sensitive to the interaction of light and darkness. Its leaves are true shade leaves in their finer structure, but this changes when more light plays about them. The seeds, however, germinate in the light and are reluctant to sprout in the deep shade.

The being of the deadly nightshade is characterized not only by the interplay of light and darkness, but also by the interweaving of water and air. The roots and sprouts greedily suck the water from the damp humus of the woods, transpiring it into the atmosphere. This intensive process of giving the fluid element to the air is revealed when a stem is broken off; after a short time it hangs down limply, since no new water can replenish the strong evaporation. Continually, forces from the astral element, air, try to take hold of the plant, urging toward slackness and wilting, but this is always balanced by the etheric element, water, pulsing through it afresh. A strong life process compensates to a large extent for the effects of excessive "astralization."

Atropa belladonna is poisonous to man in all its parts, but birds, rabbits, and generally all animals with dominant nerve-sense processes feed on it with impunity. The chemist discovers in it the typical nightshade alkaloids. In the ash there is a notable content of silicic acid and magnesium, as well as a trace of copper. The first two substances speak of the nightshade's hidden longing for light, since both silicic acid and magnesium are "light elements."

No one who has perceived the relationship of the nightshade process to light and darkness will be surprised to find that, among the specific bodily regions, the eye assumes a special role. The encounter between the worlds of day and night, however, takes place not only in a single organ such as the eye, which is "created in the light for the light," but also, as the transition between sleeping and waking consciousness, in the whole human being. The "night man" is, as it were, brought up against the "day man," and projects into him everywhere. The eyes are open, but in broad daylight they behave as though they had opened in complete darkness. The lower, blood man presses out of his subconscious, unconscious depths into the nerve region of the head, because the organism is awake only in the head; in the metabolism it is always asleep, even during the day. Under the influence of the deadly nightshade toxin, the blood presses upward; the head becomes hot, the face red. The blood principle breaks out into the nerve-sense region. The blood vessels of the eye are overfilled, nosebleed occurs, the salivary glands, tonsils, and tongue swell. Oversensitivity to outer cold appears. Since similar conditions occur in many diseases characterized by acute fevers and inflammations in their initial stage, the homeopathic use of belladonna has proven an important remedy in these initial stages. Migraine and congestive headaches are also indications for its use; it is used as well as treatment of the aftereffects of viral encephalitis ("Bulgarian treatment"). The strong efficacy of belladonna root on the head is manifested in these uses.

It is understandable that a plant into which astral activities are so abnormally pressed is efficacious in conditions where the human organism displays excessive astral engagement in certain organic regions, manifesting as spasms. Consequently, belladonna has been used to treat whooping cough, asthma, stomach and intestinal cramps, gall bladder and kidney colic, uterine cramps, and even paralytic states—of the bladder sphincter for example.

In the nerve-sense region, the "day man" can live in conscious activity of the spirit; in the metabolic-limb system he is active in a form of consciousness dimmed to the point of sleep. This activity, in which the "night man" lives, is eminently spiritual, but it is unconscious. In remaining unconscious, the spiritual element is bound to organic activity and preparation of substances. With the poison of the deadly nightshade, a part of this spirituality can be driven out of the physical and liberated. Such a freeing of the spiritual from its organic base and support normally occurs only in the brain, the nerves, and the sense organs. When it rises unbound from the depths of the metabolic organs, abnormal soul contents are experienced as visions, etc. At the same time, a wild, pathological compulsion to movement seizes the muscular system. The significance of deadly nightshade in the treatment of so-called mental disorders results from this.

Let us recall that we found an intensive struggle between the etheric and astral principles pervading the deadly nightshade plant. In addition, it should be noted that belladonna remains quite soft and unhardened through all stages of growth. In autumn the whole stately phenomenon fades away almost without a trace. Therefore, a part of the healing action of belladonna consists, in appropriate dosage, in a stimulation of the vital processes (the activity of the etheric body) and in combatting processes of induration and mineralization such as may appear with premature aging of the whole organization or a single organic region (chiefly the eye).

Readers interested in a more detailed exploration of the great variety of medicinal possibilities are emphatically referred to the comprehensive and detailed studies in the book, *Die unbekannte Heilpflanze* by W. Chr. Simonis.

The genus Hyoscyamus, which settles in gypsy fashion throughout Europe, North Africa, and Asia in regions of temperate climate, has its most characteristic and important representative in *henbane* (Hyoscyamus niger), a unique variant of the basic type and yet a nightshade plant through and through. In "normal" plants, the spiral tendency arranges the foliage rhythmically around the shoot and fulfills itself in the leaf process before going on to flower formation. In henbane, however, the blossom process takes over this tendency from the very beginning, deforming it. This solanaceous plant displays a distorted spiral tendency of the foliage. The crux of its whole structure is clearly the spiral interweaving of leaf and blossom, despite the turnip-like taproot, which gives up its

existence to the flowering process in that it dies after flower
and fruit are formed.

The main emphasis of the healing effects will be sought in
regions where the metabolic-limb processes come into contact
with those of the rhythmic system. The relation of the astral
body to the physical-etheric will be influenced in these regions
in such a way that, depending on the dosage, a weak astral
body is stimulated to stronger engagement, while an astral
body that is pressed within too strongly and cramped will be
forced out. The muscular organization of the limb system is
formed out of the interaction of the formative impulses of the
rhythmic region with the metabolic organization. The astral
organization, as the originator of the impulse to movement,
must engage especially powerfully, both anabolically and catabolically, into the musculature, as into an instrument. This is a
particular region of action of henbane, with its "astralized synthesis of rhythmic leaf and blossom processes." Release of
cramps, improved nutrition, and anabolic processes can be
brought about in this region with the appropriate henbane
remedy. The nourishment of the heart muscle and the musculature of the limbs is promoted by mixing appropriately processed henbane with other remedies given here. Cardiodoron,
for example, contains this plant as one of its constituents.

The solar plexus, according to Rudolf Steiner, is also stimulated by hyoscyamus, since the astral body and ego organization come to engage more strongly in it. That part of the astral
body that must act in unconsciousness engages in the etheric-
physical functions through the solar plexus and the connected
autonomic nervous system, with its interplay of sympathetic
and parasympathetic impulses. It is the task of the nervous
system to keep the astral body unconscious in this region and
to extinguish the forces of consciousness. Release of the soul-
spiritual in this region calls forth somnambulistic picture consciousness, visions, and hallucinations, as was described with
mandrake. In the Middle Ages, henbane had a bad reputation
because of these effects. It gained an important status as a
remedy for the first time in homeopathy, which employs it for

all kinds of spasms in the muscular region, agitation, epileptic seizures, and also in disorders that indicate that the brain is no longer a healthy foundation, a "mirroring apparatus," for waking day-consciousness, so that conceptual disorders and manic and also depressive states result. After all, so-called mental disorders always have physical causes.

In the science of medicine extended by anthroposophical spiritual science, hyoscyamus also plays a significant role in the treatment of semiconscious states; their cause is in a "brain not properly maintained in its structure," whose astral organization does not engage firmly enough in the physical. When the patient takes an appropriately prepared hyoscyamus remedy, his metabolic activity must be brought up to a particularly high intensity in order to overcome the constitution of this highly poisonous plant. This brings the formation of a corresponding force-form in the etheric body of the metabolic region. As a counterprocess to this activity in the lower organization, a better coherence results in the upper organization between the organizational forces of the brain and the astral body. As the lower pole overcomes a plant element in which astral forces are too strongly pressed, the upper pole can now properly draw to itself the astral principle that is too loosely connected.

If we see the development of the plant from the seed as an expiration into the physical, then the *thorn apple* or *jimson weed* (Datura stramonium) is the picture of "cramped expiration." Chemical analysis has found 1-hyoscyamine and small amounts of atropine and 1-scopolamine in this plant, much as in the Solonaceae dealt with before. Nevertheless, its medicinal action differs from that of belladonna, hyoscyamus, and mandragora in its subtler features. The leaves of the thorn apple help to release the asthmatic's astral body, held convulsively in the expiration process, from its spasm. Datura is also indicated in chorea (Choreodoron 1).

Rudolf Steiner also indicated a new application: appropriately processed extract of the unripe fruits of the thorn apple for the treatment of gallstone colic. This use will be understandable if we consider the spasmolytic qualities of this plant, as in the Solanaceae considered earlier, and if we observe how the conflict between swelling and forming, which pervades the whole plant, ends in the fruit as globes radiating out of one another. The most formed and hardened structure is the thorny fruit, which, even in rotting, leaves behind a delicate fibrous framework. This form is also imprinted on the crystalline incrustation that is excreted from the living juices as hardened mineral (calcium oxalate). The mace-like formations are an image of the centrifugal processes. This dynamic, the pushing of inner contents outward, is put to work in the remedy. The "prickles" are actually, in essence, vessels that belong to the fluid organization. What otherwise is expressed in rounded forms—drops and spheres—is radiated outward in this case.

In the *tobacco* plant (Nicotiana tabacum), the solanaceous motif sounds in an entirely different key. Obviously, the engagement of the blossom impulse has not led to deformation of the rhythmic system, as in the nightshade plants considered before. Nevertheless, here again astral impulses that would be normal in the blossom region have penetrated the whole plant from the root up. This expresses itself in the strongly aromatic, resinous scent of leaf and stem, and in the formation of one of the strongest vegetable toxins, nicotine, and its relatives. Just as the form of the Nicotiana species represents a different type from the deadly nightshade, henbane, thorn apple, etc., however, so is the alkaloid nicotine quite a different substance from hyoscyamine, atropine, and scopolamine. It is, above all, a fluid and truly volatile substance, sharing the nature of a volatile oil; it evaporates continuously, gently through the leaves into the atmosphere. A fine cloud of poison-vapor floats over every tobacco field with its spicy, musty odor. In tobacco, as well, the astral element has pressed into the physical too early and too deeply, taking part of the plant processes with it into the airy region, but this causes no deformation of the rhythmic system.

Nicotine completely lacks the visionary, hallucinatory drug-like effects. The curative uses of tobacco result from the processes proper to the essential nature of the plant. As we have learned, the strong forces of its rhythmic organization drive a part of the astrality, which grips the entire plant, back into the surroundings in the form of a vapor sphere. Remedies derived from tobacco leaves cause the astral body to engage in the human rhythmic organization. They accelerate the blood process, intensify the exhalation process, and influence the vascular and respiratory musculature. For this reason, asthma and vascular cramps are among the indications. "Tobacco regulates the activity of the astral body," according to Rudolf Steiner. In the digestive system, the astral body is promoted in its penetration of the air organization; severe flatulence as well as paralysis of intestinal activity are combatted. These stem from deficient incorporation of the astral body into this region. Tobacco as a remedy not only regulates the activity of the astral body. It also balances out "deformations" of this member of man's being that can be transmitted to the etheric and ultimately to the physical processes of the human organization.

In the species of the genus Solanum, the green leaf and sprout element develop more normally; the blossoms are left to their own development and are distinctly set off by themselves. The astral element allows the etheric its due and does not press itself into the formation of the plant too prematurely or excessively. Hence, the plants of this genus do not form alkaloids like hyoscyamine, nicotine, etc., but "glyco-alkaloids," intermediate substances between glycosides and alkaloids, primarily solanine in the fruit, and solacein and solanein in stem and leaf. Solanum dulcamara also contains mucilaginous substances —about ten per cent tannins and a considerable amount of silicic acid in the ash.

Its high content of silicic acid (18 per cent) gives *bittersweet* (Solanum dulcamara) strong connections to the sensory sphere, the ectoderm and its invaginations. Skin inflammations with itching, hotness, urticaria, and weeping eczema, and also catarrhal inflammations of the mucous membranes, the respiratory passages and the bronchi, especially when connected with a cramping of the astral body in these organic regions, are among the domains in which a plant that is both a silicic acid plant and one that is astralized in the manner of the nightshade family may be efficacious. It can even be helpful in whooping cough. Its action also extends to catarrhal conditions of the mucous membranes of the intestines and bladder. Rudolf Steiner specified the use of bittersweet blossoms, in combination with blooming pennycress, for the treatment of eczematous ailments (Dermatodoron). A mild belladonna note is added to the main effects cited here.

The *tomato* (Solanum lycopersicum) displays a somewhat egotistical nature in its habit of being "friendly" with itself, preferring to grow in a tomato compost. It shares this tendency with tobacco. Unrotted, "wild" compost suits it best. As a food plant it should be used with prudence and should be avoided when there is a disposition to proliferative and indurative diseases in which the formative forces go astray, as in cancer, gout, and rheumatism. On the other hand, the tomato is sympathetic to the liver, the most proliferating, plastic organ. Rudolf Steiner recommended the highly potentized extract of the fruit for the treatment of bone marrow inflammations.

In the *red pepper* (Capsicum annuum) the forces of astralization, which are familiar to us in the nightshade plants, take hold of the etheric-vegetative element with air and fire. It is not surprising to find in this plant a nitrogenous substance that lends it the burning taste and the blistering property. Characteristic of it are the energetic firing of the metabolism and the resulting curative inflammation. In addition, as a nightshade plant there is its effect on the cramped astral body in muscles affected by rheumatic diseases; this effect is released by capsicum. The high content of vitamin C and provitamin A (carotene) gives special nutritional value to the unripe fruit eaten as a vegetable.

Chapter XII
The Capillary-Dynamic Blood Test

In 1855, Friedrich Ferdinand Runge published his book, *Der Bildungstrieb der Stoffe veranschaulicht an selbstgewachsenen Bildern (The Formative Impulse of Substances Illustrated in Self-Grown Pictures)*, in which he introduced a new method of investigation. He allowed solutions of metal salts to spread horizontally on filter paper and described the forms, colors, and structures that grew in this way. What appeared pictorially he called the formative impulse of the substance. Thus he had discovered not an analytic but a new pictorial method.

Goppelsroeder's investigations in 1907 went in a completely different direction. He let solutions climb in strips of filter paper, measured the height of climbing, density, and color intensity, and created in this way an analytic method according to measure, number, and weight, the foundation for the analytic methods of chromatography.

At the beginning of the 1920's, Lili Kolisko undertook, at Rudolf Steiner's suggestion, to study solutions of substances with a pictorial, technically updated method in two phases in a diffusion picture. This provided a glimpse into the inherent dynamic of the substances and proved to be exceedingly fruitful in a great variety of fields.

Supplementing the analytic procedures, which give the content, type, and amount of constituent substances according to measure, number, and weight, a pictorial method was evolved that represented an expression of the forming forces underlying all living things. These are what Steiner called the etheric formative forces, which are described in anthroposophical literature.

Work on the capillary-dynamic blood test began in 1928. It grew out of the critical situation in which doctors found themselves in regard to the disease of cancer. It was repeatedly found, and this has changed little today, that cancer patients came into treatment when it was already too late for a thorough-going therapy. It became imperative to face the question of early diagnosis. Steiner had indicated the existence of a precancer-ous state that, to be sure, had also been presumed to exist by in-dividual medical schools, but without specific foundations.

In 1924, Rudolf Steiner had answered the author affirmative-ly as to the possibility of early diagnosis. Ita Wegmann, the founder of the Clinical-Therapeutic Institute in Arlesheim (now the Ita Wegmann Clinic) was responsive to the idea, so that in 1928 it was possible to begin testing on a large scale in this clinic. At that time, Iscador therapy was in its initial stages. Kolisko had published her capillary diffusion tests, and it was a logical next step to adapt this method to this specific complex of questions.

Steiner had provided basic material for the development of an early diagnosis for cancer and it was possible, step by step, to establish it experimentally over the course of the years. Begin-ning in 1930, the progress made in this research was reported at intervals and the results gathered into a monograph.[1]

The threefold nature of the human organism served as a foundation for the development of the method; it has proven uncommonly fruitful for the entire approach of medicine. Another fundamental idea behind the research was the polarity of the two force-systems of blood and nerve,[2] and the opposi-tion of antimonizing and albuminizing forces in the organism.[3] An additional basis was Steiner's indication that a system of forces that maintains health in the region assigned to it will have a pathological effect when shifted into another system. This also is applicable to the disease of cancer, in which forces proper to the nerve-sense system show, at an early stage, the tendency to move into the metabolic zone. Such processes have structural force, however, and it could be expected that something that affects the systems so profoundly ought to be detectable in the all-encompassing blood. The way to do this was shown by the capillary-dynamic blood test.

As the aforementioned monograph describes in detail, a particular physical system serves as an indicator. First, the blood, diluted to about eight per cent (depending on paper quality), climbs in rolls of absolutely clean filter paper of uniform structure, under an exactly normalized relation of temperature and humidity (20° to 70 per cent). Then follows Aqua dist.

Besides the standardization of blood dilution and room conditions, the quality of the paper plays a critical role. While too-soft paper produces unsharp or blurred contours, too-hard paper hampers the development of the pictures.

Looking at the forms arising with normal blood (fig. 1) in the completed diffusion process, we see a fairly regular wave-line with a linear contour (type I).

The waves that arise are to be thought of as the product of two components: a force-current going from below upward in the direction of the diffusion process, expressing itself in the wave mountains, and one acting from above downward, producing the wave valleys. The further observations presented show that the force-current acting from above downward is also an active process.

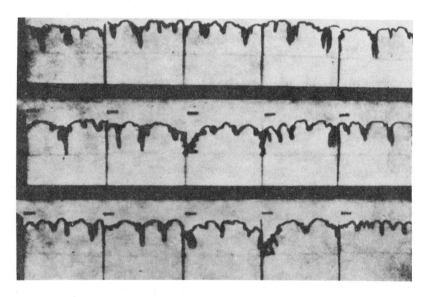

Fig. 1. Normal series of 15 sheets

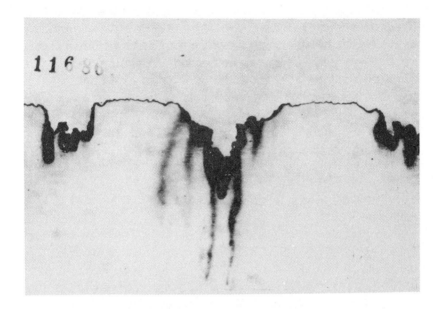

Fig. 2. "Empty" forms

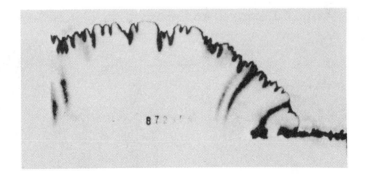

Fig. 3. Inflammation forms

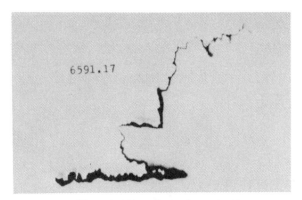

Fig. 4. Simple sclerotic form

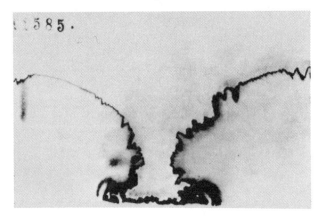

Fig. 5. Deformed end phase of the picture

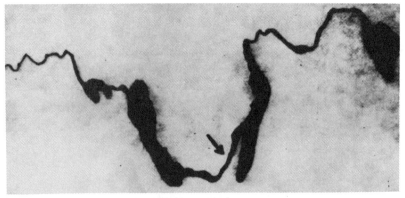

Fig. 6. Erosion with leaning form, on the right at the base

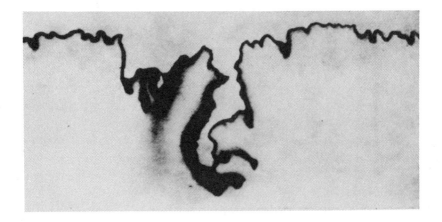

Fig. 7. Erosion with proliferation form, to the side of the base

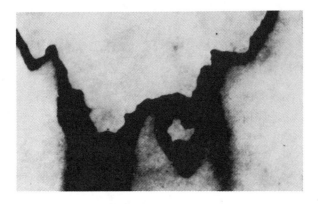

Fig. 8. Enclosure (island formation)

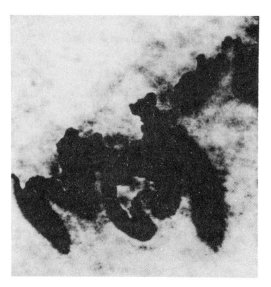

Fig. 9. Pre-explosive situation

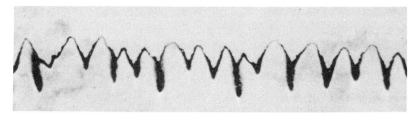

Fig. 10. Adynamia forms

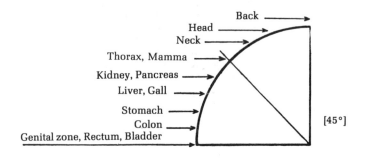

Localization Scheme

Both in the occurrence of the more or less regular wave peaks and in the rising of the wave valleys, the basic capillary phenomenon is distinctly influenced by forces that are super-imposed on the purely physical process and must be attributed to factors lying in the blood itself. These become more clearly perceptible when we go to the metamorphosis of the basic phe-nomenon in the pathological cases. Following Rudolf Steiner's terminology, we call the forces acting from below upward and superimposed on the physical capillary flow the "dissolving, albuminizing" forces, and those that form the wave valleys we call the "forming, antimonizing" forces. When one or the other group of forces predominates, the following results are seen.

1. If the dissolving forces predominate, they bring about a partial dissolution of the upper line with unclear, blurred con-ditions and all variants thereof.

2. With predominance of the forming forces, which normal-ly lead to the formation of the wave valleys, normal diffusion of the blood solution is impaired and special organ-specific formations of precancerous significance appear. For example, one part of the primary line may be dissolved, leaving a re-mainder behind; or, in the most extreme case, the forming principle can be so intensive that a breaking through of the primary blood line is not possible at all. There is a "blockage."

Phenomena of the first group, expressing dissolving forces, are encountered wherever the forces of the astral body diminish in the periphery—in hay fever, for example, and other allergic symptoms. A similar but much more intensive loosening is found in advanced cases of carcinoma, with long flat forms of the secondary line (fig. 2).

Inflammatory conditions produce pictures that are another variant of the first group; they are rhythmically structured, but their individual elevations show no differentiation (fig. 3).

In the second group, with predominance of the forming forces, we have on the one hand sclerotic-indurative conditions and on the other the large group of precancerous forms; these can be distinguished from the simple sclerotic forms by their combination with the typical precancerous patterns (fig. 4). The regular "breaches" through the primary blood line in normal blood (fig. 1) are found only singly in cancer. They are deformed quite early, and in their further development they often show grotesque, chaotic formations (fig. 5) that cannot be explained in terms of the capillary forces. Their final form at the end of the picture's development is usually a cauliflower-like configuration.

Observation of the metamorphosis of form from the breach through the first blood line to the stage of complete development of the pictures requires continous monitoring. The reason for this is as follows. Since my first publications, it has been shown that the forms appearing during the development of the picture reveal a strict and unequivocal relation between the clinical-pathological processes and their localization in the diffusion picture; this is true not only for their malignant process but also for the pathological process in general, insofar as this is caused by displacement and deformation of the formative forces. The connection of certain form-forces with certain pathological states has been confirmed in the course of decades of testing (see localization schema).

Awareness that the whole human being is mirrored in the blood, even in the smallest quantities, was completely new when this method was being developed. Understandably, it still meets with the greatest skepticism today—in fact, with total, usually untested, rejection.

Examining a particular case of cancer, for example, one of stomach carcinoma, it will be found that the same, or similar, pathological forms occur after an operation has taken place. Furthermore, a great number of seemingly healthy people show pictures that are similar to those occurring in cancer. These are the "cancer-prone." It is possible for cancer patients who remain disposed postoperatively, as almost all do, gradually to rid themselves of the dispositional element. This is true to a greater extent in the cancer-disposed group, but it is possible with relatively great certainty to turn the precancerous type back to the norm through Iscador treatment.

It has been determined in follow-up investigations that preventive Iscador treatment can lower the cancer morbidity considerably in relation to the present average level. We have also dealt with patently precancerous cases in which the individuals concerned refused a prophylactic Iscador cure and then fell ill with cancer in one-half to two years.

Along with Iscador prophylaxis, the attempt should be made, insofar as this is theoretically and practically possible, to gain an insight into the dangers that lie hidden in man's environment as pathogenic factors. Furthermore, a certain hygiene of the soul may be even more important. The significance of the individual environmental factors for the human being is dealt with in detail in other chapters of this book. In regard to the precancerous state, these questions have been treated thoroughly by W. Kaelin.[4]

The form world observable in my blood test follows the cancer patient with absolute reliability from the inception of his disposition through the development of the tumor, to the lethal end.

Experience with the clinical development of malignant tumors has shown that a temporal factor is also revealed in the development of the pictures. If malignant deformations appear in the early phase, they indicate a deep constitutional anchoring of the disease. If they appear later, then the intensity of the disease dynamic is more superficial and more likely to be accessible to therapy. This temporal factor is also shown, for example, in the fact that affections that do not arise until later life, such as the formation of concretions and arthritis, never appear pictorially in the early phase but only in the middle or even the end phase of the picture's development.

The form groups of the precancerous condition mostly do not yet have a physical manifestation, though they do have a corresponding psychic one, which I have described in the work mentioned above as "cancer psyche." They are also to be found in most cases of cancer, because the dispositional element continues to exist after the appearance of the tumor. They are also found, however, in all precancerous cases in which no malignancy is yet present.

The first stage of the precancerous motif is *erosion* (figs. 6 and 7). It is a more or less deep involution or cleft appearing in the secondary line and can be thought of as having arisen through a force operating from above downward, hindering the development of the picture. It is the expression of a psychological shock, a depressive stage of life, and the various other factors that influence the attitude in the direction of the "cancer psyche."

The transition to the next stage is represented by partial enclosures (fig. 7).

The erosion may be closed off above to form an island, an enclosure, as a visible counterpart of the next stage in the psychological process, namely, that of shutting oneself in or off with one's difficulties (fig. 8). This attitude of soul is characteristic of a person threatened with cancer. It was first described as the "cancer psyche" by G. Suchantke in 1928.[5]

A further precancerous stage is shown in a form in which a polypous, proliferating formation grows up inside the enclosure: a sign of the pre-explosive situation (fig. 9).

Another regular pattern of events in the cancer process must still be mentioned. The relatively simple, plant-like form of healthy blood, which we have designated type I, goes over into a type II, which is more similar to animal forms. This builds up until the outbreak of the tumor to create a form group designated type III, which assumes a grotesque, ragged, and chaotic character. This is the group of forms typical of carcinoma.

The metamorphosis of forms in the cancer process from the beginning of the precancerous stage to the lethal termination of the disease can be expressed in a regular curve. Let us take the first precancerous phase from the beginning up to the onset of the tumor. The formative forces of the nerve-sense system press themselves increasingly into the metabolic region. The more the formative forces predominate, the smaller the possibility of harmonious diffusion becomes. Deformed, cauliflower-like forms arise, leaving remnants of the first blood line on the side. In most cases, the implantation of the tumor coincides with the maximum pathological formation. Then, however, a reversal sets in and the formative force abates as the tumor progresses.

The forming, antimonizing forces recede increasingly in face of the dissolving, albuminizing forces. The pictures begin to display a certain formlessness. This is the adynamic state, in which the formative forces are extinguished and thus the defense against the disease is totally exhausted.

Consequently, in the course of the disease of cancer, we have a predominance of the formative forces in the rising part of the curve, a maximum of them at the apex, the onset of the tumor, and then a diminishing to the point of complete disappearance in the descending portion, that is, adynamia (fig. 10).

The transition from the dynamic to the adynamic phase is a fluid one. The advanced precancerous state just before the onset of the tumor is often hard to separate from the appearance of the tumor with its first cancer cells. The capillary-dynamic blood examination of such critical cases makes it possible to indicate to the doctor the exact degree of danger and also the organ region affected.

Hence, the capillary-dynamic blood test is not a direct tumor test for the detection of an existing tumor; rather, it is a special test intended to show precancerous states as well as the organism's status in regard to disease and defense. Since it provides a faithful image of the inner condition in the course of cancer, however, it also has a high reliability in diagnosis and prognosis.

For the practical manipulation of this technique, it is found that the language of forms reaches its maximum intensity shortly before the outbreak of the tumor, and that the main use of this method of investigation is detecting the precancerous stage and controlling the postoperative cancer condition.

The diagnostic difficulty of determining the exact point when the "first cancer cell" arises can be seen from the schematic curve. The phase to the left of the apex and that to the right of it become increasingly similar to one another in form the nearer they are to the peak. A highly advanced precancerous state differs in no way from the state when cell proliferation sets in; it merely indicates a highly dramatic situation, and this may continue to exist for a limited time past the apex despite an operation.

Accordingly, it can be seen that there is no one uniform picture in cancer. There is a variability depending on the course

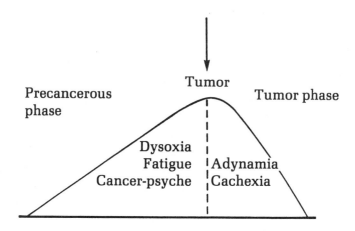

of the disease, and it can be further modified by influences such as surgery, radiation, cytotoxic drugs, and above all by Iscador therapy.

In the course of more than forty years, the author has come to the conviction that with this method of investigation all possible pathological conditions, such as rheumatic processes, sclerosis, asthma, etc., that are connected with a displacement of the formative forces are mirrored in the blood. It is thus relevant not only for precancer and cancer, although in cancer the disharmony of the two groups of forces plays the fundamental role. Therefore, this method offers a great variety of possibilities, which have been worked out only partially today, and it opens insights into new patterns that remain to be clarified. Errors in observation and interpretation are to be ascribed less to the method than to the physician entrusted with the evaluation.

The development of these capillary pictures, which resembles plant growth, should be approached with a certain intuition. Whoever is able in this way to experience them as the active picture of an organic process, developing what Goethe called an intuitive power of judgment, will become a skillful interpreter in this method.

Chapter XIII
Blood Crystallization
as a Diagnostic Technique

*My whole mind aspires to pene-
trate form and life.*
                    —Johannes Kepler

Copper chloride crystallization provides a morphological reagent sensitive to blood and its changes of state. The principle of the method is based on the well-known scientific fact that crystallizing salt solutions are, by certain additives, specifically modified in their form of growth and the arrangement of the carrier substance crystallizing out (additive-specific pictures of structure as a test method). Such crystallizations gained significance for biology and medicine after Ehrenfried Pfeiffer[1] succeeded in obtaining additive-characteristic and reproducible copper chloride crystallization pictures that permit references about the additives used and about their change of state, for example, the blood of healthy or sick individuals.

Since Pfeiffer's work, blood crystallization has been developed as a many-sided direction for diagnostic technique. In the blood, the entire functional organism is mirrored in its action on the intermediate metabolism as is found in alterations of warmth, oxidation, and of the chemical nature in each organ and tissue. Copper chloride reacts with delicate precision and with characteristic and reproducible crystal modifications, and produces tissue, organ, and disease-characteristic crystal forms by the polyvalent lability test of the subtlest alterations of the constitution of the blood. The method makes it possible to determine quite early a great variety of states of reactivity, functional disturbances, and diseases.

For a systematic description of the method, the reader is

referred to the book, *Die Kupferchloridkristallisation in Naturwissenschaft und Medizin* (Copper Chloride Crystallization in
Natural Science and Medicine).[2] In the introduction of this
book, A. Neuheus gives the basic principles of the method in
relation to modern crystallography. Then a description of technique and laboratory installation is given, along with the fundamentals of crystallization using various mineral salts, and
vegetable and animal substances. A systematic description of
blood and its components follows, including the blood crystallization of healthy individuals showing physiological variations. The blood crystallizations of diseased persons reveal,
through abundant pictorial material, the organ and disease-
characteristic alterations. They were obtained in clinically
verified cases of disease and were 80–90 per cent accurate.
Case histories indicate the practical application of the method
in relation to diagnosis and early diagnosis. When the book
was written in 1957, the investigative material consisted of
36,000 test series, including about 140,000 test plates. Since
then, these figures have doubled.

In the following, several selected areas of blood crystallization, referring to functional diagnostics and therapy, will be
described briefly.

Technique of Testing

To produce a crystallization, blood is taken from the finger-
tip, if possible in the morning, during fasting or three hours
after a light meal. It is dripped onto a medium soft filter paper
(Schleicher and Schüll, No. 604) and dried. In the laboratory
this dried blood is dissolved in twice-distilled water, mixed
with a 12 per cent solution of copper chloride, and poured on
ringed test plates 12 cm in diameter.

The test solution contains 0.1–0.015 g blood, 1.2 g $CuCl_2.2H_2O$
and 6.0 ml twice-distilled water per plate, and at least four
plates are made per test. The test is run in a chamber with the
temperature and relative humidity held constant at 28° C and
50–55 per cent relative humidity. The solution crystallizes out
in about ten hours. The blood crystallizations obtained are

then compared morphologically, regarding the formations occurring in them.

General Directions for Diagnostics

The blood crystallization picture is evaluated by considering the harmony of the whole, the type and arrangement of the needle crystals, and disease and organ-specific formations.

Blood crystallizations of healthy individuals display uniform needle lines usually radiating from a crystal center (center of gravity) toward the periphery; this is called a crystallization field. On the periphery there is a transition to a narrow, clearly delimited margin. The total picture reveals a clearly and uniformly articulated whole. This ideal norm corresponds to an organic principle of order that keeps all individual functions in equilibrium.

Blood crystallizations of diseased individuals, in contrast, show characteristic alterations; for example, those in the marginal zone are indicative of altered vitality.

Characteristic changes in the crystal's needle arrangement point to various states of reaction:

Dense, fine, dry needles	- physicalization, deposition, tendency to mineralization
Water infiltration	- metabolic disorders, congestive symptoms
Loose needle arrangement	- altered oxidation
Fibrotic brushes ("brooms")	- fibrotic processes
Soft or sharp gaps	- spastic or sclerotic tendency
Star or sparkling images (figs. 1 and 2)	- inflammatory tendency, inflammatory or allergic reaction
Hollow acorn signs (fig. 3)	- benign growth tendency

Directions for Diagnosis of Cancer

In the blood crystallizations of cancer patients, we meet with "transverse arrangements," needle strokes that have separated from the whole formation and lie crosswise or diagonally to the basic ray arrangement. Depending on how strongly they are pronounced, they appear in the crystal picture as a "separate formation tendency," or a "separate formation" (Figs. 4 and 5).

As early as 1935, Pfeiffer had recognized the relationship between transverse placement and cancer; this was confirmed by a number of others. It was soon noticed that not every transverse form indicates the existence of a manifest tumor, however, and also that atypical forms occur that should not be taken as "signs of cancer," although the inexperienced observer can easily confuse them with those typical of the disease.

We distinguish two different transverse arrangements, that is, a general, atypical tendency to separate formation without reference to cancer, and the characteristic separate formation found in cancer patients.

The Particular Formation Tendency in Tumors:
Pre- and Post-Tumorous Stages

Diagonal arrangements occur quite frequently in the blood crystallizations of cancer patients. They are found while the malignant tumor is present, before it appears and after it has disappeared. In their degree of markedness, they indicate the stage of the cancer (fig. 5, stages 1–4).

In the pre-cancerous stages, we find uncharacteristic, loose, larger or smaller slanted arrangements showing a general or incipient tendency to separate formation (stage 1). In the course of time, their placement becomes more transverse and they appear sharper and denser (stage 2).

With a malignant tumor, we see sharp, usually short-rayed, transverse needle strokes that often break into the basic radiating pattern or completely interrupt it (stages 3 and 4). They correspond to a "pronounced tendency to separate formation" or to "separate formation" (stage 4).

Pathological Blood Crystallization Pictures

Fig. 1. Star form in inflammation   Fig. 2. Cross form in tuberculosis

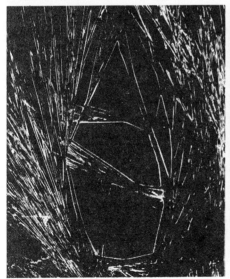
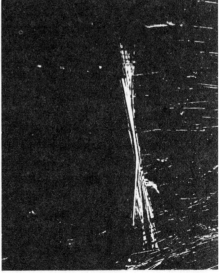

Fig. 3. Acorn form in
benign tumor

Fig. 4. Transverse arrangement
in cancer

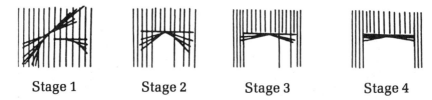

Stage 1   Stage 2   Stage 3   Stage 4

Fig. 5. Transverse arrangements, their progression and regression. Development of the transverse form.

In the resultant conditions of cancer, after surgery or radiation, transverse elements persist for weeks and months. In subsequent relapses and metastases, typical transverse structures remain for years. With healed cancer, transverse elements can be completely absent, or isolated atypical elements may appear.

In summary, the behavior of the transverse arrangements found in repeated blood crystallizations corresponds to the direction of the course of the cancer.

A growing tendency to separate formation (in the transition of atypical diagonal elements—stages 1 and 2—into transverse elements breaking into the structure—stages 3 and 4) corresponds to a situation of tumor progression. This is confirmed by many early diagnoses of cancer in which the crystallographic tendency to separate formation preceded the histologically determined cancer by one or several years.

An unvarying tendency to separate formation reflects a standstill of the tumor disposition.

A regression of the separate formation tendency corresponds to a regression or healing of the cancer after successful therapy (assuming adynamia can be excluded).

Separate Formation Tendency and Indications of Cancer in Organs

Transverse arrangements frequently occur in conjunction with organ signs—for example, intestinal, glandular, or genital signs, etc. In these cases, the crystallization indicates a separate formation tendency and a simultaneous organic disorder. The two may exist independently of one another. Nevertheless, experience has shown that this may also refer to a cancer, or the beginning of a cancer, in the given organ system. Numerous organ diagnoses and early diagnoses have confirmed this. For this reason, it is wise to watch carefully over the organ indicated in the crystallization test for a tendency to separate formation.

A Tendency to Separate Formation and the General State of the Patient

The degree of definition of transverse arrangements in the blood crystallization picture is influenced by the general condition of the patient. In early stages of the tumor, when the general state is not noticeably disturbed, transverse arrangements are especially obvious in about 85 per cent of the patients.

When the cancer is advanced and the general state poor, transverse elements are less pronounced. The highly disturbed picture reflects manifold metabolic disturbances that occasionally overlay the transverse elements.

In the adynamic stage, in severe anemia or in loss of vitality, the typical transverse elements may occasionally disappear. The dwindling formative force of the blood is unable to bring forth typical formations; the total picture tends toward the copper chloride picture. For this reason, a knowledge of the patient's general condition is especially important for an evaluation of transverse elements.

Thus we regard transverse arrangements, since they appear as early as the pre-cancerous stages and can persist postoperatively, as the expression of a functional "tumor situation" that is not necessarily identical with the presence of a tumor in the body.

Of course, it is impossible to say with certainty whether or not the tendency to separate formation, once begun, will lead to a malignant tumor. The picture only tells us that a cancer can result from these processes but not that it must. Therefore, it is appropriate to remain within the limitations of the picture and to speak of a "tendency to separate formation" without using the concept of a precancerous state, which clinically immediately suggests a cancer. The appearance of a tendency to separate formation is, however, also a reason for the physician to search carefully for a malignancy and to undertake appropriate preventive treatment.

A thorough description of transverse arrangements, their statistical certainty, and their behavior in cancer in patients of different ages and in cancers of different stages and organ systems is to be found in the book, *Kupferchlorid-Kristallisation* (*Copper Chloride Crystallization*) by A. Selawry. It includes illustrations and diagrams of morphogenesis and morphology of transverse arrangements, blood crystallization pictures in malignant tumors, comparative cancer statistics of various authors, cancer of different organ systems, case histories and illustrations of gastrointestinal, breast, and lung cancer.

Directions for Diagnosis
of Functional Disorders of the Organs

It is known that extracts of particular organs, when added to copper chloride, yield typical and reproducible type-pictures. Such organ type-pictures also occur in the blood crystallization pictures of patients with particular organic diseases; they may be based on organ-specific proteins in the blood of these patients. We call them "organ-characteristic" signs, or "organ signs" for short, and regard them as the expression of an organ dysfunction or disease.

Types and Arrangements of Organ Signs
in the Blood Crystallization Picture

We will briefly mention the most important organ signs. Most of them are like cavities or "pockets" within the radiating needle pattern. Each organ system has its type, which is distinguished by its kind of pockets, angles, and position in the crystal picture (see fig. 5). Each of these structural types relates not just to the organ but to the whole organ system.

In the blood crystallization pictures of pulmonary patients, striking pulmonary U-forms occur, reminiscent of sketches of

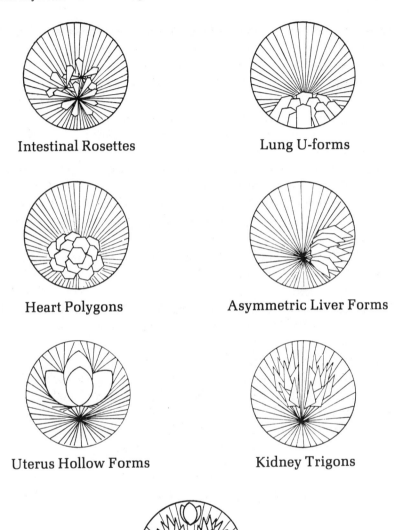

Intestinal Rosettes

Lung U-forms

Heart Polygons

Asymmetric Liver Forms

Uterus Hollow Forms

Kidney Trigons

Collective View of the Organ Signs

Fig. 6. Organ signs in their preferred situation
(From: A. and O. Selawry, *Die Kupferchlorid-Kristallisation in
Naturwissenschaft und Medizin,* Stuttgart 1957.)

"mountain crystals." They are usually located in the short-rayed upper field. The lung-characteristic U-forms are seen in diseases of the lungs, bronchi, larynx, sinuses, and nose.

Cardiac patients display sharp "heart polygons," five- or six-cornered cavities reminiscent of a honeycomb, situated around the midpoint of the plate. "Heart polygons" are observed in diseases and functional disturbances of the vascular system—the heart, arteries, and veins.

In liver patients, "asymmetric liver signs" or half-moon forms are found, chiefly in the right mid-field. The liver signs apply to diseases of the liver, the bile ducts, and gall bladder.

Spleen patients show sharper, angular, likewise "asymmetric spleen forms," usually in the left mid-field.

In gastrointestinal diseases, so-called "gastrointestinal rosettes" appear, mainly around the mid-point of the plate or in the long-rayed field. They also occur in diseases of the tongue and esophagus and may thus be regarded as the formative principle of the entire digestive tract, encompassing all of its separate members.

Blood pictures of kidney patients show typical triangle forms with lateral radiation, the "kidney sign." They are usually located in the long-rayed field; "kidney trigons" embrace diseases of the kidneys, renal pelvis, bladder, urethra, etc.

In genital diseases soft hollow forms are found; they are also found in the lower field by the kidney signs.

In disorders of the endocrine glands we find so-called "glandular wing-pairs," crystal forms reminiscent of butterflies, showing characteristic variations for the individual endocrine glands.

Indications of Organic Dysfunction and Disease

Organ signs in the blood crystallization pictures indicate an existing organic disease or functional disorder. They appear in a great variety of diseases of inner organs (with about 90 per cent probability).

In contrast to other methods, blood crystallizations clearly react to disturbed organic functioning as a whole. The direction of the disease (inflammatory, spastic, fibrotic, tending to sclerosis, tending to tumor formation) can often be perceived from other disease-charecteric configurations (see general directions for diagnosis).

Organ signs also occur in more subtle functional disorders of inner organs that are manifested in oversensitivity, transitory ailments, or latent organic dysfunction.

Organ Signs as the Expression of the Disturbed Sphere of Action of Organs

Lastly, organ signs also occur in disorders of organic activity whose effect, physical or psychic, relates to an extended sphere of functioning of this organ. Here, they form the common denominators of many disorders of organic functioning.

Some of these disorders are so subtle that they elude the customary clinical methods of examination. The sensitive test of blood crystallization, however, reflects even these "organ signs." So organ signs occur in skin diseases and allergies, rheumatism, disorders of the water balance and of excretion, discharges, digestive disorders, or migraines; they also occur in psychic disorders such as depression, schizophrenia, or epilepsy. All of these disorders belong to the sphere of action of different organs and become accessible to treatment when the organic dysfunction has been detected.

Direction for Multilevel Organic Diagnosis

If we take the organs as carriers of principles of action, we find that there is a sequence of levels of action for each organ.

On the physical level, the organ offers a specific physical center for its principle of action. Here, organ signs speak of material organic alterations or organic diseases. On the functional level, each organ-principle manifests in the particular dynamic of its functions or of its chemical action. Here, an organic reference indicates various kinds of organ function disorders. On the psychic level each organ principle forms the basis of the soul qualities associated with it. Here, an organic reference points to organ-related psychic disorders. On the level of related principles of action in the macrocosm and microcosm (in Paracelsus's sense), a metal principle corresponds to each organ principle; this regulates the equilibrium of physical, functional, and psychic organic activity.

Thus, each organ reference also points to disturbances of the organ-related metal process. To be sure, it is not only the organ sign that speaks here, but above all the "organic constellation"; the relation of the organ signs to one another and to the disease signs speaks of the metal process disturbances, occasionally even indicating their excess or deficiency.

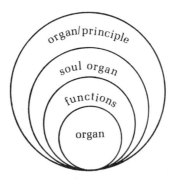

Fig. 7. Direction for multilevel organic diagnosis

The "organ signs" speak of the physical organ, a "potential" functional organ, an organ-related soul organ, and an organ-related metal principle.

A multilevel organ principle is reflected on the functional level in the blood crystallization picture. Knowledge of this provides new kinds of insights into the functional interrelationships in the organism.

We shall confine ourselves to this brief overview within the framework of diagnosis from blood crystallization. For a scientific foundation of organ-related metal regulating systems and the metal therapy following from them, the reader is referred to A. Selawry's work,[3] which provides a methodical introduction to the relationships between metal, organ, and psyche. Definite correspondences are found between the metal process and the organ function and soul faculty. Following this, a comprehensive metal-organ system is developed using the model of tin and the liver, in which many functions are held in equilibrium. For example, this system controls liver function and hepatogenic metabolic disorders in the widest sense, plastic and dysplastic processes, the functioning of serous membranes (serositis and exsiccosis or drying out; dropsy or arthrosis), and also hepatogenic psychic disorders. All of these functional, organic, and psychic disorders of the liver-tin processes are expressed in the blood crystallization picture in liver signs—their common denominator. Experience has proven them to be accessible to one or another form of tin therapy of the liver. A. Selawry's work[4] also describes a silver-regulating system in relation to urogenital functioning and the skin. This system is responsible for dysfunction and diseases of the urogenital system and disorders in regeneration and elimination (metabolic disturbances and emaciation, vegetative dystonia, inadequate defense against infection, slow wound healing, juvenile or climacteric skin diseases, or psychic disorders).

In the blood crystallization picture, this great range of disorders is expressed in the genital signs—the common denominator of the silver equilibrium system. Silver, in appropriate application, can often restore equilibrium in such disorders.

Corresponding mutual relationships exist between the organic sphere of functions and the metal regulating system for the other primary metals as well.

In summary, organ signs provide, in their constellations, indications of disturbances of organ-related metal processes and offer prospects for a metal therapy.

Blood crystallization broadens the physician's realm of observation. Qualitative alterations of the blood are captured in these characteristic and reproducible crystal phenomena.

The crystallization picture offers insights into the harmony or disharmony of the whole and into the state of vitality and various states of reaction (rheumatic, allergic, spastic tendency to mineralization, physicalization).

The disease-characteristic signs provide a direction for diagnosis of an existing inflammatory tendency or a tumor situation.

The organ signs point to lability, functional disorder, or disease of organs. Furthermore, experience has shown that organ signs give indications of little-noticed organ dysfunction in metabolic disorders (for example, skin diseases, rheumatism, migraines, etc.) and in psychic disorders (developmental handicaps, psychopathy, epilepsy, depression, etc.). Hence, this is a many-sided approach to diagnostics.

Moreover, connections are revealed between functional indications in the crystal picture and corresponding metal processes.

A knowledge of such connections makes it possible to translate organic indications, reaction states, and disease directions in the blood crystallization picture into the language of disturbed metal functions. We come to see metal equilibrium systems as common denominators of the functional organism; they point the way to a treatment with metals of a great variety of disorders, often the ones that have defied all treatment.

Naturally, a laboratory method cannot be expected to provide ready diagnoses. Like any empirical finding, blood crystallization merely contributes information to the total picture. It is the task of the physician to test these, to order them within the whole picture, and to supplement them with specific clinical examinations.

The more comprehensively the physician weighs the results, the more functionally he evaluates them, the more helpful this method will be to him.

Notes and References

(GA refers to volumes in the Rudolf Steiner *Gesamtausgabe*)

Chapter II. The First Epoch of Life

1. See Günther Wachsmuch, *Reincarnation as a Phenomenon of Metamorphosis*, Philosophischer-Anthroposophischer Verlag, Dornach (Switzerland), 1937.
2. This section was revised by H. Matthiolius.
3. W. Zeller, *Konstitution und Entwickelung.*
4. Rudolf Steiner, *The Education of the Child in the Light of Anthroposophy*, 2nd ed. Rudolf Steiner Press, London, 1965, 4th reprinting, 1981.
5. Alfred Nitschke, *Das verwaisteste Kind der Natur.* 2nd ed., Tübingen, 1968.
6. The appearance of ego consciousness can also be traced in many autobiographies. See: Carl Gustav Carus, Ludwig Ganghofer, Friedrich de la Motte-Fouqué, Carl Spitteler, Ernst Reitschel, Herbert Spencer, and many others. There is comprehensive material in *Die Früherinnerung* by Hanns Reinhardt (Halle, 1926) and also in C. von Heydebrand's essay in *Erziehungskunst*, 1934, number 2/3.
7. R. Steiner, *Spiritual Science and Medicine*, Rudolf Steiner Press, London, 1948, reprinted 1975, lecture 7.
8. R. Steiner and Ita Wegman, *Fundamentals of Therapy*, 3rd ed., Rudolf Steiner Press, London, 1967, chapter 1.
9. R. Steiner, *Spiritual Science and Medicine*, lecture 7.
10. *Ibid.*, lecture 6.
11. We can observe a physiological preliminary stage of this behavior, for example, when a person in "intense" expectation of a certain event—that is, with intense involvement of the astral body—reacts to a noise with a convulsive start; here the strong muscular reaction is caused by the heightened tension of the astral body.

12. Whether we are dealing with a viral substance or a product of reaction with body protein will not be discussed. This distinction has no bearing for the basic consideration.
13. H. Schmid, *Schw. Arch. Neur.*, 33(1934):81.
14. B. Döring et al., *Z. Kinderheilk.*, 109(1971):216.

Chapter III. The Second Epoch of Life

1. Express mention should be made here of the pedagogical writings of Rudolf Steiner, which contain abundant, highly important hygienic and pedagogical tips for teachers and doctors.
2. From K. Klare-Scheidegg in *Handbuch der jugendärztlichen Arbeitsmethoden*, Wilfred Zeller, Ed.
3. See the detailed presentation of H. Müller-Weidemann, *Mitte der Kindheit. Das neunte bis zwölfte Lebensjahr. Eine biographische Phänomenologie der kindlichen Entwicklung*, Stuttgart, 1973.
4. Falta, *Die Zuckerkrankheit*, Vienna, 1936.

Chapter IV. The Third Epoch of Life

1. K.H. Schäfer, *Erg. d. Inn. Med. und Kinderheilkd*, 4(1953): 773.
2. Wolff, *Beiträge z. erw. Heilkunst* (1955):15.
3. H. Reuter, *Beiträge z. erw. Heilkunst* (1954):142.

Chapter V. The School Child

1. E. Zeigler, *Die Ursachen der Akzeleration*, Basel, 1966.
2. Richard Nold, *Wachstumsbeschleunigung und Zivilisation*, Munich, 1965.
3. Further literature on the theme of acceleration: A. Sälzer, *Ursachen und Erscheinungsformen der Akzeleration*, Berlin (East), 1967; S. Schöffler, *Das Kind im Wandel des Jahrhunderts*, Stuttgart, 1971, p. 83; Bennhold-Thomsen, "Die Entwicklungsbeschleunigung der Jugend," *Erg. d. inn Med. u. Kinderheilkd.* N.F., Vol. 62, Nov. 1954.

4. R. Steiner, *Geisteswissenschaftliche Gesichtspunkte zur Therapie* (GA 313), Rudolf Steiner Verlag, Dornach, 1963.
5. Erich Gebertg, *Das mütterliche und das väterliche Element in der Erziehung*, Stuttgart, 1949.
6. W. Holtzapfel, "Das mütterliche und das väterliche Element im kindlichen Blut," *Erziehungskunst* (Stuttgart), 1956, No. 3.
7. R. Steiner, *Geisteswissenschaftliche Gesichtspunkte zur Therapie*.
8. Pfaundler, in *Kinderheilkunde*, Feer, Ed., Jena, 1934.
9. E. Beutler, "Tissue effects of iron deficiency," *Series Haematologica*, 6(1965):41–55.
10. Samuelsson, cited in L. Hallberg, *Nordiskt symposium "Järnbrist och Järnterapie,"* Göteberg, 1964, p. 135.
11. C. von Pirquet, "Allergie des Lebensalters," *Wiener Klinische Wochenschrift*, 1929, p. 65.
12. T. Hellbrügge, J. Rutenfranz, and O. Graf, *Gesundheit und Leistungsfähigkeit im Kindes- und Jugendalter*, Stuttgart, 1960.
13. W. Brenner, in *Biolog. Daten für den Kinderarzt*, Brock, Ed., Berlin, 1954.
14. Feer, in *Kinderheilkunde*, Feer, Ed., Jena, 1934.
15. R. Steiner, *Geisteswissenschaftliche Gesichtspunkte zur Therapie*.
16. *Ibid.*
17. R. Steiner, *Menschliches Seelenleben und Geistesstreben im Zusammenhang mit Welt- und Erdentwickelung* (GA 212), Rudolf Steiner Verlag, Dornach, 1978.
18. R. Steiner, *Discussions with Teachers*, Rudolf Steiner Press, London, 1967.
19. W. Holtzapfel, *Kinderschicksale—Entwicklungsrichtungen*, Dornach, 1966.
20. R. Steiner, *Curative Education*, Rudolf Steiner Press, London, 1972, reprinted 1981.
21. H. Klüver, cited in W. Bargmann, "Das Gehirn und die Tätigkeit des Nervensystems in der Sicht heutiger Forschung," *Universitas* (Stuttgart), 1966, No. 7.

Chapter VI. Developmental Disorders in Childhood

1. R. Steiner, *Curative Education*, Rudolf Steiner Press, London, 1972, reprinted 1981.
2. K. König, *Mongolismus*, Stuttgart, 1959.
3. J. Bort, *Heileurythmie*, Arlesheim (Switzerland), 1958.
4. R. Steiner, *Menschenwerden, Weltenseele und Weltengeist* —*Erster Teil* (GA 205), Rudolf Steiner Verlag, Dornach, 1967.
5. *Acta Paedopsychiatrica*, Vol. 35, IV-VIII, Basel, 1968.
6. J. Lutz, *Kinderpsychiatrie*, 4th ed., Zurich, 1972.
7. W. Pache, *Heilende Erziehung*, 3rd ed., Stuttgart, 1972.
8. H. Engel, K. König, and H. Müller-Wiedemann, *Ueber schwere Kontaktstörungen im Kindersalter und deren Behandlung*, Stuttgart, 1956.

Chapter VII. Inflammation and Sclerosis as Basic Tendencies

1. E. Letterer, *Allgemeine Pathologie*.
2. André Lwoff, Pasteur Institute, Paris. Nobel laureate, 1966.
3. J. Johnson, *Phytopathology* 11(1921):446; 12(1922):438.
4. L. Kunkel, *Phytopathology* 26(1936):819.
5. R. Thompson, *Infectious Diseases* 62(1938):307; J. Marshall, *Journal of Hygiene* 57(1959):484; Boring, Zu Rhein, and Walker, *Proc. Soc. Exp. Biol. Med.* 93(1956):273; Baron and Buckler, *Journal of Immunology* 80(1958):39; Kirn, Schieffer, and Braunwald, *Ann. Inst. Pasteur* 111(1966):645; Walker and Boring, *Journal of Immunology* 80(1958):39.
6. Kirn, Dammron, Braunwald, and Wurtz, *C.R. Acad. Sciences* 261(1965):1923.
7. Lwoff *et al.*, *C.R. Acad. Sciences* 250(1960):2644; Lwoff, *Bact. Review* 23(1959):109; Lwoff and Lwoff, *Ann. Inst. Pasteur* 101(1961):313; Lwoff and Lwoff, *C.R. Acad. Sciences* 246(1958):190.
8. See F. Husemann, *Vom Bild und Sinn des Todes*, Stuttgart, 1954.
9. M. Bürger, *Geschlecht und Krankheit*, Munich, 1958.
10. E. von Rindfleisch, *Die Elemente der Pathologie*, 3rd ed., 1896. (This reference is from the basic work of G. Huse-

mann, "Entzündung und Geschwulst," in *Beitr. Erw. Heilk.* vol. 25 (1972) and also in *Die Drei* 1972, No. 9.

11. Lambotte, *Erg. Ges. Med.* 19(1896):63 (cited by Ungar, see note 20).
12. R. Schmidt, *Med. Klin.* 6(1910):1690, and *Therap. u. Prophylaxe innerer Krankh.*, 2nd ed. (1948).
13. Engel, *Wiener Kl. Wochenschr.* 47(1934):1118, and 48(1935): 112.
14. Sineck, *Zeitschr. f. Krebsf.* 44(1936):492.
15. Schier, *Biol. Erf. Heilkd.*, 1936, and *Die Kinderkrankh.*, 1937.
16. A. Feld, *Die Anamnese d.* Magencarcinom-Kranken, diss. 1941 (cited by Ungar, see note 20).
17. H. Kürten, *Arztl. Forschung* 5(1):179 (1950/1951).
18. E. Hass, *Carcinoma u. Entzündung*, Leipzig, 1942.
19. Feyrter and Kofler, *Z. Histol. u. Biol. d. epithelialen Geschwülste d. menschl. Enddarmes*, 1953.
20. Kofler and Hussarek, *Krebsarzt* (Vienna) 9(1954):89.
21. Felix Ungar, *Die Medizinische*, 1954, 1563.
22. Greuer, *Hippokr.* (1965):189; Holler, *Krebsarzt* (1964):35; Holler and Tischer, *Ars. Med.* (1965):25; Stöger, *Wien. Med. Wschr.* (1948):416, and (1950):318; Stöger, *Med. Welt* 18 (1967):3183.
23. G. von Bergmann, *Funktionelle Pathologie*(1932):173.
24. Ruth Lohmann, *Klinische Wochenschrift* (1931) No. 39 (cited by von Bergmann, see note 22).
25. E. Huth, in ang. Diss. Erlangen 1951. E. Huth, in *Körpereigene Abwehr und bösartige Geschwülste*, H. Lampert and O. Selawry, eds., Ulm, 1957.
26. Busch, *Berliner klin. Wschr.* (1866):23 (cited by Huth, see note 24).
27. Bruns, *Beitr. Klin. Chir.* 3(1887):445.
28. F. Fehleisen, *Die Aetiologie des Erysipels*, Berlin, 1883.
29. W.B. Coley, *Ann. Surg.*, 1891 and *Am. J. Med. Sci.*, 1893, 1894 (cited by Huth, see note 24).
30. Coley-Nauts *et al.*, *Canc. Res.* 6(1946):205 and *Acta med. scand.* (Swedish) 145(1953) supplement 276.

31. Chranova, *Zeitschr. f. Krebsforsch.* 53(1942) Nos. 3 & 4 (cited by Husemann, see note 7).
32. H. Lampert, *Tumorbeeinflussung durch Hyperthermie und Hyperämie*, Ulm, 1956; M. von Ardenne, *Grundlagen d. Krebsmehrschritt-Therapie*, Berlin, 1970; J.A. Dickson, "Hyperthermy in the Treatment of Cancer," *The Lancet* No. 8109, pp. 202–205, Jan. 27, 1979. Further literature: H. Lampert, *Überwärmung als Heilmittel*, Ulm, 1948; H. Lampert, "Physikalische Therapie und Forschung" in *Forschung und Praxis*, 1976, chap. B.

Chapter VIII. Hysteria and Neurasthenia

1. See also R. Treichler, *Vom Wesen der Hysterie*, Stuttgart, 1964.
2. Paracelsus used this expression for what is called the etheric body in spiritual science (editor).
3. R. Steiner, *Spiritual Science and Medicine*, Rudolf Steiner Press, London, 1948, reprinted 1975, lecture 2.
4. R. Steiner, *Geisteswissenschaftliche Gesichtspunkte zur Therapie* (GA 313), Rudolf Steiner Verlag, Dornach, 1963, lecture 5.
5. See the detailed work of R. Treichler, "Vom Wesen der Neurasthenie" in *Anthroposophie und Medizin*, Dornach, 1963.
6. R. Steiner, *Spiritual Science and Medicine*, lecture 2.

Chapter IX. Fundamentals of a Biochemistry

1. R. Steiner and Ita Wegman, *Fundamentals of Therapy*, 3rd ed., Rudolf Steiner Press, London, 1967, chapter 17.
2. See H. Krüger, "Von Substanzbildung und Substanzprozessen," *Beitr. zur Substanzforschung* 1(1951).
3. See G. Schmidt, "Die Milch als Erdenstoff" in *Beitr. zur Substanzforschung* 1(1951):155.
4. R. Steiner and I. Wegman, *Fundamentals of Therapy*, chapter 8.
5. F.M. Pottenger, Jr., *Amer. J. of Orthodont. and Oral Surgery* 32(No. 8):467–485 (1946).

6. See also Pfeiffer, *Sensitive Crystallization Processes*, 2nd ed., Anthroposophic Press, Spring Valley, N.Y., 1967, reprinted 1975.

7. Bruker, *Der Zucker als pathogenetischer Faktor*, Bad Homburg v.d.H., 1962.

8. A. Katase, "Der Einfluss der Ernärung auf die Konstitution des Organismus," *Pathol. Inst. d. Med. Akademie*, Osaka, 1931.

9. Benjamin Sandler, *Sonderernährung verhütet Kinderlähmung*, Krailling, 1959.

10. E. Ziegler, "Der moderne Zuckerkonsum und die Akzeleration," *Schweizer Med. Wochenschrift* 96(No. 40):1345 (1966).

11. T.L. Cleave and G.D. Campbell, *Die Saccharidose und ihre Erscheinungsformen*, Bad Homburg v.d.H.

12. R. Steiner and I. Wegman, *Fundamentals of Therapy*, chapter 8.

13. *Ibid.*

14. G. Schmidt, "Die Milch als Erdenstoff" in *Beitr. zur Substanzforschung* 1(1951):155.

15. *Beitr. Erw. Heilk.* 6(1953):64.

16. R. Steiner and I. Wegman, *Fundamentals of Therapy*, chapter 8.

17. See G. Schmidt, "Zur Alkoholfrage," in *Anthro. Med. Jahrbuch* II (1951).

18. R. Steiner and I. Wegman, *Fundamentals of Therapy*, chapter 8.

19. Kohl, *Zeitschrift für Altersforschung* 2(No. 4) (1940).

20. See W. Pelikan in *Beitr. Erw. Heilk.* 1947, No. 5.

21. R. Steiner and I. Wegman, *Fundamentals of Therapy*, chapter 10.

22. *Ibid.*

23. *Ibid.*

24. *Ibid.*, chapter 6.

25. G. Wachsmuth, *Erde und Mensch*, 2nd ed., Dornach, 1953.

26. R. Steiner and I. Wegman, *Fundamentals of Therapy*, chapter 11.

27. Hermann Poppelbaum, *Tierwesenkunde*, 2nd ed., Dornach, 1954.

28. R. Steiner and I. Wegman, *Fundamentals of Therapy*, chapter 11.
29. *Ibid.*, chapter 12.
30. *Ibid.*, chapter 11.
31. C. von Pirquet, *Allergie des Lebensalters*, 1930.
32. R. Steiner, *Spiritual Science and Medicine*, Rudolf Steiner Press, London, 1948, reprinted 1975, lecture 12.
33. R. Steiner and I. Wegman, *Fundamentals of Therapy*, chapter 9.
34. Overview in F. Hollwich, *The Influence of Ocular Light Perception on Metabolism in Man and Animal*, New York/Heidelberg/Berlin, 1979.
35. Gigon, "Zuckerstoffwechsel bei Licht und Dunkelheit," *Klin. Wochschr.* 9(1930):1947.
36. In this regard, see R. Steiner, *The Philosophy of Freedom*, Rudolf Steiner Press, London, 1964, reprinted 1970 by Anthroposophic Press, Spring Valley, N.Y.

Chapter X. Pharmacodynamics

1. T. Schwenk, *Grundlagen der Potenzforschung*, 2nd ed., Stuttgart, 1972, and Potenzierte Heilmittel, Stuttgart, 1971.
2. Continuation of these tests, with statistical verification of reproducibility, by Wilhelm Pelikan and Georg Unger, *Die Wirkung potenzierter Substanzen: Pflanzenwachstumsversuche mit statistischer Auswertung*, Dornach, 1965. Also, Anselm Basold, "Physiologischer und physikalischer Nachweis der Wirksamkeit kleinster Entitäten: Eine statistiche bearbeitung und Würdigung der Versuche von Lili Kolisko aus dem Jahre 1923," *Elemente der Naturwissenschaft* 7 (1967):34; Anselm Basold, "Potenzforschung als Weg zum Erfassen der Substanzbildekräfte," *El. d. Nat.* 8(1968):32; Jochen Bockemühl, "Die Wirkung von potenzierten Pyrit verschiedener Verreibungsverfahren auf das Wurzel- und Sprosswachstum von Keimpflanzen," *El. d. Nat.* 8(1968):27.
3. R. Steiner, *Geisteswissenschaftliche Gesichtspunkte zur Therapie* (GA 313), Rudolf Steiner Verlag, Dornach, 1963, lecture 2.
4. R. Steiner, *Ursprungsimpulse der Geisteswissenschaft* (GA

96), Rudolf Steiner Verlag, Dornach 1974, lecture given October 22, 1906.
5. W. Cloos, *Lebensstufen der Erde*, 2nd ed., Stuttgart, 1970.
6. R. Steiner, *Geisteswissenschaftliche Gesichtspunkte zur Therapie*, lecture 3.

Chapter XI. Toward a Science of Healing Plants

1. See W. Pelikan, *Heilpflanzenkunde*, 3 vols., Dornach, 1962/63.
2. Regarding teucrium, see W. Simonis, *Die unbekannte Heilpflanze*, Frankfurt, 1955.
3. R. Steiner, *Spiritual Science and Medicine*, Rudolf Steiner Press, London, 1948, reprinted 1975, lecture 10.
4. R. Steiner, *Knowledge of the Higher Worlds and Its Attainment*, 3rd ed., Anthroposophic Press, Spring Valley, N.Y., 1947, reprinted 1977.
5. R. Steiner and Ita Wegman, *Fundamentals of Therapy*, 3rd ed., Rudolf Steiner Press, London, 1967, chapter 11.

Chapter XII. The Capillary-Dynamic Blood Test

1. W. Kaelin, *Der kapillardynamische Bluttest zur Frühdiagnose der Krebskrankheit*, Dornach, 1965. This book also contains a detailed description of the procedure.
2. R. Steiner and Ita Wegman, *Fundamentals of Therapy*, 3rd ed., Rudolf Steiner Press, London, 1967, chapter 6.
3. R. Steiner, *Spiritual Science and Medicine*, Rudolf Steiner Press, London, 1948, reprinted 1975, lecture 19.
4. W. Kaelin, *Krebsfrühdiagnose—Krebsvorbeugung*, 4th ed., Frankfurt a.M., 1966.
5. G. Suchantke, *Natura* 3(No. 28):36 (1928).

Chapter XIII. Blood Crystallization

1. Ehrenfried Pfeiffer, *Empfindliche Kristallisationsvorgänge als Nachweis von Formkräften im Blut*, 1935.
2. A. Selawry and O. Selawry, *Die Kupferchlorid-Kristallisation in Naturwissenschaft und Medizin*, Stuttgart, 1957.
3. A. Selawry, *Wissenschaft eine Metalltherapie von Organ und Psyche*, Vol. I: *Zinn und Zinntherapie*, Ulm, 1963.
4. Ibid., Vol. II, *Silber und Silbertherapie*, Ulm, 1966.